THE LIVING STREAM

THE
LIVING STREAM

Evolution and Man

by

SIR ALISTER HARDY

Meridian Books

THE WORLD PUBLISHING COMPANY

CLEVELAND AND NEW YORK

A MERIDIAN BOOK
Published by The World Publishing Company
2231 West 110th Street, Cleveland, Ohio 44102
First Meridian Printing September 1968
Reprinted by arrangement with Harper & Row, Publishers, Incorporated
Library of Congress Catalog Card Number: 67-15975
Printed in the United States of America.

CONTENTS

CONTENTS

PREFACE

In the opening lecture I express my deep sense of the honour of being invited to be a Gifford Lecturer; here I wish to thank the Principal and his colleagues for their kindness to my wife and myself during our stay in the University of Aberdeen. It was a most happy experience to be back for a time to renew many old friendships both in the University, where I once held the Regius Chair of Natural History, and in the City of Bon Accord. I want particularly to thank Professor V. C. Wynne-Edwards, my successor in that Chair, for so kindly allowing me to give my Giffords in his lecture theatre and thus making me feel so very much at home.

I must now acknowledge the help I received from members of my audience. With the Syllabus of the Lectures which was issued at the beginning of the course, on the suggestion of the late Principal Sir Thomas Taylor, I invited any who might be interested to attend informal seminars to discuss the subjects raised and to ask questions. These were well attended and were certainly most helpful to me in enabling me to clarify some of the more difficult points. I am particularly grateful to Dr. Michael Begg who kindly and most ably acted as chairman at these meetings, keeping them pleasantly informal and preventing them from straying too far from the subject in hand.

The lectures in general are published as they were delivered, but have been slightly amplified as a result of the discussions just mentioned and a little expanded because I had not always found it possible to compress what I wanted to say on some particular aspect into exactly an hour's discourse. I thank Sir Cyril Hinshelwood for kindly giving me permission to quote in lecture x a longer passage from his Presidential Address to the Royal Society in 1959 than I was able to include in the actual lecture as given.

Most of my illustrations are similar to the blackboard sketches which I made as I lectured; the others were shown as lantern slides. I wish particularly to thank Dr. Alfred S. Romer and the University of Chicago Press for kindly allowing me to reproduce, on a slightly different scale, charts from his *Vertebrate Palæontology* in my figures 1 to 5, and to Dr. Hugh Cott for permission to make a number of sketches from his excellent photographs in his *Adaptive Coloration in Animals*. Other sources of figures are acknowledged where they occur. I wish also to express my appreciation of the care and skill with which Mr. J. F. Trotter has redrawn the graphs and diagrams from my sketches.

Finally I should record that some of the themes developed in this volume have had their beginnings in earlier lectures which I have given in the past twenty years. Usually I have quoted from such a previous discussion, giving the source, but sometimes, not wishing to break the thread of an argument with a reference, I have used very similar wording without acknowledging the repetition. These former lectures were *Natural History Old and New* (my inaugural lecture at Aberdeen in 1942), *Zoology outside the Laboratory* (my Presidential Address to Section D [Zoology] of the British Association for the Advancement of Science at the meeting at Newcastle-upon-Tyne in 1949), *The Faith of a Scientist* (published in *Faith and Freedom*, vol. 2, 1949) and *Science and the Quest for God* (one of the annual Essex Hall Lectures, delivered in 1951); I should also include an article *Biology and Psychical Research* which I contributed to a jubilee volume, the 50th, of the *Proceedings of the Society for Psychical Research*, 1953.

LECTURE I

INTRODUCTION

I am indeed conscious of the honour of being invited to be a Gifford Lecturer; and I realise the responsibility that is mine in trying to uphold the great tradition built up by my distinguished predecessors.

You have elected me knowing that I am a biologist and a naturalist who is interested in the subject which was so dear to the heart of Lord Gifford: Natural Theology. You will know that I am neither trained as a theologian nor as a philosopher, and I am sure you will not wish me to pretend that I have a depth of knowledge in these subjects to which I cannot lay claim. Some may feel that it is presumptuous to attempt to give the Gifford Lectures without such a training; if so, let me assure them that I shall not trespass very far into these philosophical fields without seeking guidance. I accepted the invitation because I am convinced that both science and natural history—and I make a distinction between them—have, in their own right, contributions to make to the discussion of Natural Theology.

Was it not the great naturalists of a hundred years ago, Darwin and Wallace, who, perhaps more than anyone else in their century, influenced the outlook of philosophers and shook at least some of the walls of theology? After such a remark let me hasten to disclaim any idea that I think my lectures might have a similar revolutionary effect. Nevertheless among the company of biologists following Darwin, Wallace and Huxley to the present day there have been many who have helped to modify our views on the mechanism of evolution and so have changed the emphasis of the impact of the theory upon the world of ideas. My lectures will deal with a restatement of evolution theory which I have been considering for the past twenty years and which I believe may have a bearing upon theological thought.

I shall be devoting a whole lecture to the changes which have come about in our understanding of the process since Darwin's day, but let me now give one example of the importance, for the welfare of the world, of a proper appreciation of this mechanism. It had often been implied that the action of natural selection must *always* make a race of animals or plants fitter in its struggle with its environment. Professor J. B. S. Haldane in his *Causes of Evolution*, in 1932, was perhaps the first to give prominent attention to this fallacy—" a fallacy which," he says, " has been responsible for a good deal of poisonous nonsense which has been written on ethics in Darwin's name, especially in Germany before the war and in America and England since." He was of course referring to the first world war and writing just before Hitler came to power. He clearly showed that there are many subtle ways in which competition between members of the same species may lead to the selection of features that eventually must spell ruin to the race. Some of these features, however, are more obvious, such as the weapons evolved for combat between rivals of their own kind. " The geological record," as Haldane says, " is full of cases where the development of enormous horns and spines (sometimes in the male sex only) has been the prelude to extinction. It seems probable," he continues, " that in some of these cases the species literally sank under the weight of its own armaments." It is indeed a lesson for mankind today.

Recent developments in our knowledge of the chemical nature of the genetic material, of its apparent random changes and of the power of natural selection, have inclined some to believe that there is no room left for Natural Theology at all in what appears to them to be a process entirely at the mercy of chance, governed, as it has been said, by the shake of Nature's dice box. This idea of evolution being governed by chance is another fallacy, as is well recognised by all the leading evolutionists of today. It is selection which *guides* the process, not the chance interplay of the genes and their mutations from which the selection is made; and this selection is far from random. Do we know, however, all there is to know about the different selective agents and their true nature? This I very much doubt and a lot hinges upon it.

I am a Darwinian in the modern sense, but I venture to suggest that there is something more about the process of evolution than is generally conceded by most biologists today; and that this " something more " does, I believe, link Natural Theology to the biological scheme. My first series of lectures, which I am giving under the general title of " The Living Stream ", will essentially be a biological discussion, yet I trust it comes well within the scope of Lord Gifford's wishes in showing, as I hope to do, that Biology and Natural Theology are not opposed one to the other, but are in fact closely linked. My second series, which I shall give next session, will be a contribution to the study of Natural Theology of a rather different kind; I will there, as a naturalist, attempt to look at Man and discuss his religious behaviour and experience as a part of his Natural History and see what conclusions we can draw from such a study.

Before going any further I should say just what I mean by the term Natural Theology and by the Spirit of Man. Natural Theology is sometimes taken to be synonymous with " Rational Theology ", but more often an important difference in meaning is recognised. Rational Theology has usually maintained that God's existence could be proved, as convincingly as is a theorem of Euclid, by reason alone—to this I do not subscribe. The Natural Theology I am interested in concerns a Theism which is derived empirically from the study of nature, man and human history. In making this distinction I am following theologians such as the late Dr. F. R. Tennant[1] of Cambridge, who defined Natural Theology in just the way I have indicated; I feel sure that it was in this way, too, that Lord Gifford used the term.[2] By the Spirit of Man I mean that side of him which experiences spiritual and religious feelings and loves adventure, natural beauty and the arts.

Let me remind some of you and perhaps inform others—for I think it is not as well known as it should be—what were the exact conditions and wishes set out by Lord Gifford in making his splendid benefaction for, to use his own words, " Promoting, Advancing, Teaching and Diffusing the study of Natural Theology, in the widest sense of that term."

In his will he laid down that:

the lecturers appointed shall be subjected to no test of any kind,

---

[1] I have taken my concise definition from his article on Theology in the fourteenth edition of the *Encyclopædia Britannica*; he has, of course, developed the theme of Natural Theology at length in vol. II of his *Philosophical Theology* (1930).

[2] I should perhaps point out that to talk of Natural Theology today does *not* imply any following of the views of Paley who in his famous book *Natural Theology or Evidences of the Existence and Attributes of the Deity* (1802) put forward the thesis that the wonderful adaptations of living things pointed to the existence of God as creator and designer just as a watch signified a watchmaker. Such ideas were eclipsed by the coming of Darwinian evolution with its explanation of adaptations. A true Natural Theology must be progressive and not afraid to modify its views (and modify them yet again if need be).

and shall not be required to take any oath, or to emit or subscribe to any declaration of belief, or make any promise of any kind; they may be of any denomination whatever, or of no denomination at all (and many earnest and high-minded men prefer to belong to no ecclesiastical denomination); they may be of any religion or way of thinking, or as is sometimes said, they may be of no religion, or they may be so-called sceptics or agnostics or free-thinkers, provided only that the " patrons " will use diligence to secure that they be able, reverent men, true thinkers, sincere lovers of and earnest inquirers after truth.

He then went on to discuss how the subject should be treated:

I wish the lecturers to treat their subject as a strictly natural science, the greatest of all possible sciences, indeed, in one sense, the only science, that of Infinite Being, without reference to or reliance upon any supposed special exceptional or so-called miraculous revelation. I wish it considered just as astronomy or chemistry is. I have intentionally indicated, in describing the subject of the lectures, the general aspect which personally I would expect the lectures to bear, but the lecturers shall be under no restraint whatever in their treatment of their theme; for example, they may freely discuss (and it may be well to do so) all questions about man's conceptions of God or the Infinite, their origin, nature, and truth, whether he can have any such conceptions, whether God is under any or what limitations, and so on, as I am persuaded that nothing but good can result from free discussion.

You may know that it was your Principal, the late Sir Thomas Taylor, who wrote on behalf of the Senatus inviting me to give these lectures, and when I came to Aberdeen a few weeks later we had a talk about them. I was hoping for many more such talks, but alas it was not to be, for as you know, he died very soon afterwards. He was most emphatic in saying that he hoped I would treat my subject in a more popular fashion than had often been the case in the past, for that, he said, was indeed Lord Gifford's wish. It was this that made me consult Lord Gifford's will and thus I read: " The lectures shall be public and popular, that is, open not only to students of the Universities, but to the whole community without matriculation, as I think that the subject should be studied and known by all, whether receiving University instruction or not. I think such knowledge, if real, lies at the root of all well-being." And a little later he again refers to " a general and popular audience."

I shall endeavour to speak in as non-technical a fashion as I can so that those who have had no scientific training may follow the biological argument. At the same time I shall hope that in using as simple and direct a diction as possible I shall not be forfeiting the standard of scholarship, for the two are perfectly compatible, if only more difficult to achieve; the danger lies, of course, in being misunderstood through an over-simplification.

Let me now return to say a little more about the distinction I made at the beginning between science and natural history. I believe it is a valid and useful one; natural history is the qualitative description of nature whereas science is the quantitative and experimental analysis of its interactions. It is right that we should applaud the advance of measurement and scientific exactitude but let us not forget the contributions of the naturalists who, in the spirit of explorers, have revealed for us the marvellous world of living creatures and the facts of their structures and habits. Discoveries by observation may be just as fundamental as those made by experiment; both are important. Today the success of the scientific method tends to overshadow the part played by the naturalists; I shall be stressing in these lectures that the naturalists have still their contributions to make both to the theory of evolution and to the study of natural theology.

The phase of the great traveller naturalists reached its zenith in the middle of the last century with Darwin, Wallace, Hooker, Huxley, Bates, Trimen, Fritz Muller, Wyville Thomson, Mosley, Agassiz and so many more. Some people seem to forget that T. H. Huxley was a field naturalist before he was the more famous Professor; his voyage on the *Rattlesnake*, when he made such splendid pioneer discoveries regarding pelagic life, was only one year shorter than Darwin's five years on the *Beagle*. It was the harvest from the observational natural history of this period, so patiently gathered in by Darwin, which, together with his and Wallace's joint theory, gave the convincing demonstration of the reality of evolution. The application of the scientific method which has followed, through the mathematical studies of heredity and the chemistry of the genetical material, has thrown a great light on the mechanism of the process; so brilliant are these discoveries that today most of the leading evolutionists appear as if dazzled, even blinded, by them, in that they imagine that the main, or even the whole, puzzle of evolution has been solved. They fail, I believe, to see other truths from the world of natural history—and human history too—which are just as vital to an understanding of the process. Let me give an example of this assurance.

Dr. George Gaylord Simpson, late Director of the American Museum of Natural History and one of the world's leading authorities on evolution, says in his Terry Lectures delivered at Yale University under the title of *The Meaning of Evolution*:[1]

It would be brash, indeed, to claim complete understanding of this extraordinarily intricate process, but it does seem that the problem is now essentially solved and that the mechanism of adaptation is known. It turns out to be basically materialistic, with no sign of purpose as a working variable in life history, and with any possible Purposer pushed back to the incomprehensible position of First Cause.

And again:

In fact, as the geneticists' studies progressed they were providing the last major piece of the truth so long sought regarding the causes of evolution.

I could give similar statements from most of the present-day writers on evolution. Whilst they present a mechanistic outlook, it is only fair to say that most of them see Man emerging in a unique " ethical " phase of evolution. Let me quote Simpson again, from the Epilogue of the same book:

Man is the result of a purposeless and materialistic process that did not have him in mind. He was not planned. He is a state of matter, a form of life, a sort of animal, and a species of the Order Primates, akin nearly or remotely to all of life and indeed to all that is material. It is, however, a gross misrepresentation to say that he is *just* an accident or *nothing but* an animal. Among all the myriad forms of matter and of life on the earth, or as far as we know in the universe, man is unique. He happens to represent the highest form of organisation of matter and energy that has ever appeared. Recognition of this kinship with the rest of the universe is necessary for understanding him, but his essential nature is defined by qualities found nowhere else, not by those he has in common with apes, fishes, trees, fire, or anything other than himself.

[1] Oxford University Press, 1950.

Sir Julian Huxley has gone much further in his ideas of this new phase which he calls the psycho-social stage of evolution. His outlook can briefly be expressed in two passages from the address he gave to the Darwin Centennial Convocation at the University of Chicago in November 1959.

The broad outlines of the new evolutionary picture of ultimates are beginning to be clearly visible. Man's destiny is to be sole agent for the future evolution of this planet. He is the highest dominant type to be produced by over two and a half billion years of the slow biological improvement effected by the blind opportunistic workings of natural selection; if he does not destroy himself, he has at least an equal stretch of evolutionary time before him to exercise his agency.

During the later part of biological evolution, mind—our word for the mental activities and properties of organisms—emerged with greater clarity and intensity, and came to play a more important role in the individual lives of animals. Eventually it broke through, to become the basis for further evolution, though the character of evolution now became cultural instead of genetic or biological. It was to this breakthrough, brought about by the automatic mechanism of natural selection and not by any conscious effort on his own part, that man owed his dominant evolutionary position.

And a little later he continues:

Nor is he [Man] individually alone in his thinking. He exists and has his being, in the intangible sea of thought which Teilhard de Chardin has christened the noösphere, in the same sort of way that fish exist and have their being in the material sea of water which the geographers include in the term hydrosphere. Floating in this noösphere there are, for his taking, the daring speculations and aspiring ideals of men long dead, the organised knowledge of science, the hoary wisdom of the ancients, the creative imaginings of all the world's poets and artists. And in his own nature there is, waiting to be called upon, an array of potential helpers —all the possibilities of wonder and knowledge, of delight and reverence, of creative belief and moral purpose, of passionate effort and embracing love.

For many years Huxley has preached the new religion of humanism with much feeling:

The essential religious reality [he writes], the experience which seeks to embody itself in symbols and to find intellectual expression in theologies—what is it? Is it not the sense of sacredness? And is not this sense of sacredness, like the feeling of hunger or the emotion of anger or the passion of love, something irreducible, itself and nothing else, only to be communicated to others who have the same capacity, just as the sensation of colour is uncommunicable to a blind man? ...

He regards it, however, as is shown by the title of the book from which I have just quoted, as *Religion without Revelation.* He makes this quite clear in his preface thus:

... this question of God or no God, external Power or no external Power, non-human absolute values against human evolving values—this question is fundamental. Until it is settled, and the idea of God relegated to the past with the idea of ritual magic and other products of primitive and unscientific human thought, we shall never get the new religion we need. ... Once we have rid ourselves of this doctrine of a Divine Power external to ourselves, we can get busy with the real task of dealing with our inner forces.

This is where I feel a discussion of evolution theory in relation to natural theology is so important. Has modern biology destroyed the basis for a theistic religion? I should at once explain that by theism I do not mean a belief in a deity with an anthropomorphic image. I do, however, at least mean—and this is where I differ from Huxley— a belief in an " extra-sensory " contact with a Divine Power which *is greater than, and in part lies beyond, the individual self*; towards this we have a feeling, no doubt for good biological, or psychological, reasons (linked with the emotions of an early child-parent affection, but none the worse for that) of a *personal* relationship, and we can call it God. My second series of lectures will deal with our evidence as to the nature of this experience; here I will only say in passing that I am not led to conclude that the Freudian super-ego gives us the complete explanation. In this present series I am attempting to enquire whether in fact biological theory is contrary to such a theistic belief or not.

Does modern biology destroy such a concept? Is atheism justified by the findings of evolutionary science? No one I think can doubt that the future of our civilisation will depend upon what sort of answers the majority of people give to these questions. Already a large part of mankind is governed by a policy based upon materialism and has a desire to convert the rest of the world to its point of view. I know, of course, that dialectical materialism is very different from the old-fashioned so-called classical materialism, but it is nevertheless atheistic in outlook; I am not entirely without hope that in time, with the development of a natural theology in harmony with a scientific out-look, it may not come to drop the " materialism " in favour of a dialectical theism.[1] That, indeed, would remove a cloud from humanity. Meanwhile in the rest of the world we see a larger and larger pro-portion of thinking people who find it increasingly difficult to reconcile the findings of science with a faith in spiritual reality. It is a puzzled world; so many people still feel religion in their hearts but find their minds deciding that such yearnings must be the product of a childish wishful thinking.

It was, I believe, largely because of this feeling that so many people clutched at Pierre Teilhard de Chardin's *Phenomenon of Man* with such thankfulness and enthusiasm. Was not this, they thought, a truly scientific work, by a theologian, demonstrating the Divine Power in the evolution process? There can be no doubt that it is a book by a profoundly spiritual man who believes passionately in God: " Then as St. Paul tells us, *God shall be all in all.* . . . The universe fulfilling itself in a synthesis of centres in perfect conformity with the laws of union. God, the centre of centres. In that final vision the Christian dogma culminates."[2] To those who did not read carefully Sir Julian Huxley's introduction to the book, or did not read to its end, it may well have seemed that he (Huxley) had actually been converted by the science of the book from his former atheistic position; he vouches for Teilhard's evolutionary views in this introduction as follows:

. . . he has effected a threefold synthesis—of the material and physical world with the world of mind and spirit; of the past with the future; and of variety with unity, the many with the one. He achieves this by examining every fact and every subject of his investigation *sub specie evolutionis*, with reference to its develop-ment in time and its evolutionary position. Conversely, he is able to envisage the whole of knowable reality not as a static mechanism but as a process. In consequence he is driven to search for human significance in relation to the trends of that enduring and comprehensive process; the measure of his stature is that he so largely succeeded in the search.

Later in his introduction, however, Huxley clearly shows he is not really so converted and admits that " Here his [Teilhard's] thought is not fully clear to me . . . at one place, for instance, he speaks of a trend as a *Christogenesis*; and elsewhere he appears not to be guarding himself sufficiently against the dangers of personifying the non-personal elements of reality."

Teilhard himself begins his preface by saying, " If this book is to be properly understood it must be read not as a work of metaphysics still less as a sort of theological essay, but purely and simply as a scientific treatise."

From a scientific point of view I am afraid I must regard the book as a work full of loose thinking and false analogies; to my mind it is in no sense a logically argued thesis at all. I hate to say this, because at the same time I cannot help hailing it as a magnificent epic, almost a poem, of the rise and emergence of the spirit of man and his feeling after Divinity. If it had been published as such, one would have regarded it as a glorious, if somewhat wildly metaphorical, expression of faith, and that indeed is how I like to regard it. One feels that it might well be illustrated with engravings by Blake. When he makes out, however, that he is presenting it as a truly scientific work, then those members of the general public who have had no scientific training may well be misled, since it deals with evolution, into believing it to be as much a work of science as Darwin's *Origin of Species*. With an introduction by Sir Julian, our best known contemporary writer on evolution, the illusion was, unfortunately, complete. It has even been proclaimed as " The book of the century ".[1]

I want to be careful not to give the impression that I believe that Teilhard was in any way trying to deceive his public. I think in his enthusiasm for his idea of this new phase in the evolution of life, which he calls the emergence of the noösphere, he lets his fancy overrun his reason. This idea is indeed very close to the important conception that Huxley has developed and calls the psycho-social phase of evolution; it was this, no doubt, that made him (Huxley) write as he did in the introduction. I think Teilhard came to believe that the steps he was

[1] A reviewer in *The Sunday Times*.

taking in his argument could be regarded as logical ones, when actually they seem to be based upon no more than metaphor and analogy.[1] It was a pity, I think, that Professor Medawar in his review in *Mind* should have used the word " dishonesty ", although it must be noted that he did so by saying " its author can be excused of dishonesty only on the grounds that before deceiving others, he has taken great pains to deceive himself." That remark hurt many who think of Teilhard as a saint—as indeed he was—but surely Medawar is only saying, albeit strongly, that Teilhard deceived himself into

[1] To give an example of what I mean by calling it just metaphor and analogy I must quote him at some length: for otherwise I should be taking him out of context. But I should first explain that by " the tangential " and " the radial " he means two kinds of energy as he says on his p. 64: " We shall assume that, essentially, all energy is physical in nature; but add that in each particular element this fundamental energy is divided into two distinct components: a *tangential energy* which links the element with others of the same order . . .; and a *radial energy* which draws it towards ever greater complexity and centricity—in other words forwards." This conception we should note is not a part of generally accepted scientific theory. I shall now quote my example from his p. 271:

During immense periods in the course of evolution, the radial, obscurely stirred up by the action of the *Prime Mover ahead*, was only able to express itself, in diffuse aggregates, in animal consciousness. And at this stage, not being able, above them, to attach themselves to a support whose order of simplicity was greater than their own, the nuclei were hardly formed before they began to disaggregate. But as soon as, through reflection, a type of unity appeared no longer closed or even centred, but punctiform, the sublime physics of centres came into play. When they became centres, and therefore persons, the elements could at last begin to react, directly as such, to the personalising action of the centre of centres. When consciousness broke through the critical surface of hominisation, it really passed from divergence to convergence and changed, so to speak, both hemisphere and pole. Below that critical " equator " lay the relapse into multiplicity; above it, the plunge into growing and irreversible unification. Once formed, a reflective centre can no longer change except by involution upon itself. To outward appearance, admittedly, man becomes corrupted just like any animal. But here and there we find an inverse function of the phenomenon. By death, in the animal, the radial is reabsorbed into the tangential, while in man it escapes and is liberated from it. So we come to escape from entropy by turning back to Omega: the *hominisation* of death itself.

He had, of course, earlier on, also explained what he means by such terms as punctiform, hominisation, etc., but this is hardly the way to conduct a *reasoned* scientific argument. His so-called " radial energy ", which began as physical, gradually, as the book proceeds, becomes converted into " spiritual energy " which is, as we have just seen, liberated in the case of man from the physical system at death. How can he maintain, as he does, that the book " is not a work on metaphysics . . . but purely and simply a scientific treatise "?

believing he was enunciating a scientific theory. The book has its place in literature, not as a scientific work but for its spiritual insight.

Those who, by intuition and religious experience, are convinced of the reality of what we may call the spiritual side of man, want to see a closely reasoned statement of how this can be reconciled with, indeed linked to, evolution theory as accepted by the majority of orthodox biologists. This, I believe, is one of the most urgent needs of the present day. I think it is not impossible, but it must be presented with the greatest care. It is so easy for those who have the enthusiasm of spiritual conviction to imagine that they are using logic when all the time they are unconsciously presenting a sadly biased or unbalanced argument. I know very well that I am taking this risk; I will do my best to guard against it.

Now in what remains of this first introductory lecture let us take a brief general view of the evolutionary process as a whole. You will not expect me to spend any time in reviewing the facts which support the doctrine of descent; I will only remind you of the five main sources of such evidence which were collected together by Darwin and his followers to establish its reality. They are the study of comparative anatomy, embryology (the study of the development of an animal from its egg to its adult state), palæontology (the fossil record of evolution in the rocks), the facts of the geographical distribution of animals, and lastly the science of plant and animal breeding: *i.e.* genetics. If anyone is doubtful about it all there are legions of books at hand to provide the information, not forgetting, of course, Darwin's mine of evidence in *The Origin of Species*. I want instead to ask you to look for a moment a little more closely at the actual record of the process as seen in the long fossil history, without at present discussing the theory behind it; that will come later.

The far-off Cambrian period, now dated with reasonable certainty as beginning just over 500 million years ago, shows us, by its fossils, that quite advanced representatives of all the main divisions of the animal kingdom, except the true vertebrates, were already well established. Before that the rocks are so old or have undergone such changes that very few remains have survived and those which have are exceedingly obscure. It is quite clear, however, from the highly organised nature of the animals found as fossils at the beginning of the Cambrian era—the crustaceans, the molluscs, the brachiopods (lamp-shells), the echinoderms (sea-urchin-like animals), the worms, etc.—

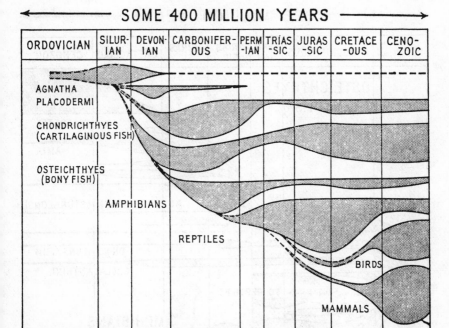

SOME 400 MILLION YEARS

ORDOVICIAN	SILUR-IAN	DEVON-IAN	CARBONIFER-OUS	PERM-IAN	TRÍAS-SIC	JURAS-SIC	CRETACE-OUS	CENO-ZOIC

AGNATHA
PLACODERMI

CHONDRICHTHYES
(CARTILAGINOUS FISH)

OSTEICHTHYES
(BONY FISH)

AMPHIBIANS

REPTILES

BIRDS

MAMMALS

MAN

1. A graphic representation of the origin and relative success of the main vertebrate groups with the passage of time since the Ordovician period of some 400 million years ago. The comparative abundance of the different groups is roughly indicated by the thickness of the bands. Redrawn and slightly rearranged from a chart by Professor Alfred S. Romer in his *Vertebrate Palæontology*.

that life, of some kind, must have been in existence for at least some 1,500 million years before that. There must have been a long evolution before even the appearance of the multi-cellular animals.

As we examine the various layers of sedimentary rocks which have been laid down in the different periods with the passage of time, we find the fossils in a definite sequence from below upwards; these indeed show us the actual changes which have taken place in long lines of related forms from the more primitive in the past to the modern types of today. They do not fit together in just one or a few paths, but in hundreds, nay thousands upon thousands of lines in a branching system. In different periods of the earth's history we see some groups

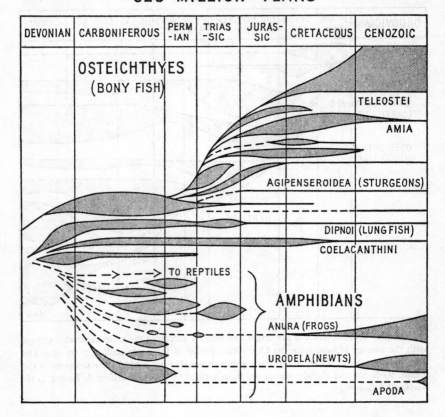

2. The evolution of the main groups of bony fish and amphibians arranged similarly to fig. 1 and also redrawn from Romer. Note the arrow marked " to reptiles " among the most primitive amphibians; at this point should be added the chart in fig. 3.

of animals being more successful than others. A few time-charts will illustrate this. In fig. 1, for example, we see in broad outline the development and relative success of the main vertebrate groups over the last 400 million years. We see the approximate points of origin of one group from another: the reptiles from the amphibia, the amphibia from the bony fish and so on. The varying width of the bands representing the different groups indicates their relative success

← ——— **225 MILLION YEARS** ——— →

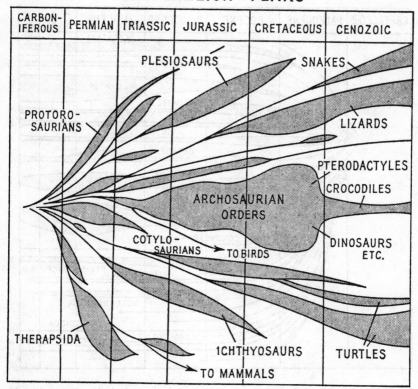

CARBON-IFEROUS	PERMIAN	TRIASSIC	JURASSIC	CRETACEOUS	CENOZOIC

3. The evolution of the main groups of reptiles arranged as in former figures and again redrawn from Romer. The archosaurian orders (crocodiles, pterodactyls, dinosaurs, etc.) have been massed together in one band for simplicity; they should be represented by eight separate diverging lines (shown by Romer in another chart) each as important as the other main lines shown here and each, except for the crocodiles, becoming extinct at the end of the Cretaceous period. The thin line reaching the present day, between the bands representing the lizards and the crocodiles, is for *Sphenodon punctatus*, the tuatara, the single representative of an ancient mesozoic group of reptiles, lingering on in isolation on some small islands off New Zealand. Note the arrows showing the points of origin of the birds and mammals; the latter leads on to fig. 4.

with the passage of time as judged by the numbers of the different kinds of fossil found in the succeeding periods. We see clearly the great outburst of reptiles in the Mesozoic period with their subsequent decline and replacement by the birds and mammals; we also see the

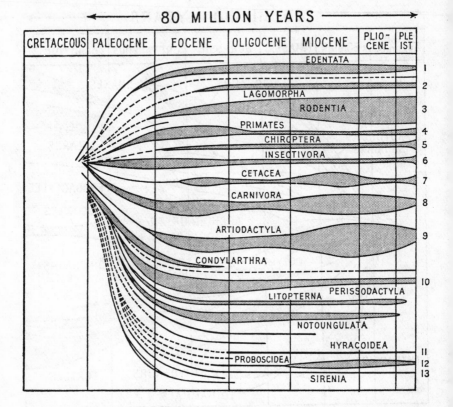

4. The history of the different orders of the placental mammals showing their remarkably rapid radiation in the early Paleocene; also redrawn from Romer. The common names of the main representatives of the different orders, which are referred to by the numbers on the right of the chart, are as follows: (1) anteaters, sloths and armadillos; (2) hares and rabbits; (3) rats, mice and other rodents; (4) lemurs, monkeys, apes and man; (5) bats; (6) shrews, moles, hedgehogs, etc.; (7) whales, dolphins and porpoises; (8) cats, dogs, bears, seals, etc.; (9) oxen, sheep, deer, antelopes, camels, etc.; (10) rhinoceroses, tapirs and horses; (11) the hyrax (or rock coney); (12) elephants; (13) sea-cows: the manatee and the dugong.

earlier rise and decline of the amphibia, and the continued and increasing success of the bony fish which, of course, were never in competition with the newer terrestrial stocks. We shall see just the same sort of thing if we look in a little more detail: for example in

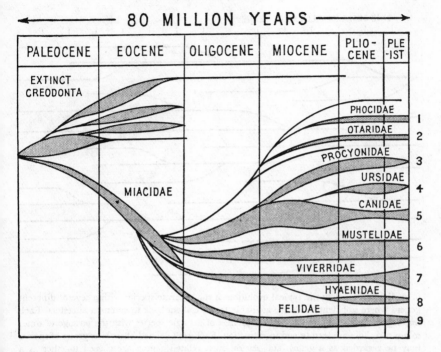

5. The evolution of the main families of just one of the orders of placental mammals: the Carnivora. Note the radiation of the modern forms replacing the more primitive creodonts which became extinct at the end of the Eocene. The common names of the typical members of the families, referred to by the numbers at the right of the figure, are as follows: (1) seals; (2) sealions; (3) racoons and pandas; (4) bears; (5) dogs; (6) weasels, martens, otters, skunks; (7) civets; (8) hyenas; and (9) cats.

figs. 2, 3 and 4 we see respectively similar time-charts of the main groups comprising the amphibia and the bony fish, of the reptiles and of the placental mammals. All these charts, and the next one, are redrawn in a simplified form from those given by Professor Alfred S. Romer in his *Vertebrate Palæontology* and are made with his kind permission. In fig. 3 all the archosaurian reptiles have been massed together for simplicity of representation; they should really be shown as eight distinct diverging lines each as prominent and as important as the other lines in the chart; the great outburst of these many different kinds of reptile adapted to various kinds of life, such as swimming, running, flying, etc., in the Mesozoic age is as striking as the later

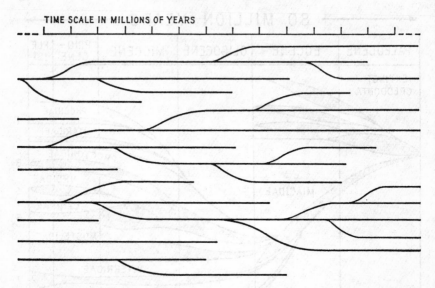

6. A diagram to show the typical evolution of the separate species within several different genera where sufficient fossils are available to trace them back to common ancestors. Each line represents the continuing *whole population* of a single species with the passage of time; many such lines are seen to end in extinction. Each well defined branching group of species may be regarded as a genus, and several such related genera are classed together as a family.

adaptive radiation of the different orders of placental mammals shown in fig. 4. These outbursts of new forms in a relatively short period of time are striking features in the evolutionary story which have not, I believe, hitherto been fully understood; I shall return to them again in a later lecture (p. 198) and discuss their significance in the light of later findings. Fig. 5, in still more detail, shows the evolution going on, differentiating the various families, in just one order of mammals: the Carnivora. Similar charts could be shown for all the important orders of vertebrates, and for the different groups of invertebrate animals as well: the molluscs, the echinoderms (*i.e.* sea-urchins and starfish-like animals), the crustaceans and so on. The occurrence of evolution is no theory; it is a well documented history.

Now if we look still more closely we shall see within each of these lesser groups, if sufficiently well represented in the fossil record, the intricate branching of the evolutionary tree giving the descent of the

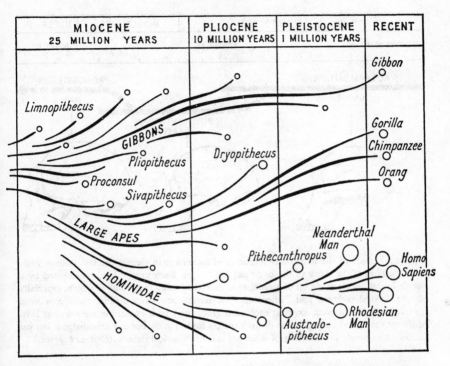

| MIOCENE 25 MILLION YEARS | PLIOCENE 10 MILLION YEARS | PLEISTOCENE 1 MILLION YEARS | RECENT |

7. The evolution of the main groups in the anthropoid branch of the primate stock, redrawn, and slightly rearranged, from Professor Sir Wilfred Le Gros Clark's *Antecedents of Man*. The sizes of the circles represent the relative sizes of the brains judged by the sizes of the cranial cavities. Note that the large brain of modern man only appeared in the Pleistocene and that Neanderthal man apparently had a larger brain than *Homo sapiens* (and yet he became extinct).

genera and the individual species; and we shall see line after line ending in extinction as represented in fig. 6. Far more evolutionary lines come to an end than continue. For every species existing today there must be perhaps hundreds of lines which have perished in the past; and it is estimated that there are close on a million different species of animals existing at the present day.[1]

Parts of the fossil record are now surprisingly complete in detail such as those of the history of the horse, the elephants, the camels and

[1] Over 600,000 arthropod species are known in the museums of the world, the majority being insects.

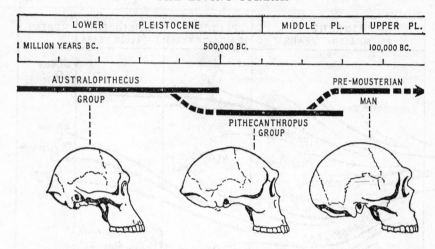

8. A time chart of the immediate forebears of modern man during the last million years
with outlines of the skulls of the principal fossil types. Each group, here represented by a
single broad line, is made up of a number of different fossil forms, some of which, especially
in the Australopithecus and Pithecanthropus groups, are given distinct specific or even
generic rank by different experts; each such group may be a branching system of at least
different races, and perhaps some distinct species (as in fig. 6), but our knowledge is not yet
sufficient to justify the charting of what are still hypothetical details. (*Continued opposite*)

many more mammalian groups; almost equally complete are a number
of invertebrate histories, and as Professor Sir Wilfred Le Gros Clark
said to me the other day, the fossil history of Man's ancestors is now,
with all the wonderful African discoveries, getting almost as complete
as that of the horse. Fig. 7 shows a time-chart of the main anthropoid
branches of the Primate Stock and fig. 8 the immediate forebears of
modern Man in the last million years. It is not my intention at this
point to discuss the factors concerned with the emergence of Man such
as the development of speech, making possible the association of
ideas, accompanied by the selection of larger and larger brains to
give vastly more nerve-cell connections; that will come later. Here I
merely want to show the extent to which modern research has demonstrated that Man is indeed part of the same evolutionary process; to
round off the series I will compare, in fig. 9, charts of the cortical
areas of the brain of an ape, and of Man.

If we look for a moment at the *proportion* of the total time scale of

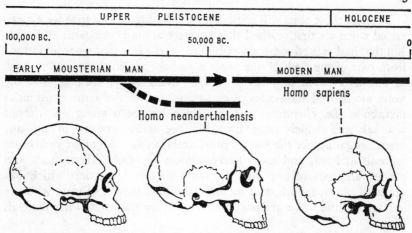

8 (*continued*). The point of origin of Neanderthal man is disputed; I follow Le Gros Clark in his *Antecedents of Man* in showing the species as an offshoot from early Mousterian man (some authors would trace the descent either from pre-Mousterian man or direct from a Pithecanthropus stock). The outlines of the skulls representing each group, which are drawn to the same scale and are one-sixth natural size, are also taken from Le Gros Clark. Rhodesian man which is shown separately in fig. 7 is here included with *Homo neanderthalensis*.

life occupied by *Homo sapiens* we see it as less than $\frac{1}{2000}$th of it,[1] and, of course, the period of civilised man is far, far less. Evolution is still proceeding, only now we call it history, being in the new psychosocial phase as Huxley calls it; it is surely unlikely that we have yet completely unravelled the puzzle of it all. It is but a few hundred years since Copernicus and Galileo shattered the mediæval dream by showing Man that his earth was not at the centre of the Universe; and their successors have revealed the immensity of space around him. It is only a century since Darwin and his followers showed not only that Man is not a separate creation, but one of a vast number of evolving organisms and one that has had its human characters for only a tiny fraction of life's time scale. We must return to this later when we consider the relation of natural theology to Man in the next series of lectures. We may well ask, Where in this long history did the theistic or (to use Otto's term[2]) numinous thread begin?

[1] We have just seen (p. 21) that life must have been in existence for some 2,000 million years.

[2] Rudolf Otto: *The Idea of the Holy* (English translation, 1923).

I expect most of us will remember the feeling of awe that we experienced when we first realised that we were actually one with an organism that had existed some 2,000 million years ago—that we were formed from part of the flesh of our parents and they from theirs and so back in one long chain into the past. Our living body, although not the same atoms and molecules of course, is part of the same continuous metabolic (*i.e.* chemical) process which has been going on without a break and which once provided the basis for life in an ancestral organism in the far off pre-Cambrian age. All other vertebrate animals at least, and most likely, almost certainly, all animals and plants, are part of one and the same chemical reaction which has gradually been modified in an almost infinite variety of ways with the passage of time. We are part of a vast living stream flowing through time.

This is the stream we shall be discussing in different aspects as our lectures proceed. This metaphoric, metabolic, river of life flows forward and is continually splitting up into separate streams, those of the newly evolving species, as it advances; likewise we see countless such specific streams in the past becoming less and less, mere trickles, and eventually drying up as this or that rarity becomes extinct. In spite of these losses the advancing stream has extraordinary powers of building itself up. Life, if unchecked and with sufficient food to nourish it, would in all too short a time smother the world. We see it pushing itself into all kinds of unlikely corners and parasitically into the bodies of other forms of life. Far back in the fossil record of the Palæozoic age we see branches of the stream leaving its original home in the sea and advancing upon the newly raised continents of the land, first the plants derived from the marine algæ and then the animals feeding upon the plants.

When we look at the life that has invaded the land and consider it as a floral and faunistic layer, the biosphere as it is sometimes called, covering the earth, we realise how thin a film it is compared with the bulk of the globe; it is like a mould growing on the surface of a cheese, nay, finer still, almost like the bloom on the surface of a plum. We ourselves are part of that film; how insignificant it might seem to a distant observer from another world and yet how wonderful! We are living in an age far greater than that of the conquest of the land by the first amphibians; at any moment now, if disaster does not overtake us, this living stream will hurl its first drops of humanity across the

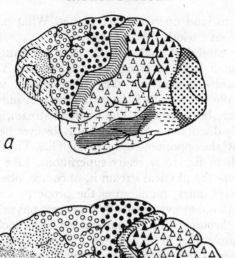

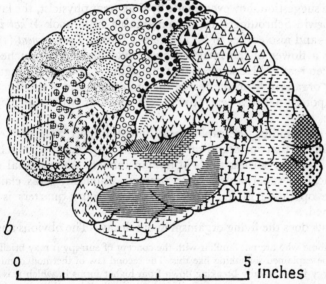

9. A comparison of the brain of *a*, a chimpanzee, and *b*, of man, drawn to the same scale and seen from the left side. The various regions of the cerebral cortex having similar functions in the two brains (sensory, motor and association areas of different kinds) are shown by similar marking. Apart from the general increase in size, the enormous enlargement (in proportion to the rest of the cortex) of the frontal region with its new association areas, in the brain of man, is particularly striking. From *Human Biology*, by Harrison, Weiner, Tanner and Barnicot, after Walker and Brodmann.

vault of space to land upon another planet. What power this living process has! What curiosity! What spirit!

We must be careful of analogies, for they are dangerous; we may easily be bemused into mistaking fancy for reality. Yet is it entirely folly to compare—or contrast—this living stream with a physical river system? We see that as it flows in *time* it is indeed like a river flowing in space, but *in reverse*. The physical stream, always running downhill, rarely divides into branches but is for ever being fed by little tributaries—just the opposite to our stream of life. The fact is so obvious that my sketch in fig. 10 is really superfluous. Like the rest of the material universe the physical stream is, of course, obeying the second law of thermodynamics; manifesting the property we term entropy. Was the suggestion, however, made by that great physicist, the late Professor Erwin Schrödinger in his remarkable little book *What is Life?* (1944)—and also earlier in his *Science and Human Temperament* (1935)— entirely a flower of the imagination or had his insight touched here some deep reality? He suggests that one of the characters distinguishing a living organism from the rest of the material world is the fact that it feeds upon "negative entropy".[1] He explains what he means as follows:

It is by avoiding the rapid decay into the inert state of "equilibrium", that an organism appears so enigmatic; so much so, that from the earliest times of human thought some special non-physical or supernatural force (*vis viva*, entelechy) was claimed to be operative in the organism, and in some quarters is still claimed.

How does the living organism avoid decay? The obvious answer

[1] For those who are not familiar with the concept of entropy it may briefly, if too simply, be explained something like this. The second law of thermodynamics states that energy is continually breaking down from higher forms in which it is capable of performing work to lower ones in which it is finally " bound " or unable to do work. The universe appears to be gradually running down as the amount of degraded energy continually increases. This degradation of energy is termed entropy, and its increase might be spoken of as " positive " entropy. By " *negative* " entropy is implied the reverse as when, for example, the energy of sunlight is used by plants to build up, through more complex chemical states, *higher* forms of energy which may later be used to do work in the plants themselves, or when, as food, their products are stored by animals for use as fuel for muscular exercise, or indeed when they are stored (by chance) to do work *at a much later date*, as in the fossil plants which we burn as coal, or as the oil remains (from long dead marine organisms) with which we drive our cars and jet aircraft.

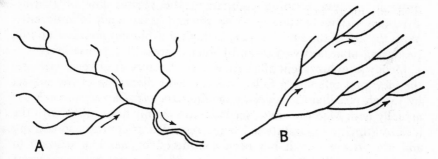

10. A comparison between the physical river system (A) flowing downhill in space and the stream of life (B) flowing in *time* and continually branching into new streams as its reproductive pressure forces it into new channels.

is: By eating, drinking, breathing and (in the case of plants) assimilating. The technical term is *metabolism*. The Greek word (μεταβάλλειν) means change or exchange. Exchange of what? Originally the underlying idea is, no doubt, exchange of material. (e.g. the German for metabolism is *Stoffwechsel*.) That the exchange of material should be the essential thing is absurd. Any atom of nitrogen, oxygen, sulphur, etc., is as good as any other of its kind; what could be gained by exchanging them? . . .

What then is that precious something contained in our food which keeps us from death? That is easily answered. Every process, event, happening—call it what you will; in a word, everything that is going on in Nature means an increase of the entropy of the part of the world where it is going on. Thus a living organism continually increases its entropy—or, as you may say, produces positive entropy—and thus tends to approach the dangerous state of maximum entropy, which is death. It can only keep aloof from it, *i.e.* alive, by continually drawing from its environment negative entropy—which is something very positive as we shall immediately see. What an organism feeds upon is negative entropy. Or, to put it less paradoxically, the essential thing in metabolism is that the organism succeeds in freeing itself from all the entropy it cannot help producing while alive.

As to whether this idea is really a valid one, opinion seems divided. I agree with Huxley in liking it; in his introduction to Teilhard de Chardin's *Phenomenon of Man* he says of evolution: " It is an anti-

entropic process, running counter to the second law of thermodynamics with its degradation of energy and its tendency to uniformity.
With the aid of the sun's energy, biological evolution marches up hill,
producing increased variety and higher degrees of organisation."

Medawar in his recent Herbert Spencer Lecture at Oxford[1] criticises
the view and refers to a fuller and excellent discussion of the subject
by Joseph Needham in an essay on *Evolution and Thermodynamics*.[2] But
actually both Medawar and Needham are mainly quarrelling with the
idea of " higher organisation " being regarded as contrary to entropy
and also in the way it has been considered by some in relation to
what is now called " information theory ". I am not here concerned
with this; although it is clear that throughout the whole organic progression from the simpler molecules up to the more advanced animal
structures we see higher and higher levels of integration being developed,
as Needham himself[3] and others have emphasised. It is the simpler
side of it, that of the living stream " marching up hill " that I find
interesting in relation to the analogy of a river in reverse. This idea
may be thought just too naïve to be considered, but sometimes the
simple hides the more profound. Of course I realise that any animal
goes up hill by using fuel just as does a man-made engine—and as
a rule it may be driven up mountains, or from the sea on to the
land (or in the reverse direction for that matter) by competition for
food; and further that it is the great reproductive pressure, driving
its stream forward, together with new adaptations fitting the animal
to more and more difficult terrains, that we are considering, and
not simply upward locomotion. Nevertheless out of this process of
evolution, from *somewhere* has come the urge, or love of adventure, in
Man that can drive him to risk his life in climbing Everest or in reaching the South Pole or the Moon. Is it altogether too naïve to believe
that this exploratory drive, this curiosity, has had its beginnings in
some deep-seated part of animal behaviour which is fundamental to
the stream of life?

I am not a vitalist in the old-fashioned sense of the word. I fully
expect that the whole of an animal's bodily mechanism will be resolved
in terms of biophysics and biochemistry; but I am not a materialist in

[1] Published in *Encounter*, vol. 21, pp. 35–43, 1963.
[2] In his *Time: the Refreshing River*, 1943.
[3] In his 1937 Herbert Spencer Lecture at Oxford: " Integrative Levels: a Revalua-
tion of the Idea of Progress " also published in *Time: the Refreshing River*.

that I am blind to the reality of consciousness in the organic world. As yet we just do not know where, or how, it relates to the physio-chemical system; and our science, at present, cannot deal with it. As a naturalist, however, I do not pretend that it does not exist, and I do not subscribe to the quite unproven dogma that consciousness only appeared at some point in the anthropoid stock. To me, from observations of natural history, but *not yet* of science, it appears likely (perhaps only because we know them best through our horses and dogs) that the higher vertebrates are conscious. To the part of the universe to which consciousness belongs, I think it likely that the " forces " (note the inverted commas) of curiosity, love and the numinous also belong but that they are somehow experienced not by means of the ordinary bodily sense organs. And what do we really know of the nature of the sub-conscious, although we know of its existence through psycho-analysis? But I go too fast, all this is not for this lecture, but much later. Here I am merely echoing Schrödinger and Huxley in pointing out that the stream does in fact flow up hill or against resistance. I would only remark that just as some physicists feel uncertain about the nature of gravity we would do well at present not to be dogmatic about the springs of animal behaviour; and for the moment I will leave it at that.

There is one other aspect of this living stream I would like to emphasise in this introduction before proceeding, in the next lecture, to discuss the various theories that have been advanced to explain it. In presenting the stream of life in such diagrammatic sketches as I have used one may easily be misled into loosely imagining these lines to represent lines of evolving individuals. Individuals don't evolve—only populations do. Each one of these paths represents a vast population. A great deal of faulty evolutionary thought has resulted in the past from neglecting this very obvious fact. The error has come about by people forgetting for the moment—and it is extraordinary that they should—that we and most other animals are bi-sexually reproducing creatures. Either in the asceticism of the cloistered study many seem to have overlooked it—or they have found it easier to work out their theories as if animals reproduced without sex, by budding or simple division, as may an amœba or a sea anemone. They seem to have thought that sexual reproduction would not markedly change the picture, but only slightly complicate it. The truth is, of course, that it is *radically* different.

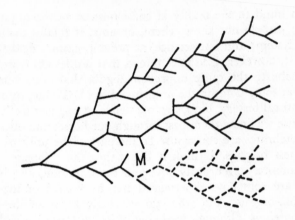

11. Evolution in a non-sexual organism which reproduces by budding or by dividing in two; the species goes on multiplying with no genetical change until a mutation occurs at M and gives rise to a new strain (shown in broken line).

In the diagram in fig. 11 (above), we see how many people loosely think of evolution—each little branch representing a new individual; so the process is thought to proceed until a new mutation at M leads to a new and slightly different race which will come into competition with the more normal kinds and eventually either be more successful, to become the new dominating type, or be eliminated. This, of course, is nothing like the real process, except for very lowly forms which have no sex. A somewhat better conception of the stream is that shown in fig. 12 which is taken from H. S. Jennings's *Life and Death*, but even that is too much of a simplification. The joining and branching lines are here intended to represent the parental and filial gametes (reproductive cells) and the horizontal lines the individuals, each with its soma (or body) represented by the dark blob. I like, instead, to represent a section of the stream as I have shown it in fig. 13 where the horizontal line with a circle attached represents an individual at the present time; it is just one of the thousands or millions of individuals making up the species stream at any one moment (a few other members are shown in broken line). The two horizontal lines to the left of it represent the parents, further to the left are four lines representing the grandparents and so on; to the right are the gametes pairing with those from other lines to give the coming generations.

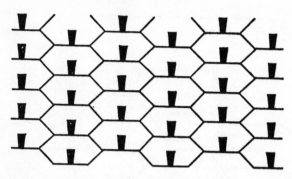

12. The living stream in a sexually reproducing organism as seen by H. S. Jennings in his *Life and Death*. The lines represent the flow of the genetical material and the black objects the bodies of the individuals; the line of ancestry from any individual, if traced back, forks into the two parents at each generation. This diagram, however, does not convey the actual multiplexity of the genetic stream; a truer expression of it is attempted in fig. 13.

Have you ever thought how many direct ancestors you might have had living at the time of say the Norman Conquest, nine hundred years ago? I believe it was H. G. Wells, in one of his books, who surprised his readers by asking this question. If we take as an average period for a generation, *i.e.* from one birth to the next in the chain, as 30 years, there will be 30 generations going back to 1066. If we did not have the same great-great-grandparents again and again the little table, Table 1 on p. 39, will show that we would have had over 1,000 million ancestors alive at that time! The total population of Great Britain at the time of Queen Anne was said to be only about five million and at the time of the Norman Conquest it was probably much less. What does it mean? It can only mean that we have all not only had the same great-great-great-grandparents, as it were, again and again, but also that most of us have more likely than not shared the same ancestors many times and that we are all more closely related to each other than we ever suspected.

It is such complex populations that are evolving. This is the nature of the living stream we must consider, one stretching back over 2,000 million years. It is a stream in which the little genetic currents continually meet and split apart again; and at each meeting and splitting the genetic material is shuffled into new arrangements giving new variations. We individuals are the little eddies at these junctions—

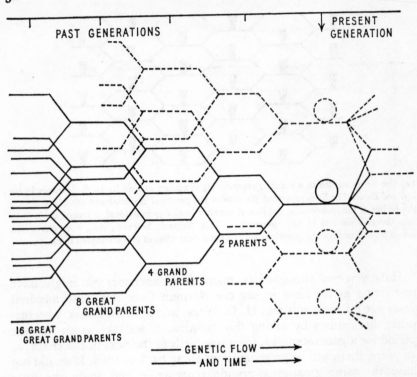

13. A diagram of the genetic stream of life. The horizontal unbroken line with a circle attached represents *one* individual of a population at the present time; the lines linked to it coming from the left represent its past ancestral individuals and the radiating lines to the right, joining with the lines from the other individuals (shown in *broken* line) represent the reproductive cells fusing to form the coming new generation to the right. If we consider a population of millions, many having common ancestors, we may imagine the true complexity of the stream.

dare I say it?—little eddies caused by love. When Gilbert sang so gaily in *Iolanthe*, " It's love that makes the world go round," he was expressing a profound truth of natural history. He sang, surely of the round of life and not the rotation of the world as a philosopher of my acquaintance thought.[1] Sexual attraction is certainly one of the forces

[1] Gilbert's line, of course, is found earlier in *Alice in Wonderland* and can indeed be traced back to Dante's " Love . . . that moves the sun in heaven and all the stars " as seen in *The Oxford Dictionary of English Proverbs*, II, Second Edition, p. 391, which

TABLE I

Generations back	Ancestors	Generations back	Ancestors
1	2	16	65,536
2	4	17	131,072
3	8	18	262,144
4	16	19	524,288
5	32	20	1,048,576
6	64	21	2,097,152
7	128	22	4,194,304
8	256	23	8,388,608
9	512	24	16,777,216
10	1,024	25	33,554,432
11	2,048	26	67,108,864
12	4,096	27	134,217,728
13	8,192	28	268,435,456
14	16,384	29	536,870,912
15	32,768	30	1,073,741,824

that makes the river of life flow forward. But I don't believe that all love is sexual, parental or filial love; there is the love of life and love of adventure, and for some of us what we call the love of God. If some feel shocked at what may seem the frivolity of my quotation in this context, let me assure them that I am indeed earnest in my intention. I believe what I have just said about love is not out of harmony with the findings of biblical scholars; in that great mine of evidence for Man's religious experience, the Bible, we see a striking and significant change in the meanings and use of the words for love.[1] Here a long period of history is showing us some important changes in that psycho-social phase of evolution we are now in. But this, again, is another story and part of the natural theology which comes later.

The river is not always calm; there are rapids at times and occasion-

---

also notes that Blackmore, 1712, refers the belief to Aristotle. So my philosophical friend was right in his origin but not surely in Gilbert's meaning.

[1] In the volume on *Love* by Quell and Stauffer 1933 (translated by J. R. Coates, 1949), in the series on *Bible Key Words from Gerhard Kittel's Theologisches Wörtebuch zum Neuen Testament* we see, for example, the change in emphasis in the Old Testament of the Hebrew word *ahebh* from sexual love to love of righteousness; or in pre-biblical Greek we see the transition from sensuous *eros*, through the friendly love of *philia* to the *agape* which becomes the predominant love in the New Testament.

ally, where different waters meet, hate—racial hatred—may throw the torrent into turmoil. Love and hate, joy and sorrow, beauty, zest and despair—yes, and the sense of the sacred—are all in the nature of the stream as we ourselves see and experience it, as a part of it. But they cannot be shown in my diagram. And again what about consciousness? When we consider such problems, as indeed we should, we realise how little biology yet touches the things that really matter in life. But we must be patient; science must go slowly over this difficult ground, making certain of each step. The new science of animal behaviour is leading us forward.

If there are parts of reality, like beauty and joy, with which, by its nature, the scientific method can *never* deal, we must not fall into the error of denying their fundamental importance in the stream of life just because they lie more in the fields of natural history, art and religion.[1] What we are looking at in my diagram of the stream may only be, as it were, its " physical skeleton "; and along with it may flow a paraphysical element which is no more, and no less, mysterious in its nature and relation to the physical than is consciousness to the physiology of the body.

Whether there is anything or not in such a speculation, and we must consider it later, we *do* know that there *is* now another " paraphysical " stream flowing forward in time: the stream of thoughts and ideas handed on by the spoken, written and printed word—and by works of art. It is the stream that Sir Julian Huxley and Teilhard de Chardin rightly talk so much about. It goes without saying that this stream of thought—continually made manifest in the consciousness of Man— has also its physical (man-made) skeleton extending in time: to be found in libraries, art galleries, collections of gramophone records, films and the like. This naturally grows, evolves and throws out new branches like the organic stream to which it is related; the old wax cylinders of Edison Bell's phonograph give way to plastic discs and to the magnetic tapes of the modern sound recorders.

We now begin to see the possibility that this new element, so recent in time, may come to modify the nature and course of the whole stream itself.

---

[1] I do not wish to be dogmatic about the limits of science; as I shall explain later (p. 265), I do not believe that all science can be resolved into physics and chemistry.

LECTURE II

EARLY STREAMS OF EVOLUTIONARY
THOUGHT

Today, as I briefly reminded you at the end of the last lecture, it is being realised that with the development of modern man organic evolution has passed into a new phase of operation—one which is almost as striking an innovation as the beginning of life itself. It is what Sir Julian Huxley has called the psycho-social phase or what Teilhard de Chardin means by the emergence of his " noösphere ". It is characterised by what Waddington calls the working of the socio-genetic system; by this he means that evolution is no longer proceeding just by the transference of the physical genetical material—the hereditary genes—but by the handing on and development of ideas. Acquired knowledge is continually passed on: at first it was transmitted in speech, then in writing, next in printed books, and now in all manner of new means of communication. It is constantly being added to by experience. We see emerging a new element in our stream of life: the verbal inheritance of acquired experience and ideas.

In this and the next lecture I want very briefly to discuss the development of the ideas concerning the mechanism of the evolutionary process. It is important that we should be clear just how the present-day views have been built up. For some of you I will be covering familiar ground, but even so, I think, it will be worth while, in view of later discussions, for you to know whether I do or do not hold the same views regarding some of these ideas as you do. Also it will be convenient for me to have briefly reviewed this history, because, later on, I shall want to refer back to some of these earlier conceptions; indeed we shall see some of them coming to life again in a new form.

Yet again, there is another reason for recounting what to some will be a familiar story, for it provides an excellent illustration of this new phase in the nature of the living stream; in it we see the emergence, conflict, rejection or survival of various ideas which are thrown up as it flows along in time. Few lines of thought, considering the short time since its acceptance, have affected history more.

In this lecture I want to follow the growth of the idea of evolution up to and including the publication of Darwin's *Origin of Species*. This is the period which shows us the emergence of the two great rival doctrines: that of Darwin and the earlier one of Lamarck. We must be quite sure about the implications of each, for about one at least there has been, and still is, a good deal of misunderstanding; it is well to clear this up as soon as possible. In the next lecture I shall deal with the modern period; here we must go to the beginnings.

The idea of evolution goes back, of course, to classical times. Let us hear what Lucretius had to say on the extinction and survival of species. I quote from R. E. Latham's new translation of Book V.[1]

In those days the earth attempted also to produce a host of monsters, grotesque in build and aspect—hermaphrodites, halfway between the sexes yet cut off from either, creatures bereft of feet or dispossessed of hands, dumb, mouthless brutes, or eyeless and blind, or disabled by the adhesion of their limbs to the trunk, so that they could neither do anything nor go anywhere nor keep out of harm's way nor take what they needed. These and other such *monstrous and misshapen births were created. But all in vain.* Nature debarred them from increase. They could not gain the coveted flower of maturity nor procure food nor be coupled by the arts of Venus. . . .

In those days, again, *many species must have died out altogether* and failed to reproduce their kind. Every species that you now see drawing the breath of life has been protected and preserved from the beginning of the world either by cunning or by prowess or by speed. In addition, there are many that survive under human protection because their usefulness has commended them to our care.

How he reminds us of Darwin in comparing the survival of animals in nature and in domestication, but he was writing nearly two thousand years earlier; he was in part probably getting his ideas from still earlier days—from Empedocles who held a most extraordinary notion which nevertheless had something of a Darwinian flavour.

[1] In the Penguin Classics—Lucretius: *The Nature of the Universe.*

What little we know of Empedocles comes second-hand from fragments of early writings which tell us that he

held that the first generations of animals and plants were not complete but consisted of separate limbs not joined together; the second, arising from the joining of these limbs, were like creatures in dreams; the third was the generation of whole-matured forms. ... Here sprang up many faces without necks, arms wandered without shoulders, unattached, and eyes strayed alone, in need of foreheads. ... But as one divine element mingled further with another, these things fell together as each chanced to meet other, and many other things besides these were constantly resulting. ... Wherever, then, everything turned out as it would have if it were happening for a purpose, there the creatures survived, being accidentally compounded in a suitable way; but where this did not happen, the creatures perished and are perishing still as Empedocles says of his " man-faced ox-progeny ".[1]

It is thought that he was attempting to account for the origin of some of the creatures of Greek mythology, centaurs, chimeras, etc., which he believed had some foundation in fact, having once lived and become extinct. In doing so he had the glimmerings of the natural selection theory: only those chance combinations which were efficient in relation to their environment survived.

Actually the concept of evolution goes back still earlier to the Ionian philosophers, Thales and Anaximander. Thales is said to have taught that all life arose from an aquatic or marine origin and Anaximander had the fantastic idea of man having arisen directly from a fish-like form.[2]

We come now to Aristotle, one of the greatest naturalists of all time. Whether he was an evolutionist is doubtful; most Aristotelian scholars would certainly say that he was not, and there is no doubt that he emphatically dismissed the ideas of Empedocles. However, there are others, including Henry Fairfield Osborn, the author of that well-known history *From the Greeks to Darwin*, who take the opposite view.

[1] I quote from the translation given by G. S. Kirk and J. E. Raven in *The Presocratic Philosophers*, Cambridge, 1957.

[2] Censorius *De Die Nat.* 4, 7, translated by Kirk and Raven (*loc. cit.*) writes " Anaximander of Miletus conceived that there arose from heated water and earth either fish or creatures very like fish; in these man grew, in the form of embryos retained within until puberty; then at last the fish-like creatures burst and men and women who were already able to nourish themselves stepped forth."

Osborn discusses these doubts and, after quoting the passages in which Aristotle dismisses the idea of the survival of chance adaptations, he writes:

These passages seem to contain absolute evidence that Aristotle had substantially the modern conception of the Evolution of life, from a primordial, soft mass of living matter to the most perfect forms, and that even in these he believed Evolution was incomplete for they were progressing to higher forms. His argument of the analogy between the operation of natural law, rather than of chance, in the lifeless and in the living world, is a perfectly logical one, and his consequent rejection of the hypothesis of the Survival of the Fittest, a sound induction from his own limited knowledge of Nature. It seems perfectly clear that he placed all under secondary natural laws. If he had accepted Empedocles' hypothesis, he would have been the literal prophet of Darwinism.

It is certainly remarkable what modern ideas Aristotle had, and his knowledge was based upon the study of a very large number of animals. He distinguished some 500 species of vertebrates (mammals, birds and fish) and discussed the life of many invertebrates, including sponges, polyps, cuttle-fish, crustaceans, echinoderms and many others, giving a beautiful description of the hermit crab and being much puzzled over the nature of the ascidians (sea-squirts). He understood adaptation in its modern sense, discussing, for example, the function of the teeth of mammals: incisors for cutting and molars for grinding.

Then, in a remarkable way he foreshadowed an important part of Von Baer's famous Law of Development of 1828. " The embryo," he said, " is an animal before it is a particular animal, its general characteristics appear before the special."[1] He arranged all organisms in an ascending scale of being. " Plants are animate as compared with minerals and inanimate as compared with animals. They have powers of nourishment and reproduction but no feeling or sensibility." Then come the plant animals, the zoophytes. The third step is the development of animals with sensibility—hence a desire for food and other needs of life and hence locomotion to fulfil these desires. Man is the highest point of one long series. Other animals, he said, have the faculty of thought; man alone generalises and forms abstractions. He is physically superior in his erect posture, in his purest and largest blood supply, largest brain and highest temperature.

[1] I quote the translation in E. S. Russell's *Form and Function*.

This certainly looks like an evolutionary idea, but most scholars would say that he was only outlining a grand plan of creation in much the same way as did the 18th-century German transcendental anatomists I shall be discussing presently. Yet for my part I cannot help sharing Osborn's feeling that he had some evolutionary idea but one very different from the materialistic conception of Empedocles. He has almost a Bergsonian conception. " Nature," he says, " is always striving after the most beautiful that is possible "; or again " it is due to the resistance of matter to form that nature can only rise by degrees from the lower to the higher types." In relation to this E. S. Russell has a striking passage in his *The Study of Living Things* (p. 61): " The living thing is not the clay moulded by the potter, nor the harp played upon by the musician. It is the clay modelling itself, or as Aristotle puts it in a beautiful figure, being moulded by Nature herself, without the aid of tools ' but, as it were, with her own hands '."

Here we must leave the ancients. The idea of evolution was lost for a long period, although St. Augustine (A.D. 353–430), perhaps influenced by Aristotle, taught what might be regarded as an evolutionary interpretation of the Book of Genesis.[1] His enlightened views, however, were not accepted as the orthodox teaching of the Church.

Then came the Renaissance, with its general advance in knowledge. Rondelet and Gesner in the 16th century and our own John Ray in the 17th century were the great compilers of the facts of natural history. They were not concerned with speculation, but were providing materials for future discussion. It has, I think, been generally thought that it was the astronomers and mathematicians who had more to do with the scientific revolution than the naturalists. Canon Raven, however, in his Gifford Lectures on *Science and Religion* in 1951[2], gives a very forceful argument for the opposite view. " The work of Gesner," he writes, " was for his contemporaries vastly more influential than

---

[1] He certainly implied a gradual unfolding of creation as in the development of a plant. Osborn in his *From the Greeks to Darwin* gives the following translation from his writings: " even so as in the grain itself there were invisible all things simultaneously which were in time to grow into the tree—so is the world itself to be thought of when God simultaneously created all things . . . not only the heaven with the sun, moon and stars . . . but also those things which the water and the earth produced *potentialiter atque causaliter*; before that, in due time, and after long delays, they grew up in such manner as they are now known to us in those works of God which He is working even at the present hour."

[2] Published by the Cambridge University Press in 1953.

that of Copernicus," and again, " the modern world owes its origin
not to the Renaissance and Reformation, nor yet to Copernicus and
Galileo, but to the ' New Philosophy' as the scientists of the 17th
century called it, of which Francis Bacon was the principal exponent,
and whose central purpose was nothing less than to provide a frame of
reference, consistent in theory and attested by experiment, for the
whole range of physical phenomena if not for all knowledge." He goes
on to show how the scientific outlook towards the end of the 17th
century in the early days of the Royal Society was largely influenced
by our great John Ray and indirectly through him by Cudworth and
the Cambridge Platonists.

While it was the naturalists who provided the material, it was the
philosphers who were the first to bring back the ideas of evolution.
They hit upon the importance of variation. They saw, no doubt
through the work of the naturalists, that species varied and at once
realised that this was the point to which observation should be directed
in attempting to build a theory of evolution. Francis Bacon indeed
seems to have been the first to consider the mutability of species as
possibly the result of the accumulation of variations. He has a striking
passage towards the end of his *New Atlantis* where he predicts the
establishment of a great biological research institute like those of
today. He says

> And we make (by art) in the same orchards and gardens, trees and
> flowers to come earlier or later than their seasons; and to come
> up and bear more speedily, than by their natural course they do.
> We make them also by art greater . . . *and likewise to make divers
> new plants, differing from the vulgar; and to make one tree or plant
> turn into another.*

And the subject is again treated in section VIII of his *Sylva Sylvarum*
where he writes " of the Generation of Plants ", saying among other
things:

> The transmutation of plants one into another is a capital work
> of nature, the transmutation of species being pronounced im-
> possible: it is a thing of difficulty and requires deep search into
> nature; but as there appear some manifest instances of it, the
> opinion of impossibility is here to be rejected, and the means to
> be sought.

As possible factors of change, he suggests alteration in soils, etc.

Both Leibnitz and Spinoza had evolutionary ideas, the former saying "All natural orders of beings present but a single chain in which the different classes of animals, like so many rings, are so closely united that it is not possible either by observation or imagination to determine where one ends or begins."[1] He had been particularly impressed by the infinite variations in the shells of the fossil ammonites being unearthed at that time. Immanuel Kant in 1790, in his *Kritik der Urtheilskraft* (I quote the translation of J. H. Bernard),[2] writes:

The agreement of so many genera of animals in a certain common schema, which appears to be fundamental not only in the structure of their bones, but also in the disposition of their remaining parts—so that with an admirable simplicity of original outline, a great variety of species has been produced by the shortening of one member and the lengthening of another, the involution of this part and the evolution of that—allows a ray of hope. however faint, to penetrate into our minds, that here something may be accomplished by the aid of the principle of the mechanism of Nature (without which there can be no natural science in general). This analogy of forms, which with all their differences seem to have been produced according to a common original type, strengthens our suspicions of an actual relationship between them in their production from a common parent, through the gradual approximation of one animal-genus to another—from those in which the principle of purposes seems to be best authenticated, *i.e.*, from man down to the polyps, and again from this down to mosses and lichens, and finally to the lowest stage of Nature noticeable by us, viz., to crude matter.

Let us now walk along the bank of the river of history and see the various eddies of insight and inference taking shape. I show part of this stream as a time-chart in fig. 14, with the lines representing the lives of the principal contributors to evolutionary thought. There are recognisable three separate streams of such speculation. There is the philosophic one that I have just mentioned, leading up to Kant and then there are two distinct lines of more scientific thought developing independently: one containing the name of Erasmus Darwin and the other leading up to Charles Darwin and Wallace.

Before I come to these other lines, however, I should mention the

---

[1] I quote the translation in H. F. Osborn (*loc. cit.*).
[2] Given by E. S. Russell in his *Form and Function*.

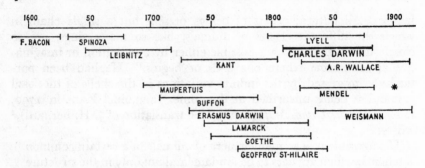

14. A time chart showing the lives of the principal contributors to evolution theory in their historical sequence in the seventeenth, eighteenth and nineteenth centuries. The asterisk marks the rediscovery of Mendel's laws in 1900.

very extraordinary zoological philosophy that developed on the continent at the end of the 18th and the beginning of the 19th centuries, particularly in Germany with the transcendental anatomists Kielmeyer, Oken, Meckel and others, and in France with Geoffroy Saint-Hilaire. It was a movement which later had its final flowering in the work of our own great comparative anatomist Richard Owen immediately before the Darwinian era. It was not directly concerned with evolution, so I have not put it in the chart; nevertheless, as we shall see, it prepared the ground. In France, a little earlier than the German school, in 1745, Bonnet had written[1] on the *échelle des êtres*—the scale of being—in which he arranged all forms of creation in a rising order from the simplest to the most complex: from minerals, through moulds and lichens, plants, sensitive plants and polyps, and up through the animal kingdom to man at the top. It was very like the ascending scale of Aristotle. Although he arranged his list like the rungs of a ladder—and it is amusing to see how he placed some of the rungs[2]—he did *not*, apparently, regard it as an evolutionary series at all but as a plan of creation.

It was the hope of discovering the plan underlying the Deity's design of the world that fired the imagination of the German transcendentalists. While all this is a digression from our main theme, it

[1] In his *Traité d'Insectologie*, 1745.
[2] For example: gall insects—insects—clothes moths—tube worms . . ., or slugs—serpents—water-serpents—eels—creeping fish—fish . . . etc.

had a noteworthy part in the development of biological thought in that it led to the idea of homology which was later going to be so important in discussions on the course that evolution had taken. Goethe was the forerunner of this German school, striving after unity of plan; he invented the term morphology for the study of form, and gave us the first idea of homology. For those who are not biologists I must explain just what we mean by this technical term " homology ". It is used in contrast to analogy and it is convenient to take the definitions given much later by Richard Owen.[1] He described what he called a homologue as " the *same* organ in different animals under every variety of form and function," and he contrasted this with what he called an analogue which he defined as " a part or organ in one animal which has the same function as *another* part or organ in a different animal." As simple examples we might say the arm of a man is homologous with the wing of a bird in that they are both organs built on the same general plan but used for different functions whereas the wing of a bird and the wing of a fly are analogous in that they both serve the same function of flight but are clearly quite different kinds of morphological structure. The interesting part about this, in relation to our present discussion, is that Richard Owen (1804–92) gave no evolutionary implication to his ideas of homology any more than did the German transcendentalists. They considered this principle of homology as an essential element in the Deity's plan—a unit upon which He played an infinite variety of changes. There were what they called archetypes, not ancestral forms but basic designs upon which the different groups of animals had been created by modifications in the essential component (homologous) parts: such were the arche-vertebrate, the arche-articulate[2] and the arche-mollusc types. When the evolution doctrine became established, the ideas of homology and analogy at once took on quite new meanings so that all the work of these early morphologists lay ready for a very different interpretation.

Goethe, although he did not use a term equivalent to homology, first introduced the idea by pointing out that the different parts of a typical plant are essentially modifications of the same structures, for example, the bracts, petals, sepals, etc., can all be derived from the leaf. It should be noted that Goethe, who incidentally became a

---

[1] *Lectures on Invertebrate Animals*, 1843.

[2] The " Articulata " was the old name for what we now call the Arthropoda (the jointed-legged animals such as insects, scorpions and crabs).

believer in evolution, did not go to the length of the wild extravagances of speculation to which his followers went in the transcendentalist school. The latter, leading through the so-called laws of " parallelism " and of " repetition ", carried the idea of similarity of structure to fantastic limits of absurdity. They finished up, for example, by supposing that in the head and body there must be repeated features of design: the upper jaw representing the arms, the lower jaw the legs! It is astonishing to see how ideas can take charge and carry seemingly otherwise intelligent men to such lengths of folly. We laugh, but it should be a warning.

In France was quite a different character, Geoffroy Saint-Hilaire (1772–1844). Although he was greatly influenced by the German transcendentalists and the idea of homology, he went to none of their excesses; he laid the foundations of a truer concept of homology and so prepared the way for its being taken over by the evolutionists. He did himself believe in a very limited evolution, for he discussed the lineal relationship between different kinds of amphibians, and reptiles, but probably thought of them as being only secondary deviations from the original plan laid down at the creation. He it was who actually first used the term homologue—saying, " Les organes des sens sont homologues "[1]—and he gave us what some zoologists still regard as the most satisfactory statement of the concept. In his earlier *Philosophie Anatomique* (1818) he opens with a question: " Can the organisation of vertebrate animals be referred to one uniform type? " ... and then he goes on to ask (and I quote from Russell's summary)[2]

Is it not generally acknowledged that vertebrates are built upon one uniform plan—e.g., the fore limb may be modified for running, climbing, swimming, or flying yet the arrangement of bones remains the same? How else could there be a natural method of classification. ... But it is a vague feeling of likeness—what general principle can be applied? ... Now it is evident that the sole general principle one can apply is given by the position, the relations, and the dependencies of the parts, that is to say, by what I name and include under the term of *connections*.

By this he means that the relative parts of any organ, for example

[1] Geoffroy Saint-Hilaire: Memoire sur la Structure et les Usages de l'Appareil olfactif dans les Poissons ... etc. *Annales des Sciences Naturelles*, Tome 6, 1825, p. 341.

[2] E S. Russell: *Form and Function*, p. 53.

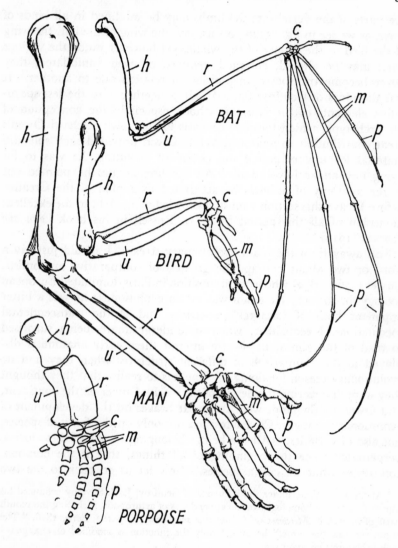

15. A comparison of the homologous bones in the forelimbs of man, a small whale (porpoise), a bird and a bat: *h*, humerus; *r*, radius; *u*, ulna; *c*, carpals; *m*, metacarpals; and *p*, phalanges.

the parts of the vertebrate forelimb, may be modified in all kinds of
ways, as we see in fig. 15, to give us, say, the wing of the bat, the wing
of the bird or the flipper of the whale, yet however much the various
parts may be altered, enlarged, reduced or even annihilated, they
never become transposed in position in relation one to another.[1] It
was the ideas of Geoffroy Saint-Hilaire, together with the less speculative elements of the German school, especially the conception of
the archetype, which formed the basis for our own Richard Owen's
great contribution to anatomy. While Owen provided such splendid
material for understanding the course of evolution, he was to his
dying day an anti-evolutionist. All the homologues he pointed out
in the anatomy of animals he attributed to a plan of the Creator.
Before I leave this section I must acknowledge my debt to the excellent
discussion of all this period by E. S. Russell in his book *Form and
Function* (1916).[2]

Still away from the main evolutionary stream, I should just say a
word or two about perhaps the greatest of comparative anatomists,
Cuvier (1769–1832) who from his position in Paris dominated European
zoology for so long. He again was *not* an evolutionist; he was a bitter
opponent both of Lamarck's doctrines and of the transcendental
speculations. I remember, when an undergraduate, being surprised
to read of the almost passionate interest these early anatomists displayed in the comparison of different structures when they had no
evolutionary reason for doing so. One has to realise that they thought
they were discovering the design of the world. Cuvier on the continent,
and Owen in England, were the great brakes on the development of
evolutionary thought. Cuvier insisted not only on the fixity of species,
but also of varieties. " All the beings belonging to one of these forms,
perpetuated since the beginning of all things, that is the creation,
constitutes what we call a species." Now let us go back to the two

---

[1] At the same time, under the influence of Geoffroy, J. C. Savigny produced his
fine studies on the homologies of the appendages of arthropods, including the mouth
parts of insects, in *Mémoires sur les Animaux sans Vertèbres*, part I, Paris, 1816. " The
organ remains the same," he says, " only the function is modified or changed—
such is Nature's constant plan."

[2] Since going to press I have now received a copy of Professor A. J. Cain's paper
"The Perfection of Animals " in *Viewpoints in Biology*, vol. 3, pp. 36–63, 1964. It
contains an excellent discussion of Owen's arguments and their influence upon
Darwin. I am only sorry it has appeared too late for me to make more than this
brief reference to it.

independent streams of evolutionary speculation that I spoke of before this digression: those shown in our chart in fig. 14 (p. 48).

The first scientist, in the modern sense, to turn his thoughts to evolution was perhaps that notable, and remarkably versatile, French mathematician and physicist, Louis Moreau de Maupertuis (1698–1759) who, through his support of Newton's theories, became a Fellow of our Royal Society and was made President of the Berlin Academy by Frederick the Great. In 1745 Maupertuis in his *Venus Physique* put forward a genetical theory to explain " the production of accidental varieties and the succession of these varieties from one generation to another, and finally the establishment or destruction of species," and in 1751 he enlarged and generalised this theory in his *Système de la Nature* when he used this idea to account for the origin of all existing species.[1] To explain inheritance he put forward a theory of pangenesis, which was not un-similar to the one that Darwin propounded more than a hundred years later. An embryo, he said, developed from the union of the seminal fluids of the two parents (the part played by cells in reproduction was not at that time understood) and each fluid, he thought, contained particles derived from all parts of the parent; and on mixing the particles from each parent united in pairs to produce the embryo. Organisms with novel characteristics might then have arisen in the past by the fortuitous change in the seminal fluids, or changes induced by the environment. Both kinds of such changes would be inherited by pangenesis. " Each degree of error would have made a new species and, as a result of repeated variations, would have been made the infinite diversity of the animals we see today." Four years later in his *Essai de Cosmologie* he anticipated the theory of natural selection: " In the fortuitous combinations of the productions of Nature . . . only those with certain adaptive relationships could survive . . . in the other, infinitely greater part, there was neither adaptation nor order. All these last have perished . . . and the species we see today are only the smallest part of those which a blind destiny produced."

Then, also in France, came the first naturalist to be an evolutionist, the great Buffon (1707–88). He indicates his belief in evolutionary change in the 1755 edition of his celebrated *Histoire Naturelle*, where he discusses the vestigial parts of animals; for example, in discussing the

[1] For an excellent discussion of his evolutionary views see A. C. Crombie " The Idea of Organic Evolution " in *Discovery*, March, 1953.

foot of the pig he says it has " useless parts or rather parts of which it cannot make any use, toes, all the bones of which are perfectly formed and which nevertheless are of no service to it." Later, in 1761, we find him writing:

How many species being perfected or degenerated by the great changes in land and sea, by the favours and disfavours of Nature, by food, by the prolonged influence of climate, contrary or favourable, are no longer what they formerly were.

One is surprised at the rapidity with which species vary and the facility with which they lose their primitive characteristics in assuming new forms.

This shows that he believed in evolutionary change as a result of the *direct influence of the environment*.

We come now to that remarkable character, Dr. Erasmus Darwin (1731-1802), the grandfather of Charles; he was one of the great leaders of intellectual activity in England towards the end of the 18th century. He it was who founded a Society, holding meetings in his house at Lichfield, to which such celebrities as James Watt, Joseph Priestley, Samuel Galton, Josiah Wedgwood, Sir Joseph Banks, Sir William Herschell and William Murdoch (the inventor of coal gas) came to discuss the philosophical problems of the day; they called it the Lunar Society—because they always met at the full moon to lessen the risk of attack by highwaymen as they drove back in their gigs over the miles of countryside in the early hours of the morning. Erasmus Darwin put forward very explicit evolutionary views in that remarkable two-volume work called *Zoonomia or the Laws of Organic Life* which he published in 1794. It is a pity they were buried among so much other matter mainly of a medical nature. It is only after he has discussed reproduction that we come to the full expression of his views on evolution on page 504 of his first volume. I will now give some brief extracts from the second (corrected) edition of 1796 (pp. 504-9).

When we revolve in our minds, first, the great changes, which we see naturally produced in animals after their nativity, as in the production of the butterfly with painted wings from the crawling caterpillar; or of the respiring frog from the subnatant tadpole. . . .

Secondly, when we think over the great changes introduced into various animals by artificial or accidental cultivation, as in horses, which we have exercised for the different purposes of strength or swiftness, in carrying burthens or in running races; or in dogs, which have been cultivated for strength and courage, as the bull-dog. . . . Add to these the great changes of shape and colour, which we daily see produced in smaller animals from our domestication of them, as rabbits, or pigeons; or from the difference of climates and even of seasons; thus the sheep of warm climates are covered with hair instead of wool; and the hares and partridges of the latitudes, which are long buried in snow, become white during the winter months: . . .

Thirdly, when we enumerate the great changes produced in the species of animals before their nativity; these are such as resemble the form or colour of their parents, which have been altered by the cultivation or accidents above related, and are thus continued to their posterity. . . .

Fourthly, when we revolve in our minds the great similarity of structure, which obtains in all the warm-blooded animals, as well as quadrupeds, birds, and amphibious animals, as in mankind; from the mouse and bat to the elephant and whale; one is led to conclude, that they have alike been produced from a similar living filament. . . .

Fifthly, from their first rudiment, or primordium, to the termination of their lives, all animals undergo perpetual transformations; which are in part produced by their own exertions in consequence of their desires and aversions, of their pleasures and their pains, or of irritations, or of associations; and many of these acquired forms or propensities are transmitted to their posterity. . . .

I should explain that throughout the book, on its medical side, he makes a great deal of *irritation*: the effects on the body of external objects; and by *associations* he means the effect of one form of muscular movement upon another part of the body.[1] We may note that in this fifth paragraph, when he speaks of perpetual transformation (*i.e.* evolution) " produced by their own exertions in consquence of their desires and aversions, of their pleasures and their pains," Erasmus Darwin is forestalling by fifteen years the doctrine of Lamarck. On the next page he also has a remarkable passage foreshadowing part of his grandson's doctrine of sexual selection:

[1] Just after this lecture was given, the excellent book, *Erasmus Darwin* by Desmond King-Hele, was published (1963). He gives (p. 48) a good discussion on Darwin's division of all bodily action, and diseases, into four classes, which he calls Irritation, Sensation, Volition and Association.

A great want of one part of the animal world has consisted in the desire of the exclusive possession of the females; and these have acquired weapons to combat each other for this purpose ... So the horns of the stag are sharp to offend his adversary, but are branched for the purpose of parrying or receiving the thrusts of horns similar to his own, and have therefore been formed for the purpose of combating other stags for the exclusive possession of the females; who are observed, like the ladies in the times of chivalry, to attend the car of the victor.

The birds, which ... are armed with spurs for the purpose of fighting for the exclusive possession of the females, as cocks and quails. It is certain that these weapons are not provided for their defence against other adversaries, because the females of these species are without this armour. The final cause of this contest amongst the males seems to be, that the strongest and most active animal should propagate the species, which should thence become improved.

He proceeds (on p. 509) to a magnificent vision of evolution as a whole:

Would it be too bold to imagine, that in the great length of time, since the earth began to exist, perhaps millions of ages before the commencement of the history of mankind, would it be too bold to imagine, that all warm-blooded animals have arisen from one living filament, which THE GREAT FIRST CAUSE endued with animality, with the power of acquiring new parts, attended with new propensities, directed by irritations, sensations, volitions, and associations; and thus possessing the faculty of continuing to improve by its own inherent activity, and of delivering down those improvements by generation to its posterity, world without end!

Turning back to France, we come to the great Lamarck (1744–1829). It appears not to be known whether or not he had any knowledge of Erasmus Darwin's doctrine. He first put forward his evolutionary views in his *Philosophie Zoologique* in 1809 when he enunciated two laws, but subsequently in 1816 in his *Histoire des Animaux sans Vertèbres* he enlarged the statement of his theory into four laws. (There is thus, unfortunately, some confusion as to what some writers mean by referring to his first or second laws.)

These propositions may be stated as follows:

First Law.—Life by its internal forces tends continually to increase the volume of every body that possesses it, as well as to increase the size of all the parts of the body up to a limit which it brings about.

Second Law.—The production of a new organ or part results from a new need or want, which continues to be felt, and from the new movement which this need initiates and causes to continue.

Third Law.—The development of organs and their force or power of action are always in direct relation to the employment of these organs.[1]

Fourth Law.—All that has been acquired or altered in the organisation of individuals during their life is preserved by generation, and transmitted to new individuals which proceed from those which have undergone these changes.

This theory, which for a time was the greatest rival to the later Darwinian doctrine, has so often been misunderstood. Its main feature is that changes in the *habits* of animals can bring about evolutionary change. So often writers have misrepresented him in supposing that he believed in the direct effect of the environment.[2] He only believed in this in regard to plants and the very lowest animals; for the majority of animals he definitely denies this. For him the real cause of evolutionary change springs from the animal's behaviour. It was Buffon, as we have just seen, who believed in the direct effect of the environment, *not* Lamarck; although it is true that he (Lamarck) believed that changes in behaviour may often be *brought about* by changes in the environment. Let me give another translation from Lamarck to make this quite clear.

Great changes in environment bring about changes in the habits of animals. Changes in their wants necessarily bring about parallel changes in their habits. If new wants become constant or very lasting, they form new habits, the new habits involve the use of new parts, or a different use of old parts, which results

---

[1] At another point he expands this into two sub-laws: " In every animal which has not passed the term of its development, the more frequent and sustained employment of each organ strengthens little by little this organ, develops it, increases it in size, and gives it a power proportioned to the length of its employment; whereas the constant lack of use of the same organ insensibly weakens it, deteriorates it, progressively diminishes its powers, and ends by causing it to disappear." This is now known as the Law of Use and Disuse.

[2] This is further discussed on p. 159.

finally in the production of new organs and the modification of old ones.

We know now that the suggested mechanism which Lamarck postulated for bringing about structural change—*i.e.* the development of some parts of the body through greater employment or the reduction of others through less frequent use, with such changes being inherited—has now been disproved. Unfortunately with the dismissal of his particular mechanism the majority of biologists also threw aside Lamarck's conception of the importance of new habits in bringing about evolutionary change, because they could not see how such a principle could possibly work. It is this idea, but with a Darwinian mechanism, which I hope to show will return into the main evolutionary theory and then Lamarck, I believe, will have the credit for his brilliant insight into this vital part of the process. Lamarck curiously enough always avowed himself a materialist;[1] yet his theory was essentially one linked to the behavioural side of life, and, consequently, with what some would regard as a form of vitalism. To this question also we must return in later lectures.

The influence of Lamarck was for the time being crushed by Cuvier, and the stream of exciting speculation on organic change which was bubbling up, particularly on the continent, but also in England with Erasmus Darwin, at the end of the 18th and beginning of the 19th centuries almost entirely dried up. Then, remarkable as it may seem, after an interval, an *entirely new stream* leading to Charles Darwin and Wallace sprang from quite another source.

If my history is to be reasonably complete, although for brevity it must be the merest sketch, I should just mention, before coming to this new stream, that the idea of natural selection was expressed by Dr. W. C. Wells[2] in 1813 and Patrick Matthew in 1831.[3] And recently Professor Darlington[4] has drawn our attention to the very interesting story of Dr. Lawrence, a professor of the Royal College of Surgeons, who published a book, *Lectures on physiology, zoology and the natural history of man*, in 1819, in which he discusses evolution treating man as

[1] Darlington in his *The Facts of Life* (p. 223) writes of " Lamarck's interest in a Supreme Being." This seems contrary to all that one knows of Lamarck; see the discussion in Russell's *Form and Function* (pp. 222–6).

[2] In a paper read to the Royal Society on " An account of a white female part of whose skin resembles that of a negro."

[3] In a work entitled " Naval Timber and Arboriculture ".

[4] C. D. Darlington: *Darwin's Place in History*, Blackwell, Oxford, 1959.

an animal. Lawrence, however, being threatened with prosecution for blasphemy, and fearing professional ruin, suppressed the book very soon after its publication, although several pirate editions were later printed by other publishers.

At first sight, looking back from today, it does indeed seem extraordinary to us that the ideas of Charles Darwin and Alfred Russell Wallace, the beginning of the modern conception, did not follow directly from that outburst of interest in evolution at the end of the previous century. So completely were the beginnings stifled by Cuvier that when Charles Darwin came to consider the problem of possible evolutionary change he began quite afresh; there can be little doubt, I think, that he believed that these early ideas had been completely dismissed as idle speculations. He has been accused, by Samuel Butler[1] and more recently by Darlington,[2] of taking his ideas, without acknowledgement, from his grandfather Erasmus Darwin and keeping him in the background. I cannot believe this is true. Charles, as a young man, read his grandfather's *Zoönomia*, and in a moment we shall see how speculative he thought it; he hated speculation unless it was supported by a large array of facts. He did not hurry to publish his own views; he kept on waiting, for over twenty years, for more and more evidence, and in the end was only forced to publish them, as we shall see, before he was actually ready to do it. That is not the behaviour of a man who steals his ancestor's ideas to gain personal fame; and his own ideas, except for that small part of his sexual selection theory, were entirely different from his grandfather's.

Darwin tells us in his autobiography[3] how as a student at Edinburgh —and he went there at the age of 16 in 1825—he met Grant who later became Professor of Zoology at University College, London. After saying Grant was his senior by several years, he writes:

He one day, when we were walking together burst forth in high admiration of Lamarck and his views on evolution. I listened in silent astonishment, and as far as I can judge, without any effect on my mind. I had previously read the *Zoönomia* of my grandfather, in which similar views are maintained, but without producing any effect on me. Nevertheless it is probable that the hearing rather early in life such views maintained and praised

---

[1] Samuel Butler: *Evolution, Old and New*, London, 1879.
[2] C. D. Darlington: *loc. cit.*
[3] On p. 49 of the complete version edited by Nora Barlow, London, 1958.

may have favoured my upholding them under a different form in my *Origin of Species*. At this time I admired greatly the *Zoönomia*; but on reading it a second time after an interval of ten or fifteen years, I was much disappointed, the proportion of speculation being so large to the facts given.

Of his days as a medical student he wrote " The instruction at Edinburgh was altogether by Lectures, and these were intolerably dull, with the exception of those on chemistry by Hope. . . . Dr. Duncan's lectures on *Materia Medica* at 8 o'clock on a winter's morning are something fearful to remember. . . ."

So it came about that his father realised that he was not going to make a doctor and decided that he should become a minister instead, sending him in 1828 to Christ's College, Cambridge, to read for a pass degree in Divinity. Whilst, as he tells us, he spent much of his time at Cambridge riding, shooting, and collecting beetles, he became a friend of J. S. Henslow, Professor of Botany, who introduced him to Adam Sedgwick, Professor of Geology. It was their influence, it will be remembered, that largely removed his parents' objections to his going as naturalist on the *Beagle*. And when he sailed he took with him, on Henslow's advice, Lyell's great book *Principles of Geology* which had recently appeared; although Henslow had told him " to take no notice of his theories."

It was Lyell's *Principles* which more than anything prepared the way for Darwin's thoughts which were to be generated by his experiences on the voyage. The great influence of Lyell and the development of geology generally on his outlook has been beautifully told in that little classic *The Coming of Evolution*[1] by Professor John Judd (a later successor to Sedgwick in the Cambridge Chair of Geology). I will only refer to this bit of history in the briefest outline, for it will be familiar to most of you; I include it because it is so important a part of this sparkling stream of ideas.

The story goes back to James Hutton (1736–97) of Edinburgh, the father of modern geology, who in 1785 published his revolutionary book *The Theory of the Earth*.[2] In this Hutton not only pointed out for

[1] In the series of Cambridge Manuals of Science and Literature, 1910.
[2] We now know that Hutton held views on the production of varieties in animals and plants by a process of natural selection; these, however, remained unpublished until 1947 so Darwin could not have known of them. They are particularly interesting in relation to the idea of Organic Selection and I shall discuss them further on p. 178.

the first time the volcanic origin of many rocks but, more important, emphasised the effects of sub-ærial erosion—the action of rivers in carving out valleys, etc.;[1] he believed that the formation of all rocks, both igneous and sedimentary, was brought about by causes in the past similar to those acting today, but over an immense period of time. It was perhaps a pity for his theory that he was bold enough at once to assert that he could see no beginning or end to the process, for this brought bitter opposition as he came into conflict with orthodox theology. At first the theory was referred to as " Vulcanism " or " Plutonism " because of his views on the volcanic origin of some of the rocks, and it was opposed by the so-called " Neptunism " of Werner (1750–1817), Professor of Geology in Saxony, who taught that all rocks, even those we now call igneous ones, were deposited by precipitation from waters which had once covered the earth. This became the Catastrophe Theory postulating a series of great floods in the past when the earth was covered by the sea and all terrestrial life drowned; the different layers of fossils were thought to represent the life so destroyed and Noah's flood was pointed to as the most recent of these great disasters. Hutton's followers became known as the Uniformitarians, and a battle was waged between them and the Catastrophists.

The great Cuvier in France and Dr. William Buckland (Professor of Geology at Oxford and Dean of Christ Church) were the powerful leaders of Catastrophism; under their influence the Uniformitarians, who were in the minority, were ridiculed, and Hutton's teaching became neglected. Now Charles Lyell, coming up to Exeter College, Oxford, in 1816, became a pupil of Buckland who gave him his love for geology; on leaving Oxford, however, after seeing the effect of the sea's erosion on the Norfolk coast and being impressed with river action when travelling in France, he became converted to the Uniformitarian point of view. In 1829 he published the first volume of his epoch-making *Principles of Geology*. It was this masterly exposition of the continuous action of natural causes acting over vast periods of time that had such an influence on Darwin when he read it on the *Beagle*. Some recent writers have asserted that Lyell was not a believer in the evolution of animal life until later convinced by Darwin, but if we read the *Life and Letters of Sir Charles Lyell* (1881) we shall see how far from the truth

[1] Actually Generelli, an Italian Carmelite friar (in 1749) and Nicolas Desmarest in France (in 1777) had already published works on the action of rivers in carving out valleys, but this, so Judd thinks, was probably unknown to Hutton.

this is. Perhaps Lyell, not wishing to become a victim of public attack on theological grounds—as had befallen his hero, Hutton, and still more recently Lawrence—had hidden his views so successfully that even modern biologists failed to perceive them.[1]

Darwin, fired with the new vision of Lyell, had on his voyage three outstanding experiences which made a lasting impression upon him and set him thinking of the possible reality of evolution. He took part in Patagonia in the excavation of some of the fossil remains of the giant land sloths of the past, such as *Mylodon*, and also of the great *Glyptodon*; in so doing he recognised the essential similarity of the skeletons of the former to those of the smaller tree sloths and of the latter to those of the modern armadillos. He pondered the question: could the living forms be descended from the same stock as the extinct ones? Also in South America he was greatly struck by the marvellous adaptations of so many animals to their surroundings particularly the beautifully protectively-coloured insects of the Brazilian forests. Then, with perhaps even greater effect, he saw how the birds and reptiles on the different islands of the Galapagos group differed from one another

[1] In his *Life and Letters* we see that Lyell wrote as follows to John Herschel in 1836, when Darwin was still out on the *Beagle*.

" In regard to the origination of new species, I am very glad to find that you think it probable that it may be carried on through the intervention of intermediate causes. I left this rather to be inferred, not thinking it worth while to offend a certain class of persons by embodying in words what would only be a speculation . . . One can in imagination summon before us a small part at least of the circumstances that must be contemplated and foreknown, before it can be decided what powers and qualities a new species must have in order to enable it to endure for a given time, and to play its part in due relation to all other beings destined to co-exist with it, before it dies out. . . ."

And again in 1837 Lyell wrote to Whewell: " It was impossible, I think, for any-one to read my work and not to perceive that my notion of uniformity in the existing causes of change always implied that they must for ever produce an endless variety of effects, *both in the animate and inanimate world*."

And to Sedgwick, a year later, thus:

" Now touching my opinion " concerning the creation of new species at the present day, " I have no right to object, *as I really do entertain it*, to your contro-verting it; at the same time you will see, on reading my chapter on the subject, that I have studiously avoided laying down the doctrine dogmatically as capable of proof. I have admitted that we have only data for *extinction*, and I have left it to be inferred, instead of enunciating it even as my opinion, that the place of lost species is filled up (as it was of old) from time to time by new species. I have only ventured to say that had new mammalia come in, we could hardly have hoped to verify the fact."

and again from the similar types of the mainland; was it not more likely that they had gradually diverged in form from one another after long periods of separation, instead of being created as slightly different types on the different islands?

On his return from the *Beagle* he began the famous notebook " for the collection of facts which bore in any way on the variation in animals and plants under domestication and in nature." He had been struck by Man's powers of developing various characters in domestic animals by selective breeding. Could there not be some similar principle operating in Nature he thought? In 1838 when reading Malthus[1] on population, he realised how selection in nature could be brought about.[2] We read in his autobiography[3] as follows:

In October 1838, that is, fifteen months after I had begun my systematic enquiry, I happened to read for amusement Malthus on *Population*, and being well prepared to appreciate the struggle for existence which everywhere goes on from long-continued observation of the habits of animals and plants, it at once struck me that under these circumstances favourable variations would tend to be preserved, and unfavourable ones to be destroyed. The result of this would be the formation of new species. Here, then, I had at last got a theory by which to work; but I was so anxious to avoid prejudice, that I determined not for some time to write even the briefest sketch of it. In June 1842 I first allowed myself the satisfaction of writing a very brief abstract of my theory in pencil in 35 pages; and this was enlarged during the summer of 1844 into one of 230 pages, which I had fairly copied out and still possess.

He sent a copy of this last essay to Lyell who begged him to publish it and warned him that if he delayed much longer he would surely

---

[1] Malthus (1766–1834), mathematician, social economist and parson, first published his *Essay on the Principle of Population* anonymously in 1798 and then a much larger and altered edition, using his name, in 1803. He showed that life tended to increase in a geometrical progression and that, unless there were severe checks on the populations, Man would soon outstrip his food supply: such checks being unwholesome occupations, severe labour, extreme poverty, diseases, war, famines, etc.

[2] Sir Gavin de Beer has recently shown (in his book, *Charles Darwin*, 1963) that the idea actually came to Darwin a little earlier, but it was Malthus who made him realise the force it could have, as is clearly shown in the quotation I give from his autobiography.

[3] *The Autobiography of Charles Darwin*, edited by N. Barlow, 1958, p. 120.

be forestalled by someone; Darwin, however, would go on collecting more and more facts to support his theory before committing himself. Ten more years passed and here, in 1855, Wallace begins to come into the story.

I must now go a little more slowly for I am anxious, in this brief history of thought leading up to our present views, to give Wallace what I feel to be a rather fairer proportion of the credit for the theory than has usually been allotted him outside strictly biological circles.

Alfred Russell Wallace, as an enthusiastic young traveller naturalist, collecting in the forests of Sarawak, in 1855 had a paper published in the *Annals and Magazine of Natural History* entitled " On the Law which has regulated the Introduction of New Species "; his main conclusions were that " every species has come into existence coincident both in space and time with a pre-existing closely allied species."[1] It attracted much attention; and Darwin entered into friendly correspondence with Wallace telling him that for a long time he had been collecting facts bearing on the question of the origin of species, but he gave no hint whatever of his theory of natural selection. He had kept it a secret from all but three: first Lyell, and then Hooker to whom he had later sent a copy of his essay, and lastly a rough sketch sent to Asa Gray in 1857. It was a good thing he let both Lyell and Hooker know, otherwise perhaps we might not be talking of Darwinism today, but Wallacism.

In the spring of 1858, Wallace lay sick of fever at Ternate in the Island of Celebes and his thoughts wandered to the species problem. He then remembered Malthus, whose book he had read twelve years before, and I will continue the story with an extract from his *My Life* (1908):

> Then I thought of the enormously rapid multiplication of animals, causing these checks to be much more effective in them than in the case of man; and while pondering vaguely on this fact there suddenly flashed upon me the *idea* of the survival of the fittest—

[1] The high merits of this paper have recently been discussed by Professor C. P. A. Pantin in the *Proceedings of the Linnean Society of London*, vol. 171, p. 139, 1960. He writes: " The importance of this essay is twofold. It is perhaps the most important ' Pre-Darwinian ' essay on the Origin of Species apart from the works of Lamarck. Further, taken together with his 1858 essay it shows that Wallace did not merely contribute the notion of natural selection but had in effect a complete skeleton for a work on the Origin of Species such as Darwin possessed at the time of his 1842 essay."

that the individuals removed by these checks must be on the whole inferior to those that survived. In the two hours that elapsed before my ague fit was over, I had thought out almost the whole of the theory; and the same evening I sketched the draft of my paper, and in the two succeeding evenings wrote it out in full, and sent it by the next post to Mr. Darwin.

The title he gave to his manuscript paper was " On the tendency of variations to depart indefinitely from the Original Type."

The paper arrived at a very bad time for Darwin. He was ill himself and very depressed; an infant son had died the day before of scarlet fever and a little daughter was dangerously ill with diphtheria. On his breakfast plate lay the letter from Wallace enclosing the paper and asking him to send it on to Lyell. Darwin was flabbergasted and wrote hurriedly to Lyell:

... your words have come true with a vengeance—that I should be forestalled ... I never saw a more striking coincidence; if Wallace had my MS. sketch written out in 1842, he could not have made a better short abstract! Even his terms now stand as heads of my chapters. Please return me the MS. which he does not say he wishes me to publish, but I shall of course at once write and offer to send it to any journal. So all my originality, whatever it may amount to, will be smashed, although my book, if it will ever have any value, will not be deteriorated; as all the labour consists in the application of the theory.

In a second letter to Lyell (June 25) he says:

But as I had not intended to publish my sketch, can I do so honourably, because Wallace has sent me an outline of his doctrine? I would far rather burn my whole book than that he or any other man should think that I had behaved in a paltry spirit. Do you not think his having sent me this sketch ties my hands? ...

and next day, he wrote to Lyell yet again:

Forgive me for adding a P.S. .... First impressions are generally right, and I at first thought it would be dishonourable in me now to publish.

Darwin would have held back his own work if he had not been persuaded to do otherwise by Hooker and Lyell who both knew of his essay written years before Wallace's. He left the matter in their hands and the two papers, Darwin's and Wallace's, were read together at the meeting of the Linnean Society on July 1st, 1858.

How did this historic event strike the contemporary scientific world? Was their exciting new conception loudly acclaimed and did its injection into the stream of ideas have an immediate effect? Not a bit of it. It fell completely flat. The human mind is such that we must always be prepared at first for indifference, yet so complete was the lack of appreciation and with such pomposity was it expressed that, on looking back, it can only be described, I think, as comic. It is almost as if some cruel demon had inspired the President of the Society (none other than Thomas Bell the great crustacean expert) to go out of his way to make so crass an error of judgment. In his Address, on May 24th, 1859, reviewing the past year of the Society's proceedings, he said:

> This year . . . has not indeed been marked by any of those striking discoveries which at once revolutionise, so to speak, the department of science on which they bear; it is only at remote intervals that we can reasonably expect any sudden and brilliant innovation which shall produce a marked and permanent impress on the character of any branch of knowledge or confer a lasting and important service on mankind. A Bacon or a Newton, an Oersted or a Wheatstone, a Davy or a Daguerre, is an occasional phenomenon, whose existence and career seem to be especially appointed by Providence for the purpose of effecting some great important change in the conditions or the pursuits of men.[1]

Darwin published his *Origin of Species* in November of the following year, 1859. It was, of course, his marshalling of such an enormous body of facts in support, from so many different fields, that convinced the thinking world of the reality of evolution. It was this weight of evidence, together with the first reasonable and simple theory of its working, which carried the day. Even the great T. H. Huxley was not fully convinced in the summer of '59[2] (a year after Darwin and Wallace's paper) but upon reading the *Origin* he was won over as we see from his brilliant three and a half column review of the book in *The Times* of December 26th of that year. In the following summer, at the British Association Meeting in Oxford, came Huxley's debate with Bishop Wilberforce which rocked the intellectual world. For all the patient labour in preparing the case and for its masterly presentation Darwin must get the greater credit, but for brilliance of insight

[1] *Proceedings of the Linnean Society of London*, 1858–9, p. viii.
[2] See Pantin, *Proc. Linn. Soc. Lond.*, 1959, p. 222.

Wallace, I believe, should get the palm. Some years later, when Darwin was working on his theory of sexual selection and trying to explain all bright colouring of animals by this means, he came to consider the many gaily adorned caterpillars and then, of course, realised that at this stage they had no sex life at all! He wrote in his perplexity to Wallace, and almost by return of post[1] came the theory of warning coloration which in all essentials is just as it is accepted today; in fact as now proved correct by experiment.

When we think of the theory of natural selection we must never forget the name of Alfred Russell Wallace. What a wonderful pair of men they were: Darwin who, after twenty years' hard work on his theory, was prepared to withdraw completely to let Wallace have the priority; and Wallace, who, if he had had a different character, might so easily have demanded his right to have his work published first, used as the title of his most important book on evolution, just one word: *Darwinism*!

How remarkably similar their two independent accounts of the theory were, can only be appreciated by carefully comparing the two papers. Osborn in his *From the Greeks to Darwin* has done this by showing side by side, in summary form, the relevant passages from each version; I reproduce this as follows:

DARWIN	WALLACE
There is in Nature a struggle for existence as shown by Malthus and De Candolle.	The life of wild animals is a struggle for existence . . . in which the weakest and least perfect must always succumb.
Rapid multiplication, if unchecked, even in slow breeding animals like the elephant . . .	Even the least prolific of animals increase rapidly if unchecked.
Great changes in the environment occur.	A change in the environment may occur.

[1] We see in *The Life and Letters of Charles Darwin* (vol. III, pp. 93–4) that he wrote to Wallace on Feb. 23, 1867, saying, " On Monday evening I called on Bates, and put a difficulty before him, which he could not answer, and as on some former similar occasion, his first suggestion was, ' You had better ask Wallace.' My difficulty is, why are caterpillars sometimes so beautifully and artistically coloured? . . ."

On Feb. 26 Darwin had obviously had Wallace's reply for he writes, " My dear Wallace,—Bates was quite right; you are the man to apply to in a difficulty. I never heard anything more ingenious than your suggestion. . . ."

DARWIN	WALLACE
It has been shown in a former part of this work that such changes of external conditions would, from their acting upon the reproductive system, probably cause the organisation ... to become plastic.	(No cause of variation assigned) Varieties do frequently occur spontaneously.
Can it be doubted . . . any innate variation in structure, habits, or instincts, adapting the individual better to the new conditions, would tell upon its vigour and health? In the struggle it would have a better chance of surviving; and those of the offspring who inherited the variation, be it ever so slight, would also have a better chance.	All variations from the typical form have some definite effect, however slight, on the habits and capacities of the individuals. Abundance or rarity of a species is dependent on its more or less perfect adaptation. If any species should produce a variety having slightly increased powers of preserving existence, that variety must inevitably in time acquire a superiority in numbers.

As Osborn pointed out, remarkable as the parallelism is, it is not complete. Darwin dwells upon variations in single characters as taken hold of by selection whereas Wallace is more concerned with *full formed varieties* as being favourably or unfavourably adapted.

Looking back, fifty years after the joint publication of their two papers, Wallace, at the age of·85, makes a contribution to the Darwin-Wallace jubilee celebration volume published by the Linnean Society and modestly compares their two qualities. " I was then, as often since," he said, " the ' young man ' in a hurry; he [Darwin] the painstaking and patient student, seeking ever the full demonstration of the truth he had discovered, rather than to achieve immediate personal fame." And later in the same article he referred to their relative share of the credit for the initiation of the principle of natural selection and suggests as a fair proportion a ratio of " twenty years to one week ", those being the periods each had devoted to it. He also showed (in the same volume) how much he too was indebted to Lyell:

Along with Malthus I had read, and been even more deeply

impressed by, Sir Charles Lyell's immortal *Principles of Geology*; which had taught me that the inorganic world—the whole surface of the earth, its seas and lands, its mountains and valleys, its rivers and lakes, and every detail of its climatic conditions—were and always had been in a continual state of slow modification. Hence it became obvious that the forms of life must have become continually adjusted to these changed conditions in order to survive.

We see clearly how the Darwin-Wallace line of thought, springing from Lyell's geological demonstration of slow change, had quite a separate course from that of the ideas of Erasmus Darwin and of the early continental evolutionists. In the next lecture we shall discuss the changes of view which have taken place as we follow the stream on to the present day.

THE DEVELOPMENT OF MODERN

EVOLUTION THEORY

In the last lecture we traced the beginnings of the various ideas on evolution up to the time of the publication of Darwin's *Origin of Species*. I now want to carry the story forward to the present time both to provide a concise statement of what I consider to be the generally accepted position of today and also to show how the views of biologists have changed, and changed again, in this relatively short period. When I hear people state, as many do, that we have now reached a stage when the major issues of the problem have been solved, I like to look back at these changes of opinion; they should at least make us cautious in accepting today's views as the final statement of the theory. You may feel impatient at my going over this well trod ground again, yet I believe it is necessary in preparation for the later lectures; I am leading up from the past to show how I think the emphasis in the present-day view must be false.

Let us resume our survey with a brief re-statement of the Darwin-Wallace doctrine as put forward in their joint Linnean Society communication of 1858. Animals and plants tend to vary in all sorts of ways and some of these variations are inherited from one generation to another. They reproduce at such a rate that there is intensive competition for available supplies of food—only a very small proportion can survive to maturity. Some varieties will be more successful in the struggle for life than others; they will tend to survive—to be, as they said, selected by nature—and so to contribute more to posterity. The less efficient strains will tend to be eliminated and will consequently appear less often in the ancestry of future generations.

Fig. 16 represents a part of a chart which illustrated Darwin's *Origin of Species* and shows how he thought evolution took place. We see organism A, one of a group of closely related species A, B, C and D,

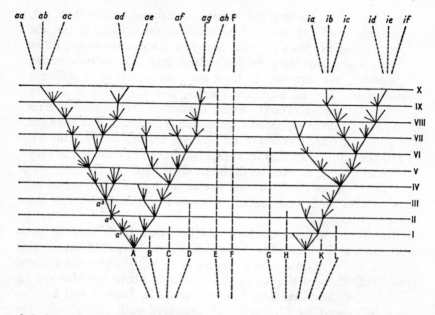

16. A chart redrawn in slightly simplified form from Darwin's *Origin of Species* to show how he envisaged the evolution of new species to take place. For further explanation see text.

having offspring varying slightly one from another and two of them at a^1 giving rise to further offspring and so on at a^2, a^3, etc. He is imagining selection working by picking out at first two distinct characters from descendants which have moved into two rather different surroundings. Actually, as he explained, the differences shown in his diagram would not take place in just a few generations, the gaps between a^1, a^2 and a^3, etc., would really represent a thousand generations or more. He is just intending to show how, with the progeny of one form spreading into different terrains, different selective forces may come into operation so that in time in different parts of the country we may get separate races such as *aa*, *ab*, *ac*, etc., and these, with the further passage of time, may become distinct *new species* in the future. Similarly with *ia*, *ib*, *ic*, etc., the descendants of species 1, but here let me quote a short passage from Darwin's explanation:

The six descendants from (1) will form two sub-genera, or even

genera. But as the original species (1) differed largely from (A),
standing nearly at the extreme points of the original genus, the
six descendants from (1) will, owing to inheritance alone, differ
considerably from the eight descendants from (A); the two groups,
moreover, are supposed to have gone on diverging in different
directions. The intermediate species, also (and this is a very
important consideration), which connected the original species
(A) and (1), have all become, excepting (F), extinct, and have left
no descendants. Hence the six new species descended from (1),
and the eight descended from (A), will have to be ranked as very
distinct genera, or even as distinct sub-families.

Thus it is, as I believe, that two or more genera are produced
by descent with modification, from two or more species of the
same genus.

Some critics at once doubted whether there really was the great
destruction of life implied by natural selection. They doubted whether
selection could normally be so severe as to bring about the changes
postulated, changes similar to those brought about by Man by his
continual selective breeding. Wallace, who like Darwin had been so
much influenced by Malthus, well answered such critics[1] with the
following simple example. A bird like a sparrow usually lays six eggs
in a clutch and usually has two or more broods in a year; and in
captivity, they will live for over 15 years. Let us be conservative, said
Wallace, and suppose that they only live 10 years and only produce
10 young a year. If all these young grew up to lead a natural breeding
life and if on an average half of them are females, a simple little sum
will show that in 10 years' time for every pair of sparrows today, there
will be over 24 million as shown in table II. Yet we know that the
sparrows are not usually increasing. This, of course, does not mean
that for every two sparrows over 24 million will die in the next ten
years, because, out of each 10 offspring per year, to keep the balance
right, there will be a loss, on an average, of eight or nine. Over
thousands of years this gives plenty of scope for selection; those variations that are the more efficiently adapted for their life will, more often
than not, tend to survive. Compared with many other animals a bird
like a sparrow has relatively few offspring; there are many insects that
lay a thousand eggs and some whose hatching grubs may become
mature adults within a fortnight. The codfish lays a million eggs and

[1] In *Darwinism*, p. 25.

the halibut five million! We can have no doubt that the competition for food is great.

TABLE II

Original parent birds	2
1st generation	10
2nd generation	50
3rd generation	250
4th generation	1,250
5th generation	6,250
6th generation	31,250
7th generation	156,250
8th generation	781,250
9th generation	3,906,250
10th generation	19,531,250
Total (if all remained alive)	24,414,062

In his first edition of the *Origin* Darwin relied almost entirely on natural selection to bring about the evolutionary change. In his sixth edition of 1872, however, he had come to admit the importance of the use and disuse effect (which was Lamarck's theory) and on p. 395 summarises his views thus:

This [evolution] has been affected chiefly through the natural selection of numerous successive, slight, favourable variations; aided in an important manner by the inherited effects of use and disuse of parts; and in an unimportant manner, that is in relation to adaptive structures, whether past or present, by the direct action of external conditions and by variations which seem to us in our ignorance to arise quite spontaneously."

It is certainly interesting to note this change when we remember that in 1844 he wrote to Hooker saying " Heaven defend me from Lamarck's nonsense " and in other letters of the same period he refers to Lamarck's work as " veritable rubbish " and " an absurd though clever book ". This weakening of his position in regard to natural selection was due to a criticism published in 1867. Not much general notice of this objection, however, was taken until much later, and for this reason I postpone an account of it (p. 79); nevertheless it affected Darwin deeply. Wallace was clearly shocked at Darwin's retreat. At the end of my last lecture I recorded how Wallace had modestly and

generously called his most important work on evolution by the simple
title *Darwinism*; I should also say that I think there was, in addition,
just a touch of irony in it, for in his preface to this book he shows that
he was now more Darwinian than Darwin.

Although I maintain [he writes] and even enforce, my differences
from some of Darwin's views, my whole work tends forcibly to
illustrate the overwhelming importance of Natural Selection
over all other agencies in the production of new species. I thus
take up Darwin's earlier position, from which he somewhat receded
in the later editions of his works, on account of criticism and
objections which I have endeavoured to show are unsound. Even
in rejecting that phase of sexual selection depending on female
choice, I insist on the greater efficacy of natural selection. This
is pre-eminently the Darwinian doctrine, and I therefore claim
for my book the position of being the advocate of pure Darwinism.

Wallace's *Darwinism* was not published until 1889 so that in the
1870's Lamarck's doctrine, following the change in Darwin's outlook,
was being accepted and came next in importance to natural selection.
Let me just remind those who are not biologists of the essential difference between the two theories. As a striking illustration, because
perhaps slightly ridiculous, let me take the giraffe, which was an
example used by Lamarck himself. The giraffe, as everyone knows,
lives in the park-like savannah country of Africa, where it feeds on the
foliage of the tall trees which are separated by stretches of grassland.
Lamarck explains their long necks and long front legs by their continual craning upwards to get their food; he thought that, over vast
periods of time, this stretching of the necks and legs had gradually
led to an increase in their length. Darwin, on the theory of natural
selection, would explain it in quite a different way. We see how the
trees in any park containing cattle are browsed off in a perfectly level
fashion showing us just how high the cattle can reach to get their food.
In the case of the giraffe, according to Darwin, if there should be
competition for such food, and if there is some variation in the length
of the neck and legs amongst the population, then those with the
shorter necks will tend to be starved, whilst their more lofty brothers
and sisters survive. If such chance variations in the length of neck are
inherited, then as the process is repeated again and again over hundreds
and thousands of years, there must be a gradual evolution leading to
the grotesque forms of today, provided of course that the animal as a

whole remains as a reasonably efficient organism. (It must indeed be near the limit of that efficiency now.)

In those days, in the 1870's, you could take your choice between these two views and many people tended to prefer the Lamarckian doctrine because they could not bring themselves to believe that the whole act of creation was brought about by the ruthless, almost mechanical, selection of small chance variations. In 1885, however, Weismann (1834–1914) dealt what appeared to be a crushing blow to Lamarckism with the publication of his *Theory of the Germ Plasm*.[1] His idea was that the germ plasm, *i.e.* the part of the organism which is destined to give rise to the reproductive cells and so to the next generation, is usually isolated from the rest of the body at a very early stage in development. The protoplasm of these future reproductive cells remains in a relatively unspecialised condition, so that an egg, which has been fertilised by the sperm cell, is able to give rise to a whole new individual; it divides and divides again, and the products go on dividing to build up a body of perhaps a hundred million cells (as in Man). Some of these cells are, as I have just said, put on one side and will form the ovary or testes which will provide the future reproductive cells; the rest, going on dividing, become specialised for different functions and form the nerve, muscle, gland, epithelial and other cells of the body. For Weismann, the specialised body is just the perambulator carrying the baby, *i.e.* the germ plasm, which will be handed on to the next generation (fig. 17); it is this precious plasm which is potentially immortal. As far as we know, it has continued from far back in time for some two thousand million years. The body, which has become specialised as a carrier, wears out; the price of such specialisation is death. Generation after generation of such bodies are cast aside as the precious stream flows on. It does not matter, said Weismann, how much a body may enlarge this or that part by exercise, such changes cannot affect the germ plasm which has already been set on one side from the rest of the body.[2] The effects of use or disuse could

---

[1] He also did experiments which he claimed disproved the hypothesis, but they were really beside the point. For many generations he cut off, at birth, the tails of mice he was breeding and then found at the end that the final offspring, if allowed to grow them, had tails as long as those of their ancestors. But amputation can hardly be equated with actual disuse by the animal!

[2] As a matter of fact, although it was not realised at the time, the strict isolation of the germ plasm is by no means a universal rule even in animals; and we know

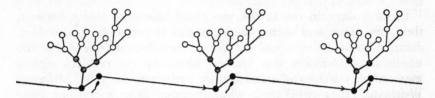

17. A diagram to illustrate Weismann's conception of the continuity of the germ plasm (the blacked-in circles connected by a line) and its early separation from the body cells of the individuals which, having divided off from it, become specialised and will eventually die. The bodies die, but the germ plasm goes on and is potentially immortal.

not be inherited. The stretching of a neck could not lead to a longer neck in the next generation; a duck (fig. 18) by stretching cannot eventually become a swan. Lamarckism appeared dead. By the 1890's the theory of natural selection seemed fully established and dominated the field. It was the heyday of Darwinism—the action of natural selection upon chance variations which were inherited.

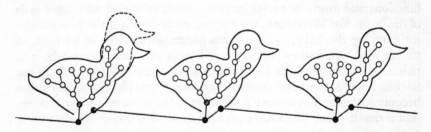

18. The same diagram as in fig. 17 but with the outline of the bodies of succeeding generations filled in. However much a duck, as an individual, might increase the length of its neck by continual stretching after food on the bottom of the pond, any such increase would not be passed on to the next generation because the germ cells had already been separated from the body cells at an early stage in development.

now that fresh germ cells in some animals can indeed be regenerated from quite other tissues. Also, although I do not think people pointed it out at the time, this separation of the germ plasm does not apply to plants at all; the flowers and the generative parts are usually produced at the very tips of the shoots from normal parts of the plant body.

It was in this period that a new form of Lamarckism came on the scene with the sparkling ideas of Samuel Butler and his concept of a gradual developing subconscious racial memory handed on from generation to generation. Many people who could not face the materialistic outlook of Darwinism clutched at Butler's ingenious idea which has sometimes been called the neo-Lamarckian theory. Actually it broke down at several points; it failed, for example, to explain the evolution of the kinds of instinctive behaviour which we see occurring in some animals, such as certain insects, only *after* they have laid their eggs. I will not, however, deal with the Butler hypothesis here because I shall refer to it again in a later lecture (p. 257).

Now when the Darwinian doctrine appeared supreme, with chance variations as the material on which selection worked, Francis Galton, Charles Darwin's cousin, began his detailed study of the nature of variation; he measured vast numbers of examples of all kinds of natural objects to see how they actually varied in weight, size, or in such characters as the number of veins in a leaf and so on. If we measure a sufficiently large random sample of any natural object of the same kind, for instance leaves, seeds, or parts of animals of the same species, we will find that there is a continuous range of measurements covered by the whole sample; and if as we measured them we kept all those of each particular unit of size separate, we shall find that there are very few of the extreme sizes, large or small, rather more of those not quite so extreme, and still more and more of those nearer and nearer to the average in size. Their frequencies of occurrence along the range of size, if plotted as a graph, will approach what we call a normal curve of error: a bell-shaped curve falling away from the mean on either side (fig. 19). They appear, in fact, to be varying according to the laws of chance.

It was then thought that if we selected examples of our animal or plant of, say, larger size than the mean, and bred from them, we should find that their offspring would tend to vary in the same sort of chance way: some being slightly larger, some slightly smaller, with the majority nearer to the *size of their parents*. So it was confidently thought, at this time, that if we went on selecting for larger size, or some other character, generation after generation, we could go on pushing evolution in this or that direction as we liked within, of course, the limits of an efficient working organism (fig. 20). This seemed an obvious deduction because, if variation was really quite a matter of

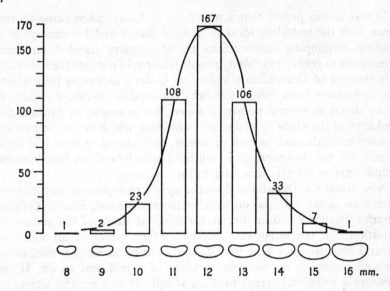

19. Histograms showing the relative numbers of beans of different sizes in a sample gathered at random; the frequency curve is the normal curve of deviation (or curve of error).

chance, then surely the offspring must continue to range in size more or less equally above and below the size of their parents. It was taken for granted that this indeed was what the stock breeder was doing in producing his different races of domestic animals: sheep with higher wool yield, hens of greater egg laying capacity and so on.

Now in the late 90's, when Karl Pearson and others, who followed Galton, began to put this to the test of experiment—when they tried, in fact, selecting some particular quality over a number of generations —they were horrified to find that selection appeared not to work. Experiment after experiment was made. They seemed to be doing what they felt sure the breeders of domesticated animals had been doing: selecting for some particular character in order to get that feature more pronounced in their chosen strain; yet each time they failed. At the very end of the century biologists were in a very uncomfortable position. They had convinced the intellectual world of the reality of evolution, including many dignitaries of the Church, and they had appeared to have shown that Darwinian selection was

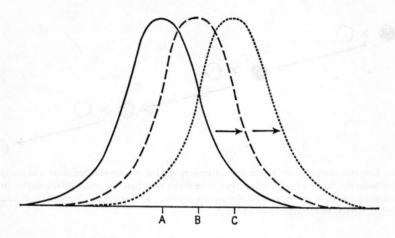

A   B   C

20. Diagram to show how it was originally thought that by selecting, say, for size, and breeding always from the larger individuals, the range of variation (see curve in fig. 19) could be shifted in the direction of selection from a mean at point A on the size scale to one at B and so on to C. The early experiments trying to demonstrate this failed (see text).

the obvious mechanism of the process, yet now when they applied the test of experiment, it appeared not to work.

There was another argument which now began to be heard. It had, in fact, been pointed out a good deal earlier by Professor Fleeming Jenkin[1] (Professor of Engineering in Edinburgh University) but few seemed to have taken any notice of it. It was said that by the then recognised mechanism of inheritance, the so-called theory of blending inheritance, Darwinism could not on theoretical grounds really be expected to work. The idea of blending inheritance was roughly this: that the inheritance received by each individual came more or less equally from the two parents and that of the parents, of course, from their parents, and so on, thus the different characters possessed by each member of a mating couple were thought to be blended together in the offspring. This idea had been expressed by Galton as the Law of Ancestral Inheritance which could be summarised by saying that the sum of the inherited qualities possessed by any individual could be regarded as having been derived on an average as follows:

[1] In a review of *The Origin of Species* in the *North British Review* for June 1867.

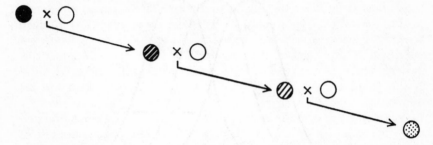

21. Diagram to show how (before the rediscovery of Mendel's laws) inheritance was thought (erroneously) to be of a blending type. The effect of a new variation (black circle) in a normal population would soon be blended away as its offspring bred with normal individuals (white circles) in subsequent generations.

$\frac{1}{2}$ of the total from the 2 parents
$\frac{1}{4}$ „ „ „ „ „ 4 grandparents
$\frac{1}{8}$ „ „ „ „ „ 8 great-grandparents
$\frac{1}{16}$ „ „ „ „ „ 16 great-great-grandparents
. . . and so on to infinity

or it could be expressed as an equation of inheritance thus:

$$\tfrac{1}{2}p + \tfrac{1}{4}gp + \tfrac{1}{8}ggp + \tfrac{1}{16}gggp \ldots = 1$$

If such a theory was accepted (as it was at that time, but, of course, no longer held today) then it would seem impossible for Darwinism to work. As soon as some new favourable variety cropped up, it would be most unlikely for such an individual to come across and mate with another quite new sort of individual of the same kind. Thus in the next generation, half of the advantage of the new type would be blended away, and it would be still further reduced by a half in the following generation and so on, as seen in fig. 21. It seemed that any new variety must be blended away by the then accepted rules of inheritance long before selection could possibly operate to make it spread in the population.

Does it not seem extraordinary to us that the great brains of the Victorian era should not have appreciated this? Some people have supposed that Darwin must actually have seen it much earlier and was, in fact, so worried by it that he delayed and delayed publishing his theory hoping always to discover more about the true nature of inheritance. This, however, cannot have been so, for we see from *The*

Life and Letters of Charles Darwin (vol. III, p. 108) how deeply he had been affected by Fleeming Jenkin's criticism (of 1867) and it was, no doubt, this which made him, as we have seen (p. 73), introduce Lamarck's theory of use and disuse into his sixth edition of the *Origin* published in 1872. It is a little disconcerting to realise, on reading this passage in the *Life and Letters*, how muddled Darwin appeared to be at this time; and once again we find him writing to Wallace in his difficulties.[1]

We see then that at the end of the century Darwinism was plunged into the shadow of a dark cloud, that of its failure to pass the test of experiment and perhaps worse still its apparent failure even as a possible theory. No wonder there was consternation in the biological camp, even if it was somewhat hidden, and many began to search for some other mechanism to explain the evolution which all the facts of anatomy, embryology, geology and geographical distribution showed must be taking place. This was the darkness before the dawn—a bright dawn was coming which would eventually bring Darwinism back again. How fascinating is this stream of ideas. Those who had ignored the difficulty of blending inheritance were going to be shown to be

[1] I quote from *The Life and Letters of Charles Darwin*; it is edited by his son Francis Darwin, who writes on pp. 108–9 about his father as follows:

" With regard to the fifth edition of the ' Origin ', he wrote to Mr. Wallace, January 22, 1869: ' I have been interrupted in my regular work in preparing a new edition of the " Origin ", which has cost me much labour, and which I hope I have considerably improved in two or three important points. I always thought individual differences more important than single variations, but now I have come to the conclusion that they are of paramount importance, and in this I believe I agree with you. Fleeming Jenkin's arguments have convinced me.'

" This somewhat obscure sentence was explained, February 2, in another letter to Mr. Wallace:—' I must have expressed myself atrociously; I meant to say exactly the reverse of what you have understood. F. Jenkin argued in the " North British Review " against single variations ever being perpetuated, and has convinced me, though not in quite so broad a manner as here put. I always thought individual differences more important; but I was blind and thought that single variations might be preserved much oftener than I now see is possible or probable. I mentioned this in my former note merely because I believed that you had come to a similar conclusion, and I like much to be in accord with you. I believe I was mainly deceived by single variations offering such simple illustrations, as when man selects.'

" The late Mr. Fleeming Jenkin's review, on the ' Origin of Species ', was published in the ' North British Review ' for June 1867. It is not a little remarkable that the criticisms, which my father, as I believe, felt to be the most valuable ever made on his views, should have come, not from a professed naturalist but from a Professor of Engineering."

right after all, but not for a little time yet, and only because the idea of blending was about to be proved false.

In looking for new mechanisms, biologists became interested in discontinuous variation. Kölliker was perhaps the first to draw attention to it and as early as 1870 Huxley wrote: " We greatly suspect that [nature] does make considerable jumps in the way of variation now and then, and that these *saltations* give rise to some of the gaps which appear to exist in the series of known forms." In 1894 William Bateson (1861–1926) produced his great book *Materials for the Study of Variation*, to which he gave the sub-title *With special regard to discontinuity in the Origin of Species*. It is a mine of information about the remarkable freakish variations reported from both the plant and animal kingdoms.

Then de Vries, the Dutch botanist, just before the end of the century, put forward his famous mutation theory. He had made a detailed study of discontinuous variations in the American evening primrose, *Œnothera lamarckiana*, which he found growing in a waste meadow as escapes from a garden. Some differed markedly from the normal type, and one of these variants, *Œ. gigas* as he called it, as well as the *Œ. lamarckiana*, was observed for several generations multiplying by self-fertilisation, when many new and true breeding types appeared. The species seemed to him to be disintegrating into numbers of forms so different from the old type as to justify their description as new species; and they led him to found his mutation theory. We know now, from more recent work, that these events were really due to highly exceptional hybrid abnormalities and were not at all what he thought them to be. In his book *Die Mutationstheorie* (1901) he says:

> The properties of the organism are made up of units sharply distinguishable from one another. These units are bound up in groups and, in related species, the same units and groups of units recur. Transitions, such as are seen in the outer forms of animals and plants, no more exist between the units than between the molecules of the chemist.

> Species are not continuously connected but arise through sudden changes or steps. *Each new unit added to those already present forms a step and separates the type as a species independent from which it arises.* The new species is a sudden appearance. It arises without visible preparation and without transitions.[1]

[1] From the translation *The Mutation Theory*, London, 1910.

The laws of inheritance which Mendel had annunciated as early as 1865, and which had been completely neglected, were re-discovered quite independently by three biologists in 1900; they were Correns of Berlin, Tschermak of Vienna and de Vries of Leyden. Each, eagerly searching the literature for possible clues as to the nature of inheritance, came across the paper which Gregor Mendel (1822–84), the Augustinian monk, had published in the *Proceedings of the Natural History Society of Brünn*. At once it was seen that Mendel's laws seemed to fit into de Vries's theory of evolution much better than Darwin's. There now came a feverish activity in the biological world to test Mendel's laws both in the breeding of plants and of animals. De Vries, Correns and Tschermak all independently confirmed Mendel's results for peas, which were the plants Mendel worked with, and for many other plants as well. Bateson, in this country, first demonstrated the application of his laws to animals.

The immediate impact of Mendel's work is well shown from the preface that Bateson wrote to his *Mendel's Principles of Heredity* published in 1902:

In the study of evolution progress had well nigh stopped. The more vigorous, perhaps the more prudent, had left this field of science to labour in others where the harvest is less precarious or the yield more immediate. Of those who remained some still struggled to push towards truth through the jungle of phenomena: most were content supinely to rest on the great clearing Darwin made long since.

Such was our state when two years ago it was suddenly discovered that an unknown man,[1] Gregor Johann Mendel, had, alone and unheeded, broken off from the rest—in the moment that Darwin was at work—and cut a way through.

This is no mere metaphor, it is simple fact. Each of us who now looks at his own patch of work sees Mendel's clue running through it: whither this clue will lead we dare not yet surmise.

In his book Bateson gives the full translation of Mendel's two papers. The first, under the title of *Experiments in Plant Hybridisation*, was read to the Brünn Natural History Society on February 8th, 1865. Two points from the opening sentences to this first paper are specially

---

[1] Forgotten would perhaps have been a better word. Mendel was not just an obscure monk, as many imagine; he became Abbot and was a prominent figure in Moravian society.

worth noting. For one thing he says he had been at work for eight years on an experimental study of *evolution*, *i.e.* from the year before Darwin and Wallace's paper was published; and secondly, in view of what we shall presently see was discovered some seventy years later, it is particularly interesting to note his stress on statistics. He explains the care necessary in determining " the number of different forms under which the offspring of hybrids appear or to arrange these forms with certainty according to their separate generations or to definitely ascertain their statistical relations." He goes on:

It requires indeed some courage to undertake a labour of such far-reaching extent: it appears, however, to be the only right way by which we can finally reach the solution of a question the importance of which cannot be over-estimated in connection with the history of the evolution of organic forms.

The paper now presented records the results of such a detailed experiment. This experiment was practically confined to a small plant group, and is now, after eight years' pursuit, concluded in all essentials. Whether the plan, upon which the separate experiments were conducted and carried out, was the best suited to attain the desired end is left to the friendly decision of the reader.

There can be little doubt that Mendel expected his labours would have been acclaimed by the scientific world; instead, they were almost completely ignored and he died nineteen years later, at the age of 62, a bitterly disappointed man. And sixteen years after his death he became world famous.

I must not turn a Gifford Lecture into a lesson in elementary genetics; I will merely remind you that Mendel chose to study those characters of the pea which he found might each be in one or other of two forms: their seeds might be round or wrinkled, their flowers red or white, their stems tall or dwarf and so on; and when he crossed say round with wrinkled or tall with dwarf, you remember he got all round seeded or all tall plants in the first generation and on crossing *these* he got round or wrinkled seeds, or tall or dwarf plants, roughly in the ratio of 3 to 1 in the next generation. It was as a result of many different carefully controlled crosses and back crosses, by using algebra, and by assuming that the factor for tallness was dominant over that for dwarfness, round seed dominant to wrinkled etc., that he concluded that for each of the many different kinds of characters there must be a pair of factors responsible. In his first and most important

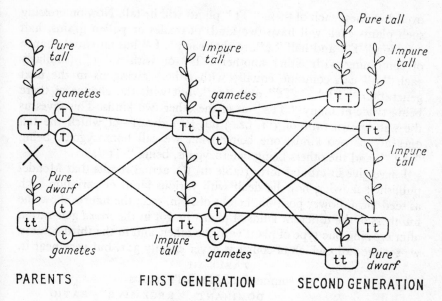

PARENTS   FIRST GENERATION   SECOND GENERATION

22. An example of the working of Mendel's first law as applied to plants; for explanation see text.

law he said that at the formation of the gametes, *i.e.* the reproductive cells (ovule or pollen grain in plants), the two members of such a pair segregate so that each gamete has one member of each kind of unit. Today, of course, we call such a unit factor a gene.[1] At the union of the gametes to form the next generation the pair of genes are restored, one coming from each parent. I give the two simple diagrams which illustrate his first law, and the following brief description merely to remind those who may now have forgotten what they learnt long ago.

In the diagram in fig. 22 showing the crossing of a tall pea with a dwarf pea, the " T's " represent the factors for tallness, and the " t's " the factors for dwarfness. Now as these segregate to give single representatives in the ovules or pollen grains (the gametes), then a factor for tallness *must* mate with a factor for dwarfness to give the constitution " Tt " in the first generation. Tallness being dominant

[1] In more strictly biological circles the term gene is now being replaced by that of the *cistron* (see p. 107).

over dwarfness each of these " Tt " plants will be tall. Now on crossing such plants each will have two kinds of ovules or pollen grains, half carrying " T " and half " t ", so that each " T " has an equal chance of combining with either another " T " or with a " t " (similarly each " t " can combine equally with either) giving us in the next generation " TT ", " Tt " and " tt ", but with the chance of there being twice as many " Tt's " as of the other two kinds. This gives us the well known ratio of 3:1, *i.e.* 3 tall to 1 dwarf—of which the tall ones are of two kinds, one being what we call homozygous, being " TT ", and the others being heterozygous, being " Tt ".

I here give in tabular form (table III) the actual results that Mendel published showing how he dealt with various kinds of variation such as seed form, flower position, height of stem, etc.; the figures show the numbers of the different kinds of plants he got in the *second* generation after crossing one type of plant with the other, and in the third column we see the ratio which of course is never exactly 3:1, but very near it.

TABLE III
A summary of Mendel's results

	DOMINANT	RECESSIVE	RATIO
Seed form	5,474 round	1,850 wrinkled	2·96:1
Cotyledon colour	6,022 yellow	2,001 green	3·01:1
Seed-coats, form	882 inflated	299 wrinkled	2·95:1
Seed-coats, colour	705 grey	224 white	3·15:1
Unripe pods, colour	428 green	152 yellow	2·82:1
Flower position	651 axial	207 terminal	3·14:1
Stem	787 tall	277 dwarf	2·84:1

14,949 (74·9 %) 5,010 (25·1 %)   2·98:1
or 3:1

I am giving these figures because in a moment I want to say something about them which perhaps is not known to many outside biological circles.

In fig. 23, for comparison with the simple diagram of the peas, I put another to show the working of Mendel's law in an animal: the inheritance of a colour variation in the little fruit fly, *Drosophila*.

The characters which were studied by Mendel and all the workers in animal genetics in the early days were naturally the rather more striking characters, such as red and white flowers, or black and normal fruit flies, etc., and it was shown that it was such characters which

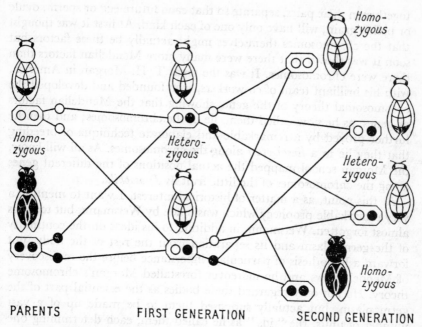

23. The inheritance of a black variation (ebony) in the fruit-fly *Drosophila* according to Mendel's first law; for explanation see text.

from time to time suddenly appeared as if from nowhere. They were what gardeners had long called " sports ", and it was these which they bred from to give us the new kinds of garden flowers; and it was the same with animals. Suddenly a different type appears and, if bred from, will be found to obey Mendel's laws. This indeed fitted well with de Vries's theory. Evolution was now thought by most biologists to be proceeding by these sudden jumps or mutations, with selection playing but a minor rôle: a mere pruning knife, as it were, instead of the great creative force the Darwinians had supposed it to be.

Very soon after the re-discovery of Mendel's laws, it was realised how very similar was the supposed behaviour of his hereditary factors to that of the bodies called the chromosomes, long thread-like bodies in the nucleus of each cell, which had been shown to occur in pairs. As the reproductive cells are formed, there is a particular kind of cell division, called meiosis, in which the chromosomes, after coming together in their pairs, separate so that each future egg or sperm, ovule or pollen grain, will have only one of each kind. At first it was thought that the chromosomes themselves might actually be these factors but soon it was shown that there were many more Mendelian factors than there were chromosomes. It was the great T. H. Morgan in America, with his brilliant team of co-workers, who founded and developed the chromosomal theory of the gene, showing that the Mendelian factors or genes, as he now called them, lie in the chromosomes; and then he further proved by a remarkable and elaborate technique of breeding that they lie in a *linear order* along the chromosomes. As all will know, the Morgan school mapped the actual positions of the different genes along the chromosomes of the little fruit fly *Drosophila*.

At this point, as a matter of historical interest, I want to mention a very remarkable prophecy which was made by Weismann, but today is almost forgotten. Weismann, in addition to his ideas on the continuity of the germ plasm and its separation from the rest of the body, put forward a hypothesis of particulate inheritance before the re-discovery of Mendel's laws and he moreover forestalled Morgan's chromosome theory. He not only regarded these bodies as the essential part of the germ plasm, but actually supposed them to be made up of a vast number of units, the " ids " as he called them, each determining one kind of hereditary character. Moreover, he predicted that some process of halving the chromosome material would be found to take place in the maturation of the germ cells before it was actually shown to be so. By the bringing together of the maternal and paternal chromosomes at syngamy (*i.e.* fertilisation) and the loss of half at the maturation of the germ cells, he annunciated his hypothesis of the nature of variation by the continual bringing together of different ancestral chromosomes in the germ plasm. It was a most remarkable prophetic speculation, and, although he was wrong in thinking that the parental chromosomes joined end to end in the offspring, I always feel that he should receive a little more acknowledgment for his brilliant intuition.

It is these flashes of insight that give the sparkle to the stream of ideas. I now come to an extraordinary little eddy in its flow discovered by the late Sir Ronald Fisher. It is the surprising fact that according to the laws of statistics, the ratios which Mendel published as the result of his experiments appear far too good to be true; never in the history of experimental breeding have such a series of ratios consistently been so near the 3:1 figures his theory demanded. Everywhere where Mendel's laws have been tested they have found to be correct, yet it appears that the detailed figures for the results he first published could never have been true, or at least could only have been true by what one might describe as an absolute miracle of chance. Fisher, perhaps our greatest biological statistician, says, after a lengthy examination,[1] that it is inconceivable that such ratios could have been obtained. I do not think that anyone supposes that Mendel himself deliberately faked the results. It seems most likely, and this, as Fisher suggests, perhaps makes Mendel an even greater figure than one hitherto thought, that, instead of his first doing a vast number of experiments and *then* coming to his conclusion, he, after a few trials, worked out his theory by mathematics in his study and then put it to the test. One can imagine him telling his gardeners of his theory, why he was doing the experiments, and why he expected to get a ratio close to, but not exactly, 3:1. As the experiments proceeded, the gardeners, who helped him, no doubt saw quite clearly that the results were coming out as he had foretold; and, assisting in the counting, it must be supposed that they saved themselves much trouble by giving Mendel the results as he had foretold, not exactly but very nearly 3:1—too near as it turned out! With painstaking care Mendel himself no doubt carried out the pollinations but perhaps left the mere counting to his assistants. We shall never know the exact truth of this story, but it appears to stand, like Weismann's, as another example of brilliant insight being confirmed by experiment. You see now why I drew attention to Mendel's emphasis on statistics at the beginning of his paper!

Darwinism was certainly in eclipse. It was strange perhaps that few people seemed to realise that Mendel's demonstration that inheritance was of a particulate nature instead of the old blending type gave back to the Darwinian doctrine half of what it wanted to make it work. A new favourable variety, instead of being blended away in the coming generations, is just shuffled backwards and forwards, generation after generation, without being changed until there comes the rare event of mutation. In fig. 24 we see how the Mendelian factors are being thrown to and fro between the members of the population at each generation without diminishing their unit values; the diagram, for

[1] R. A. Fisher (1936). Has Mendel's work been rediscovered? *Annals of Science*, vol. 1. (See his p. 132 onwards.)

GENERATIONS

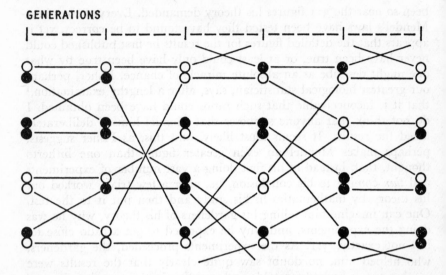

24. A diagram showing the flow of mendelian factors (the genes) in a population from generation to generation; only a single pair of factors is shown whereas there may be thousands being transmitted in a continuous reassortment. Compare this with the old idea of blending inheritance shown in fig. 21 (p. 80); here there is no dilution of the effects of a new variation.

clarity, however, shows just *one pair* of such factors, whereas actually there are thousands continually being brought together in different combinations.

Whilst the discovery of this particulate inheritance removed one great objection to the Darwinian theory, there remained the awkward fact that experimental selection had appeared to fail. This objection was in turn also swept away in 1909 by the work of the Danish botanist, Johannsen. He carried out research in what may be called " pure line " inheritance, that is, studying the effects of breeding from the same kind of self-fertilising plants over many generations. He chose for his material a self-fertilising dwarf bean. Collecting the seeds from such beans over a whole field, he found that they varied in weight from 20 to 90 centi-grams and produced the typical bell-shaped curve of frequency which Francis Galton and his followers got (p. 77). From this range of varying weight, he bred pure lines of beans by self-fertilising those of many different weights. He then found that when he bred from

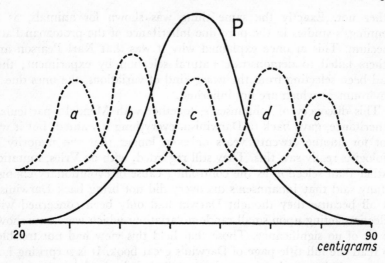

25. A diagram showing the results of Johannsen's experiments with breeding pure line beans. Whilst beans collected at random from the population in a field gave a size frequency curve P ranging in weight from 20 to 90 centigrams, he found by breeding pure lines (by self-fertilisation) he could distinguish five separate races, a, b, c, d and e each having a different and more limited range in weight variation.

beans of, say, the smallest size, 20 centigrams, he got offspring that yielded beans varying in weight from 20 to say 35 centigrams, but however long he carried on his breeding, he never got them to exceed that weight. Similarly, taking beans of the heaviest kind, 90 centigrams, he found their offspring varied from, say, 75 centigrams to 90, but never went beyond these limits. By carrying out vast numbers of such experiments, breeding pure lines from different sizes of bean, he found that, from his original collection of beans from the population in the field, there were five distinct strains, i.e. genetical races; each race varied within certain limits, but would never cover the complete range of weight shown in the population as a whole. This is shown in fig. 25. He was the first to distinguish by experiment two different types of variation, one which he called the genotypic kind, by which he meant the variation governed by inheritance, and another kind he called phenotypic, which was caused simply by differences in the environment, such as varying sunlight, moisture, mineral content of the soil, etc. One kind of variation, the genotypic, is inherited and the other not. Exactly the same thing was shown for animals, as in Jennings's studies in the pure line inheritance of the protozoan Paramecium. This at once explained why it was that Karl Pearson and others failed to demonstrate natural selection by experiment; they had been selecting from the *wrong* kind of variations, the ones due to environment which are not inherited.

This discovery of Johannsen's, together with Mendel's particulate inheritance, gave back to Darwinism everything it wanted, but it was not for another twenty years or even longer that the majority of biologists really saw this. They still regarded, with de Vries, mutation rather than selection as the controlling cause of evolutionary change. Many said that Johannsen's discovery did not bring back Darwinism at all because they thought Darwin had only been concerned with selection acting upon small random variations which were now shown to be of no significance. Those that held this view had not troubled to read the full title page of Darwin's great book. It is surprising how few people know what it was really called. It has as its main title *The Origin of Species by means of Natural Selection*, but then if you look more closely, you will see in small print an alternative title which reads *or The Preservation of favoured Races in the Struggle for Life*. His use of the word races shows quite clearly, as indeed he emphasises in his text, that he was only considering the action of selection upon *inherited* variations. It is true, of course, that neither he nor anyone else in his lifetime knew of the two quite different kinds of variation. How strange it seems, looking back, that so few people saw that the objections to Darwinism had now been completely removed. It was only after so much genetical breeding had been accomplished, and after the elegant application of the mathematical genius of the late Sir Ronald Fisher, together with the carrying of Mendelism into the field of wild population studies by Dr. (now Professor) E. B. Ford at Oxford, that the truth was realised. Darwinism had come back into its own.

The great development in evolutionary theory in the present century lies, of course, in the field of genetics. It is impossible here to give any proper account of this brilliant history (and the many changes of view within it). I will merely summarise, in a few sentences, the main contributions from genetics as I see them. I will in fact recite what I might call my genetical creed to make clear what I believe to be the salient features in the physical mechanism of inheritance. It is not *all* I believe in regard to evolution, as you may have guessed!

The Mendelian factors or genes lie on the chromosomes of the nucleus. They are arranged in linear order. Their positions on the chromosomes can be mapped with an extraordinary degree of accuracy if sufficient breeding experiments are done. They can be shown to be not evenly spread along the chromosomes, some are more crowded together, others spaced further apart. From time to time a gene undergoes a change, a mutation, whereby its effect upon inheritance is altered. We see that such mutations to be of value must be *rare* events. This rarity itself must have been the product of natural selection, for the value of different mutations can only be tested one at a time. If many changes were made together, no single beneficial change could be selected from a number of others. As Schrödinger said, if a Works Manager wants to improve the efficiency of his factory, he will make only one change at a time, otherwise he will not know which one is bringing about the desired effect; so also, he said, too high a mutation rate in nature would defeat the evolutionary ends. Unstable genes—those that mutate too easily—will thus tend to be eliminated from the system by natural selection. We see that the same kind of mutation may occur again and again, being recurrent as we say; they may also be reversible, mutating back to their original form.

In addition to gene modifications, there may be chromosomal changes, *i.e.* loss of parts, little inversions of parts, or translocations (one part of a chromosome becoming attached to another part). These are usually small chromosomal changes but there are bigger ones that we might call chromosome mutations. Among these there might be breakages giving two small chromosomes in place of one, or so-called heteroploidy, with the addition or loss of complete chromosomes, or polyploidy in which whole sets may be multiplied. Polyploidy is very common in plants,[1] but rare in animals.[2]

[1] For example, in the chrysanthemums, where the basic (haploid) number is 9, we get different species with chromosome numbers of 18, 36, 54, 72, 90, etc., or in *Solanum* (potatoes, tomatoes, etc.) where the basic number is 12, we get species with 24, 36, 48, 60, 72, 96, 108, 120 and 144 chromosomes.

[2] This, as Müller first pointed out, may be due to the preponderance of monoecious forms (= hermaphrodite in animals) in higher plants and the fact that the sexes are separate in nearly all of the genetically studied animals; as has been shown in *Drosophila* (the fruit fly), polyploidy leads to an upset in the sex-determining mechanism—the ratio of the x chromosomes to the autosomes. Actually, there are series of chromosome numbers in certain hermaphrodite animals, such as flat-worms and molluscs, which suggest that polyploidy may also occur among some hermaphrodite strains of animals.

Sex itself is now seen to be a genetical effect determined by the action of many genes situated on what are called the x (sex) chromosomes in relation to the action of those on the others (autosomes). One of the sexes being what is called the heterogametic sex in having " xy " chromosomes instead of " xx " chromosomes as in the opposite sex;[1] the y chromosome is somewhat in the nature of a dummy. Because of this we get sex-linked inheritance due to the genes carried on the x, but not on the y, chromosomes.

During the course of the present century, we have seen several changes in the interpretations of the facts observed. It was thought at first, as it was by Mendel, that there was a unit factor (or gene, as we now say)[2] governing each particular character of an animal or plant; now, however, we realise that the effects which we are seeing are the result of the interaction of vast numbers of such genes. Whilst each particular gene may have a more pronounced effect upon one part of the body than another (and so becomes labelled as the gene for this or that), it is really producing many other effects: both structurally and physiologically. One gene which may influence the colour of part of an animal may also be making it more tolerant of extremes of temperature, humidity, etc. We know now that genes may have effects in both space and time, *i.e.* some may govern the rates of development of different parts of the body of an organism, so that one part may appear earlier or later than usual in the course of development. Above all we now realise that all these different effects may be altered by the presence of other genes. In fact, all the genes are acting together to create a joint genetical influence: what we call today *the gene complex*. The appearance of any organism is the product of this internal gene complex interacting with the external environment in which it has been brought up.

This conception of the gene complex brought a further important development in our appreciation of the nature of the evolutionary mechanism. It came to be realised that the *effect* of any mutant gene may be more beneficial—or more harmful—in one gene complex

---

[1] In most animals the male is xy and the female xx as in ourselves; but in birds and butterflies (and, curiously enough, some fish) the reverse is true, xx being the male and xy the female. Why this should be so is a very interesting evolutionary story, but it is too long to go into here.

[2] On p. 107 I shall explain that in more specialised circles the term gene is giving place to that of the *cistron*, but in general discussion I am retaining the familiar expression.

than in another. In no two individuals, except identical twins, will the gene complex be exactly the same; so great is the number of possible different combinations of genes that it is inconceivable on statistical grounds that they could be the same.[1] Since the general appearance of an organism is the result of the combined action of *all* its genes, it follows that the *effect* of *any particular one* will depend in some degree upon the united action of the others. This leads to the important concept that the *effect* of any gene *is subject to genetic variation*; *i.e.* not the gene itself, but *its effect* may be altered by changes, mutations and recombinations, in the rest of the gene complex. This, therefore, means that the *effect* of a gene is *subject to selection*. The reality of this is seen in the improvement in the viability of a new mutant form after several generations of inbreeding; those individuals whose gene complex reacts unfavourably are eliminated.[2]

The gene complex then is subject to selection. The effect of a gene can be altered by the continual selection of those complexes in which its effect is more favourable and by the elimination of those in which it is more harmful. Space will not allow me to dwell further on all the refinements of modern genetic theory; but one point, however, must be made. So nicely balanced is the complex in relation to the external environment that only very rarely can we expect a new mutation to be an improvement. For the same reason it is the mutations *with very small effects* that are most likely to be successful in improving the stock. A big or violent change is most likely to be harmful.

We realise how far we are now from the conception that de Vries put forward at the beginning of the century. Instead of evolution proceeding, as he thought, by big jumps—almost new species bounding into existence with selection playing little or no part in their production—we see what are usually tiny changes developing under the influence of selection, little steps far below the species level of difference.

We are brought back to Darwinism, the action of natural selection upon small inherited variations; but it is Darwinism with an important difference: that of particulate inheritance. It is Darwinism and Mendelism united in one doctrine. What changes we have seen!

[1] R. A. Fisher: *The Genetical Theory of Natural Selection*, 1930; also T. Dobzhansky: *Genetics and the Origin of Species*, 1937.

[2] That it is the reaction of the animal to the gene that has changed, and not the gene itself, can be proved by out breeding such a stock; when this is done the original disadvantageous effects of the gene are at once recovered.

There are, of course, many other aspects of evolution theory which I cannot touch on in this one lecture;[1] but one of these must be mentioned here, for without it the present position cannot be properly understood. Once more the stream of ideas surprises us; only within the last twenty years, have most biologists grasped what we now recognise as one of the basic principles of the whole process. I refer to the nature of a species.

As several writers have pointed out, although Darwin called his great book *The Origin of Species*, he did not, strictly speaking, deal with the problem of speciation—of just how individual species do in fact originate; he dealt with the general principles of evolution. He did not recognise any real distinction between species and varieties on the one hand or between species and genera on the other; he regarded the development of such categories as one gradual general process with the distinction between them only a matter of classificatory convenience. Hardly any one, until Ernst Mayr published his *Systematics and the Origin of Species* in 1942, really understood that the species was a unique unit, having quite a different significance in the evolutionary system from that of any other category.

For a long time naturalists had accepted what had been called the practical species concept which Darwin held: he wrote in the *Origin of Species*: " In determining whether a form should be ranked as a species or a variety, the opinion of naturalists having sound judgement and wide experience seems the only guide to follow." We now realise that the species is something which is not just a matter of judgement but has a quite definite *objective reality*. I cannot here develop the modern theory of speciation; I merely want to point out that this is a recent

[1] For example the comparative forces of inter- and intra-specific selection, the modern view of what Darwin called sexual selection, and the part, if any, played by pre-adaptation and Sewell Wright's idea of Genetic Drift, and the disruptive effects of two or more selection forces acting together on a population to produce a polymorphism as recently demonstrated by Professor J. M. Thoday at Cambridge. About some other topics such as the rôles of the Lloyd Morgan, Baldwin and Waddington effects, I shall have a good deal to say later.

Then, more closely related to what we have here been discussing, can we be sure that all inherited variation is due to the chromosomal genes—to these Mendelian factors? We certainly know that there are some forms of cytoplasmic inheritance (*i.e.* factors carried in other parts of the reproductive cells than in the nucleus) and we will probably learn of more; the very nature, however, of the nuclear mechanism, which I shall briefly discuss in the next lecture, makes it clear that they must be of quite subsidiary importance to the main action of the genes.

and important development in evolution theory. The crux of the matter is this. An interbreeding population of animals (or plants) may happen to become divided by a geographical barrier (or other means of isolation) into two quite separate groups, so that, with the passage of time, the members of one, by the action of selection under somewhat different conditions, may come to differ from those of the other; so if eventually the two populations should come in contact with one another again, and if they should now be so different, either in structural or behavioural character that they will no longer interbreed, then we shall have two new species in place of the former one. This is how the *real steps* in evolutionary change take place. It was, indeed, the separation of the slightly different forms of life on the Galapagos Islands which had impressed Darwin so much and it was Wallace who made a special study of such isolation in his splendid book *Island Life*. It was not, however, until eighty years after Darwin's masterpiece was published that Mayr made us all realise exactly how the origin of species did in fact take place. Then, in *his* book, he told us how this true conception of the species had actually first been expressed, some ten years before Darwin ever went to the Galapagos, by the naturalist Leopold von Buch in a description of the fauna and flora of the Canary Islands published in 1825 (and then forgotten!):

> The individuals of a genus spread out over the continents, move to far-distant places, form varieties (on account of differences of the localities, of the food, and the soil), which owing to their segregation [geographical isolation] cannot interbreed with other varieties and thus be returned to the original main type. Finally these varieties become constant and turn into separate species. Later they may reach again the range of other varieties which have changed in a like manner, and the two will now no longer cross and thus they behave as " two very different species ".

Again we may marvel how such a clear and simple statement on so important an issue can have lain unnoticed for so long. What else is lying neglected and forgotten, and what new things are round the corner? Quite a lot I am sure. In lecture vi I shall be discussing the neglect of the ideas put forward at the end of the last century by Lloyd Morgan and Baldwin and the newer form of them in terms of Waddington's " genetic assimilation ".

THE NATURE OF THE GENE AND THE

WORKING OF SELECTION

In the last lecture we saw the development of evolution theory giving us our present-day picture of natural selection acting upon the gene complex, with the genes residing in the chromosomes of the nucleus. A great body of work in the last twenty years has gone to show us that the genes are in fact complex chemical molecules or parts of them- Whilst it is impossible here to give more than a sketch of the contribu. tions of the modern bio-chemists to our story, it is essential, I think, to give some indication of what is now known of the physico-chemical nature of the gene and the actual working of natural selection in nature. Before we discuss Natural Theology we must clearly face the facts which are thought by many to provide a most cogent argument for materialism.

The chromosomes carrying the genes have the remarkable power of reduplicating themselves in the process of cell division called mitosis, which goes on repeatedly during the growth of an individual; by this means the genetic elements are distributed in exactly equal quantities, without change, to all the cells of the body. When the time for reproduction comes, however, we see a significant modification of this process as the sexual cells are being formed.

Sex is that fundamental evolutionary device for bringing about the re-assortment of the genes as one generation follows another. It is in the preparation (or in the maturation as we say) of the germ cells for reproduction that a change in the form of cell division comes into play: the process called meiosis which halves the number of chromosomes in the resulting reproductive cells. We now realise that this division (a kind of telescoped double mitosis) does something much more than this. It is itself a product of evolution ensuring that any new mutant genes are spread through the population and tried out in different genetical combinations with all possible speed. It is a device for increasing variability: a special mechanism for shuffling the genes.

Instead of the chromosomes just coming together in pairs before division, as was originally thought, they twist round one another in pairing and in so doing break, so that corresponding parts of a pair of chromosomes are interchanged and joined up together again. One chromosome which, before pairing, may have had say, genes A, G, L and T at intervals along its length, may be changed to have A, g, I and t at the end of the process, g and t having come in with those parts of the other chromosome, with which it paired and twisted, in exchange for the parts carrying G and T.

It is interesting to note that in the primitive single-celled organisms (the Protista) from which both plant and animal kingdoms originally evolved, we find all kinds of different mechanisms of nuclear division, some more than others approaching the mitosis of higher forms. Once true mitosis had been achieved, it became established as the only type of normal cell division in all higher forms right through the animal and plant kingdoms. From this mechanism, that of meiosis was evolved with the coming of sex, and again it became universal in the two kingdoms. It is a far more complicated process than I have suggested, but the details can be gathered from any modern text-book. The working out of the nature and evolution of this elaborate machinery for generating variation is largely due to C. D. Darlington, who is now Sheradian Professor of Botany at Oxford.

Parallel with these advances in our knowledge of cell mechanics came all the wonderful discoveries of the biochemists regarding the materials of which plant and animal bodies are made. Reproduction and growth are among the most characteristic properties of living things, and naturally both can only be brought about by the production of new material similar to the old; the many different complex chemical substances of the body must be duplicated.

This capacity for growth and reproduction is astonishing. The continual biochemical multiplication of material, coupled with the organisms' sexual drive for reproduction, produces the colossal pressure which not only forces life into every niche that will receive it, but makes the process of selective survival absolutely inevitable. The corollary is, of course, clear enough for Man; unless the world controls its reproductive rate a deadly struggle for survival must ensue: one which might turn out to be not one of survival but of extinction.

An animal can only pass into its tissues relatively simple compounds. When we eat our beef, horse-radish sauce and vegetables followed by a fruit tart, all the complex substances that make up these items of the menu—the carbohydrates, fats and proteins—have to be broken down into much simpler chemicals before they will pass through the lining of our alimentary canal into our body proper. This process of digestion is the work of different chemicals, called enzymes, which are secreted by various glands as the food passes down the tract; each acts as a catalyst[1] in promoting the breakdown of just one or other of the various categories of food substances. Once inside the tissues the simple products of digestion are built up again into the new complex substances of the body giving rise both to growth and the repair of old tissues. The particular proteins of our beef, for example, will be broken down into amino-acids and then built up again into other different proteins characteristic of *Homo sapiens*. Such building processes are also carried out under the influence of other special enzymes, and these, too, are proteins.

I must not become too technical nor attempt in just a few minutes to load you with a mass of facts. It is not my purpose to lecture on biochemistry which I am not qualified to do. I merely want to give the briefest sketch of the " natural history " of some of the chemicals making up the living animal. Don't let us bother with the details or be overwhelmed by the complexity of some of the molecules. I am going to present my argument largely in pictures—in diagrams—and ask you to look at some of them in turn just as if we were visiting a molecule " zoo ". We can enjoy looking at the giraffe, the armadillo and the anteater and appreciate their main differences without burdening ourselves with all the facts of their anatomy; so here, also, don't feel you must retain all the details of molecular structure to follow the points I am trying to make. If, like me, you are not very chemically inclined, just look at them as marvels of nature; I shall draw attention to only a few particular features. All I want to do is to give you some impression of what the biochemists have revealed to us regarding the physical nature of the living organism—indeed of ourselves. No doubt their findings will be modified as their work continues, but the general outline must be true, and we should know of it in discussing the evolutionary process.

[1] *Catalyst:* a substance which aids a chemical reaction without itself undergoing chemical change.

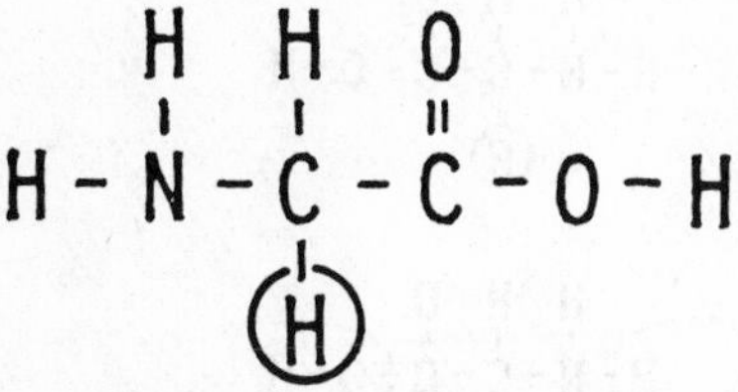

26. A graphic representation of the arrangement of the atoms in a molecule of the simplest known example of an amino-acid: glycine. The letters stand for the atoms of the different elements: c, carbon; h, hydrogen; n, nitrogen; and o, oxygen. The h within a circle is replaced by different radical groups in other amino-acids as in fig. 27.

The proteins are no doubt the most important elements in the living chemical machine. They are built up, as I have just said, from simple amino-acid units; they are linked together in long chains. *Glycine* is the simplest possible such acid unit; the atoms of carbon, hydrogen, oxygen and nitrogen are linked together in its molecule as shown in fig. 26. There are some twenty different kinds of these amino-acids each having molecules with the same arrangement of atoms as Glycine except that each has a different *group* of atoms in place of the one hydrogen (H) atom enclosed within a circle in the diagram; in fig. 27 are a few examples of the molecular structure of some of them: Alanine,

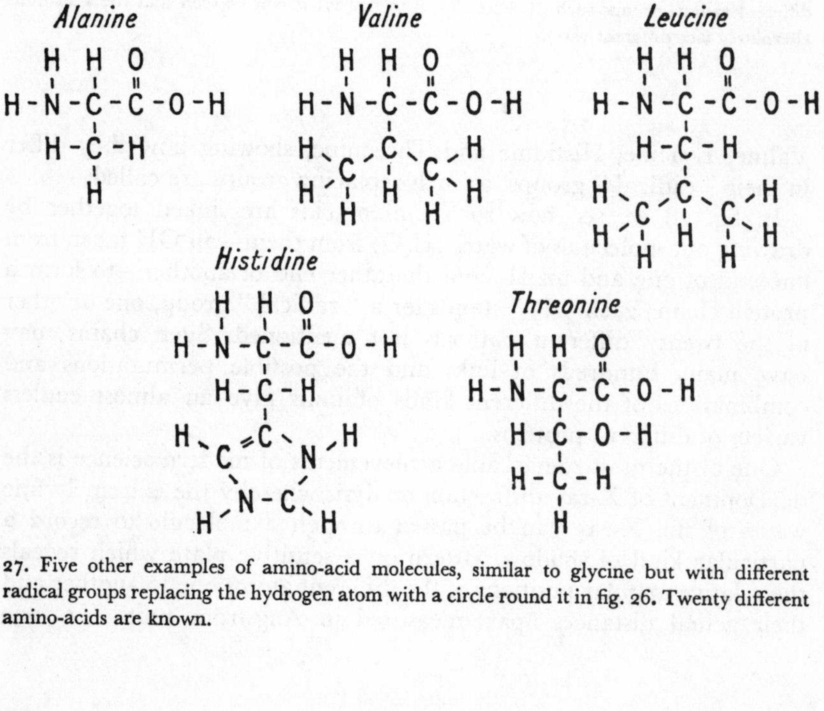

27. Five other examples of amino-acid molecules, similar to glycine but with different radical groups replacing the hydrogen atom with a circle round it in fig. 26. Twenty different amino-acids are known.

28. Showing how the amino-acid units are linked together to form long protein chains by the loss of hydrogen and oxygen to form water molecules (H_2O). Here the " R's " stand for different radical groups such as those shown in fig. 27; it will be seen that the acid units alternately face different ways.

Valine, Leucine, Histidine and Threonine, showing how they differ in their " radical " groups, as such replacing groups are called.

In fig. 28 we see how such amino-acids are linked together by drawing out molecules of water (H_2O) from them—an OH taken from one end of one and an H from the other end of another—to form a protein chain; each " R " stands for a " radical " group, one or other of the twenty different patterns just mentioned. Such chains may have many hundreds of links and the possible permutations and combinations of the different kinds of units give an almost endless variety of different proteins.

One of the most remarkable achievements of modern science is the development of X-ray diffraction analysis whereby the extremely fine waves of the X-ray can be passed through a molecule to record a particular kind of shadow pattern on a sensitive plate which reveals the relative angular positions of the different atoms one to another and their actual distances apart measured in Angström units (*i.e.* one

29. Showing the remarkable knowledge that X-ray crystallography has given us concerning the actual distances apart of the atoms in a protein chain, measured in Angström units, and also the angles that the linkage bonds make with one another.

ten-millionth of a millimetre).[1] An example of such measurements is given in fig. 29.

In fig. 30 we see a small part of the protein chain of hæmoglobin, the red pigment of our blood which carries the oxygen from our lungs to the other tissues. So far we have only considered simple proteins; such chains may be folded up in all sorts of ways or twisted in a spiral such as the *Alpha spiral* seen in fig. 31 where the coils are held together by a bond between the hydrogen attached to the nitrogen of *one unit* and the oxygen of *another unit* three steps along the chain. Or again two or more such chains may be held together in crystalline structure as in the *Beta configuration* seen in fig. 32 where the hydrogen bonds link with the oxygens of the neighbouring chains. Such is the material of our physical existence.

It is now known that modification in some of the protein molecules is under genetic control. A Mendelian factor, a gene, in Man converts the normal hæmoglobin molecule into one called the S type which produces sickle-celled anæmia by the substitution of one amino-acid radical (valine) for another (glutamic acid). In this condition the red blood corpuscles become sickle-shaped. While this anæmia is fatal, the gene which produces it continues to be carried in up to some 40 per cent of the inhabitants of some tropical countries because the disease is only manifest when the gene, which is recessive, is in the

[1] The Angström unit was originally introduced in physics for the measurement of waves of light.

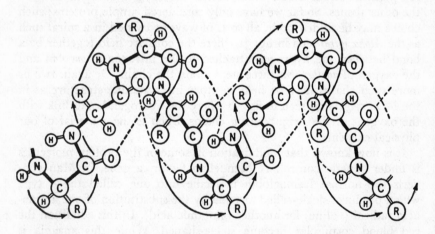

Histidine

Leucine

Valine

Leucine

30. A small part of the protein chain of the respiratory blood pigment hæmoglobin. Alterations in the arrangement: the substitution of one amino-acid unit (valine) for another (glutamic acid) is known to be under the control of a gene and produces the fatal disease of sickle-celled anæmia. The whole chain consists of some 200 such acid units.

31. An example of a protein chain twisted in a spiral—the Alpha spiral—in which the coils of the helix are held together by a bond between the hydrogen attached to the nitrogen of one unit and the oxygen of another unit three steps along the chain. For simple demonstration the spiral has been somewhat opened out; in reality it should be more tightly twisted so that the linkage bonds, shown as broken lines, would be shorter and lie parallel to the axis of the spiral.

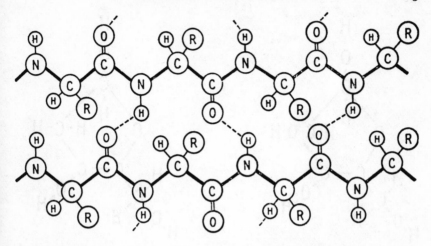

32. An example of two (or more) protein chains being held together in crystalline structure: the Beta configuration in which hydrogen bonds link with the oxygens of neighbouring chains.

homozygous (*i.e.* double dose)[1] state; in the heterozygous (or single dose)[1] state it confers upon its possessor a high degree of immunity against malaria, and so tends to be kept in the population. Here we have definite proof of what had been suggested for some time: that a mutation in a chromosome brings about a variation in the character of an individual by making a change in the chemical constitution of one or more of its proteins.

Several authors had put forward reasons for believing that the gene was a complex chemical molecule. This was well argued by H. J. Müller in his Pilgrim Trust Lecture to the Royal Society, entitled " The Gene ", in 1945; independently it was also the main theme of the very remarkable little book *What is Life?* by that great physicist, the late Erwin Schrödinger, published in 1944. Schrödinger was perhaps the first to suggest how the atomic variations in such large molecules could provide a basic code for specifying the most detailed " information " governing the step by step stages in the development of an individual. Slight changes in the atomic arrangement of a molecule—a mutation—would mean an alteration in the specification

[1] See p. 86.

RIBOSE SUGAR   DEOXYRIBOSE SUGAR

33. A comparison of the molecules of ribose and de-oxy-ribose sugars which respectively form the basis of the two kinds of nucleic acid: ribonucleic acid (RNA) and deoxyribonucleic acid (DNA). The only difference between the two sugars is the lack of an oxygen atom in the deoxy-molecule.

which would change the resulting organism. As he pointed out, a code, like the morse code, using just two signs, dot and dash, in groups of not more than four: e.g.

$$—\cdot, \cdot—, ——\cdot—, \cdot\cdot—, ——\cdot——\cdot, ——\cdot\cdot—, \text{ etc.}$$

can give 30 different specifications. If three signs were used, say ·, — and ×, and in groups of not more than ten, they would give 29,524 different specifications; and if five signs were used, say ·, —, ×, O and +, in groups of not more than 25 there would be 372,529,029,846,191,405 different specifications!

It might be argued, Schrödinger said, that this is a bad analogy with the genetic material because in such a total we are including groups of different numerical composition, as: —·, —··—, etc. To remedy this defect, he said, we could pick from the last example only the combinations of exactly 25 symbols and only those containing exactly five of each of the separate types, for example:

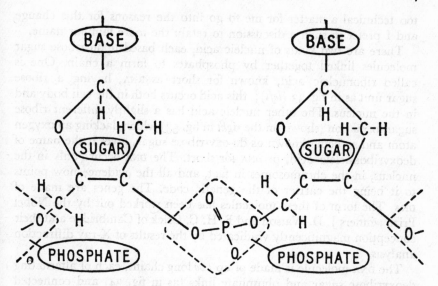

34. Diagram of a part of one of the side chains of a DNA molecule consisting of the deoxyribose sugars and phosphate units in alternating links. Two such chains are joined together by pairs of bases bridging across like the rungs of a ladder and the whole is coiled round in a spiral as shown in fig. 36.

$$\cdots \cdots ----\times \times \times \times \times OOOOO+++++$$
$$\cdot\times---\cdots+O-O\times\times\cdot++O+O\times\cdot--+\times O$$
$$-\cdot-\times O++\times\cdots-OO-+\times+\times-\cdot OO\times+,$$

etc.

A rough calculation now gives 62,000,000,000,000 such alternatives: this gives plenty of scope for a most detailed specification of development and there are many more than 25 genes, each of which may take many forms! What was then a bold speculation now seems to be the most likely solution for the way the genes influence the characters of the organism as it develops. We now know very much more about the nature of the gene; it is indeed either a giant molecule or a part of such a molecule and its substance is a *nucleic acid*. In fact molecular biology is advancing so fast that its exponents no longer talk of the gene, but of the *cistron* to mark our new knowledge of it; it would be too technical a matter for me to go into the reasons for this change and I prefer in such a discussion to retain the more familiar name.

There are two kinds of nucleic acid, each based upon ribose sugar molecules linked together by phosphates to form a chain. One is called ribonucleic acid, known for short as RNA, having a ribose sugar unit as in fig. 33 (*left*); this acid occurs both in the cell body and in the nucleus. The other nucleic acid has a slightly different ribose sugar formation (shown on the *right* in fig. 33) which, lacking an oxygen atom and so being known as de-oxy-ribose sugar, gives it the name of deoxyribonucleic acid, or DNA for short. The DNA occurs only in the nucleus, in the chromosomes in fact, and all the evidence now points to it being the carrier of the genetic code. The genes are made of DNA. The form of these molecules has been worked out by the Nobel Prize winners J. D. Watson and F. H. C. Crick of Cambridge and their conception magnificently vindicated by the results of X-ray diffraction analysis.

The DNA molecule is made of up *two* long chains, each of alternating deoxyribose sugar and phosphate links (as in fig. 34) and connected one to the other by crosslinks, of those substances called " bases ", going from the sugars of one chain to those of the other like the rungs of a ladder. There are only four kinds of these so-called bases and in the DNA molecule they are always linked together in just two kinds of pairs:

Adenine linked to Thymine
Guanine linked to Cytosine

as shown in fig. 35.

Now imagine the " ladder " twisted so that the two sides spiral round one another as seen in the diagram of fig. 36 and you have an idea of the form of the long DNA molecule; but you will note that it is not like a normal ladder. While its two sides spiral round one above the other, as on the surface of a vertical cylinder, the " rungs ", which are *horizontal*, pass obliquely across and so geometrically form chords across the inside of the cylinder. In a model showing all the atoms it looks a most complicated structure. There are many thousands of such rungs in a single ladder chain and the pairs of bases, Guanine-Cytosine, Cytosine-Guanine, Adenine-Thymine, Thymine-Adenine, may be arranged in any order. It is thought that it is the almost endless possible combinations and permutations of these pairs that provide the code system. The DNA molecule of the T4 virus is estimated

35. The molecular structure of the two pairs of bases: Adenine and Thymine, and Guanine and Cytosine which link the two side chains of a DNA molecule together, as shown in the schematic arrangement at the top of the figure. Actually these " rungs of the ladder " are somewhat oblique as shown in the lower part of the figure and so become horizontal when the " ladder " is twisted as in fig. 36. Recent research has suggested that Guanine and Cytosine are linked by a third bond (shown with a question mark) which makes them more tightly linked than the other pair.

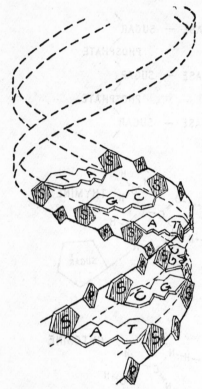

36. A simplified diagram of the double helix of the DNA molecule. The two side chains spiral round one above the other as on the surface of a cylinder, but the connecting links (the pairs of bases A and T or G and C shown in fig. 35) are horizontal and geometrically form chords across the inside of the cylinder. The parts marked S and P represent the sugar and phosphate units and A, T, G and C represent the bases adenine, thymine, guanine and cytosine respectively.

to contain some 200,000 base pairs. How it is thought that the DNA governs protein production is too technical a matter to be discussed here and space will not permit me to go into just how one molecule is thought to promote the formation of another one of a particular kind, save to say that one is thought to act as a templet. Remarkable mechanical models have been made by Professor Penrose: objects of particular shapes which, when shaken together in a box, will pick up other objects and build them into complex structures. This gives us a hint, by analogy, of how it may be done.

A very significant fact should be mentioned; the nature of the DNA molecules and their mutations appear to be of the same type throughout the organic world from bacteria to Man. The viruses appear to be made of the same material and can be held inert in crystalline form until injected into living tissues when they " come to life " and begin

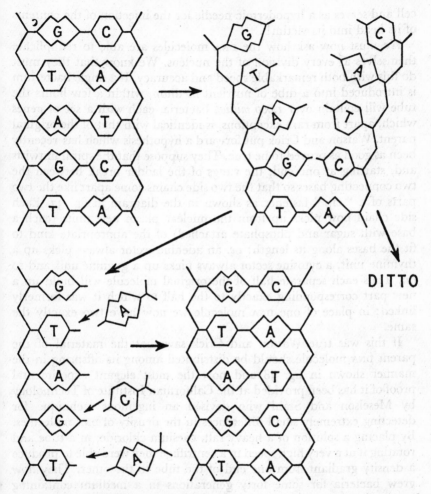

DITTO

37. Diagrams to illustrate the reduplication of the DNA molecule according to the views of Watson and Crick. For explanation see text.

to organise their surrounding molecules just as do the legitimate DNA molecules of their host, but for their own nefarious ends. The electron microscope has now revealed that viruses, on a molecular scale of size, can be distributed like tiny spores and that they have a little " head " and " tail "; the " tail " attaches itself, like a parasite, to a host cell and serves as a hypodermic needle for the injection of the contents of its head into its victim!

We must now ask how the DNA molecules are able to reduplicate themselves at every division of the nucleus. We know that they must do this with both remarkable speed and accuracy. If a single bacterium is introduced into a tube of nutrient medium, within a few hours the tube will contain over *1,000 million* bacteria, each with a set of genes which, apart from rare exceptions, is identical with that of the original parent. Watson and Crick put forward a hypothesis which has recently been as good as proved to be true. They suppose that the spiral untwists and, starting at one end, the rungs of the ladder break between the two connecting bases so that the two side chains come apart like the two parts of a " zip " fastener as shown in the diagram in fig. 37. Each side chain now picks up from the nuclear plasm new units (each a base with sugar and phosphate attached) of the appropriate kind to fit the bases along its length: *i.e.* an adenine sector always picks up a thymine unit, a cytosine sector always picks up a guanine unit and so on. Thus each separate half of the original molecule will build up a new part corresponding exactly to the half to which it was formerly linked; in place of one DNA molecule we now have two exactly the same.

If this was true Watson and Crick saw that the material of the parent DNA molecule should be distributed among its offspring in the manner shown in fig. 38 and now the most elegant experimental proof of it has been provided at the Californian Institute of Technology by Meselson and Stahl who devised an ingenious technique for detecting extremely small differences in the density of DNA molecules. By placing a solution of a heavy salt, caesium chloride, in a tube and rotating it at a very high speed in a centrifuge they were able to produce a density gradient from one end of the tube to the other. They now grew bacteria for some forty generations in a medium containing heavy nitrogen (N^{15}) so that the DNA molecules would have taken it up and become heavier than normal ones; then they diffused the culture with a medium having normal nitrogen (N^{14}) in it, so the first new generation should have, if the theory was correct, DNA molecules all with one chain heavier than the others as shown in fig. 38. In the second generation half the resulting molecules would be light ones and half intermediate between the heavy and the light, again as shown in fig. 38; and in the next generation a quarter would be intermediate

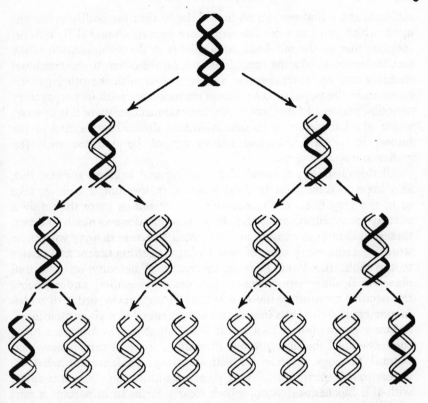

38. A diagram to show how the original material of the parental DNA molecules is distributed among the following generations by repeated reduplications. Experiment, as explained in the text, has now proved the hypothesis of Watson and Crick to be correct.

and the rest light, and so on. When the DNA molecules from these different generations were introduced into the density gradient tube and " centrifuged " their distributions in the tube appeared in exactly the right order as the hypothesis demanded. Similar independent evidence has now been obtained by growing such bacteria in a radio-active medium so that the distribution of the radio-active DNA in the descendants can be detected by photo-sensitive plates. The theory is gloriously vindicated.

This little review of some of the wonders of biochemistry must suffice to show that we can no longer doubt that the bodily variations upon which natural selection works are indeed chemical in nature; they are due on the one hand to accidents in the reduplication of the DNA molecules producing mutations and, on the other, to the continual shuffling and recombinations of such novelties with the other genetic elements in the population by sexual reproduction with its preparatory meiotic divisions. I fully accept the material mechanism of this process; whilst our knowledge of its details will no doubt be modified in the future, its general chemical nature cannot be doubted with the evidence now before us.

All this chemistry is wonderful, exciting and brilliant science, but, as I hope to show later in these lectures, it does not, I believe, take us to the very heart of the nature of life or tell us more than only a part of the evolution story. Dr. Crick who has done so much to reveal these wonders to us ends an article[1] which he wrote in 1957 with these words: " From every point of view biology is getting nearer and nearer to the molecular level. Here in the realm of heredity we now find ourselves dealing with polymers [i.e. chain molecules] and reducing the decisive controls of life to a matter of the precise order in which monomers [i.e. the units in a chain] are arranged in a giant molecule."

Many people follow him in his belief; that is why we must bring these chemical findings into our discussion. If we in turn believe that natural theology provides us with empirical evidence for what we choose to call spiritual reality we must attempt to show how it is linked with this biochemical world which clearly forms so important a part of the physical side of evolution. These molecular changes do appear to control the development of individual bodies, but how far do they control evolution as a whole? This we must come to later.

Still reviewing the present generally accepted position I want for the rest of the lecture to consider that other great factor in the evolutionary process: natural selection. What evidence have we for its actual working in nature? There has been abundant evidence for the power of selection when exercised in the laboratory breeding of animals; only comparatively recently, however, have we obtained really satisfactory evidence of its great force in the natural world.

We realise how recently this evidence has come when we look back at a special symposium organised by the Royal Society in 1936 dealing with " The Present State of the Theory of Natural Selection ", which

[1] The *Scientific American*, September 1957.

was opened by Professor D. M. S. Watson. Here we find recorded[1] the most divergent views. In his opening speech Watson says:

The theory of natural selection is the only explanation of the production of adaptations which is consonant with modern work on heredity . . . [but he goes on to say] . . . the validity of its basal assumption of a selective death-rate determined by a favourable variation has not yet been established. [He also says]: It is probable that the differences between geographical races have no adaptive significance.

Later in the discussion we find Cyril Diver, the ecologist, saying:

The degree to which Natural Selection is responsible for the production of adaptations and the origin of species is still a matter which must be discussed largely on indirect evidence. Recent genetical and mathematical work has greatly increased the reasonableness of the theory, but it has mainly been directed to demonstrating that Natural Selection could operate and not that it does operate . . . [and he goes on later to say]:

With regard to the origin of species, it has been shown that a type of evolution could be brought about by Natural Selection; but the more deeply the facts relating to closely allied species are investigated, the less likely does it become to appear that the evolution that has taken place is of this particular type; and the more likely is it that species formation may be brought about by a number of different causes of which selection might possibly be one.

In the same year G. C. Robson and O. W. Richards, leading systematists, writing in their book *The Variation of Animals in Nature* (p. 316) say:

In short, we do not believe that Natural Selection can be disregarded, as a possible factor in evolution. Nevertheless there is so little positive evidence in its favour, so much that appears to tell against it, and so much that is yet inconclusive, that we have no right to assign to it the main causative rôle in evolution.

Even by the mid-30's Darwinism could not be regarded as fully re-established; very few well designed experiments had yet been made. Actually de Cesnola, as early as 1904, had staged a very simple demonstration with that grasshopper-like insect, the praying mantis (*Mantis religiosa*)—so called because it sits motionless with its front

[1] *Proc. Roy. Soc.* B, vol. 121, pp. 43–73.

legs raised as if in prayer, waiting for unsuspecting insect victims to come within its range. It occurs in two colour variations: green or brown. De Cesnola tethered 20 green and 45 brown ones by woollen threads to green plants and observed them from time to time; after 17 days all the green ones still survived, but all the brown, which differed from their background, had been killed by birds. He did the reverse experiment of tethering 20 brown and 25 green ones to brown plants; now all the brown survived and all the green were killed.[1]

Another early and striking observation was made by J. W. Heslop Harrison in 1920,[2] who collected specimens of the November moth (*Oparabia autumnata*) in two woods, one mainly of pine and one mainly of birch, separated from one another by half a mile or so of heather. This insect also occurs in two varieties: dark and light. In the pine wood, he caught 144 of which 96 per cent were of the dark variety, whereas in the birch wood out of 71 moths only 15 per cent were dark with the remaining 85 per cent of the light variety. The real significance of this result will be seen when, in a moment, I shall discuss the magnificent evidence for selection recently obtained by Dr. Kettlewell. Before, however, I come to that, I must mention some other very striking experiments made a little earlier.

In 1941[3] Dr. E. J. Popham made a study of the variations in the colour of a species of that common aquatic insect, the so-called water boatman *Arctocorisa distincta*. He noticed, while collecting round Richmond, that most of the specimens closely resembled the colour of the bottom of the particular pond they were in and found that similar observations had been made by other naturalists. He therefore decided to make an experimental study of the subject. From a standard Ostwald's colour chart, he made a scale of greys, which, passing from light to dark, can be denoted by the letters a to p, having respectively the following percentage of black:[4]

[1] Robson and Richards (*loc. cit.*) report that Beljajeff (1927) repeated the experiments using brown, yellow and green forms of *Mantis*. On a brown background, out of 20 of each kind, 11 green, 12 yellow and 4 brown were eaten in a fortnight. In a second experiment, however, some crows in 24 hours ate 11 green, 12 yellow and 12 brown from the same background.

[2] *Journal of Genetics*, vol. 9, pp. 195–280, 1920.

[3] *Proc. Zool. Soc.*, vol. A.III, pp. 135–72, 1941.

[4] They are based on Fechner's law " that in order to produce equal stages of sensation, the amount of active stimulus providing the sensation must increase in a geometrical progression."

a	c	e	g	i	l	n	p
3·5	5·6	8·9	14	22	35	56	89

In collecting his insects he judged their colour by holding them in a glass tube against his scale of grey to see between which two shades they lay. He similarly judged the bottoms of the ponds by viewing them against the scale when looking down into them. He found in each of 9 different ponds he studied, that the majority of insects corresponded in colour to their background. Here are two examples:

Queensmere—Surrey (colour i–l)	*Pen Pond–Richmond (colour l–n)*
Arctocorisa of colour g–i: 68	*Arctocorisa* of colour g–i: 0
,, ,, i–l: 421	,, ,, i–l: 39
,, ,, l–n: 46	,, ,, l–n: 113

He then showed that the insects had instinctive colour preferences; if he kept them in aquaria with strips of different grey on the bottom, he found that different insects tended to rest more often on the background which they matched. He now made his striking experiments in selection. He used small fish, rudd, as predators. Putting equal numbers of insects " l " and " i " into an aquarium with an " i " background, and replacing, by others of the same kind, those insects that were eaten, until a total of 200 had been taken, he found that 151 of the darker colour had been taken, as against only 49 of those matching their background. Again, using fish in four separate aquaria which had background colours of " a ", " c ", " e " and " g " respectively, he experimented with 9 insects at a time, having always 3 of each colour " n ", " l " and " i " present (*i.e.* by again at once replacing those eaten). He continued the experiment until 100 insects had been taken in each aquarium, with the following results which show the percentage of the insects of each colour taken in each experiment:

	Percentage of different insects taken in each experiment		
	" n "	" l "	" i "
Experiment with background " a "	33	34	33
,, ,, ,, " c "	36	38	26
,, ,, ,, " e "	41	32	27
,, ,, ,, " g "	53	36	11

This shows clearly that it is the *contrast* between the colour of the insect and its background that determines its chances of being eaten or not.

In the first experiment the three kinds of insects are all so different from their background that they are all equally likely to be taken. As we go down the series of experiments, the contrast between the insects and their background is getting less and less. In the last experiment, for example, insect " i " is only *one* stage in his scale of colour from its background, and only 11 per cent of those taken are of this shade as compared with 53 per cent of those coloured " n " which are *three* degrees on his scale away from their background. This is a brilliant demonstration of the force of predator selection in determining colour variation.

Space will only permit me to mention one more of his experiments, this time demonstrating the relative average time taken by a fish to catch 24 insects in five different populations containing two different colour varieties " l " and " i ", in different relative proportions, each against an " i " background. The results were as follows:

	Number of insects coloured " l "	Number of insects coloured " i "	Average *time* taken to catch each of 24 insects
Experiment 1	24	0	22 secs.
2	18	6	31
3	12	12	39
4	6	18	45
5	0	24	48

We see how much more quickly an insect is caught when it differs from its background than when it is of the same shade.

If it be objected that these are really laboratory experiments and perhaps tell us something different from what is happening in the wild, no such criticism can be levelled against the remarkable work of Dr. Bernard Kettlewell. Here is a study of a widespread evolutionary change which we see actually taking place in our own day.

In 1850 a jet black variety, *carbonaria*, of the geometrid moth *Biston betularia*—the well-known salt-and-pepper moth—was first taken near Manchester, and before long other specimens of the same black form began to be taken in other such urban areas. During the latter part of the century, these black varieties were increasing in number throughout all the industrial regions of Britain and those on the continent as well, particularly in Germany. They were followed by black, or dark varieties, melanic forms as we call them, of a number of other species of moths. It was very soon suggested that they might be produced by natural selection favouring the black forms against the more sooty backgrounds, but at first this was just laughed at, for few were ready to believe that the grime was so bad as to cause such an effect. In 1926 J. W. Heslop Harrison and F. C. Garrett[1] thought they had demonstrated that such melanic forms were due to the effects of certain salts of lead and manganese being taken up by their caterpillars through their food plants as solutions of the salts were washed out by rain from the basic slag extensively used as road metal in certain districts. The supposed discovery was at first hailed as a striking demonstration of the direct effect of the environment bringing about evolutionary change, but similar experiments repeated by several workers failed to confirm the effect.[2] I mention it only because even now it is still being used quite falsely by some authors to support the case for the direct effect of the environment.

It was not until after the last war that an experimental study of industrial melanism, as the phenomenon became to be known, was tackled in earnest by Dr. Bernard Kettlewell[3] at Oxford, who showed that it gave the most striking proof of the working of Darwinian natural selection under wild life conditions. He explored the problem from several different angles and from each approach, the evidence fitted together in a most remarkable way. From a nation-wide survey he showed that the black varieties of *Biston betularia* occurred in large numbers through great tracts of country, not only in the immediate vicinities of industrial development, but also for some considerable distance to the east of such regions, where the prevailing winds were from the west. He also surveyed Great Britain for deposits of soot, taking rubbings from the trunks of trees and from their leaves, then plotting the distribution of contamination on a map. He showed that such areas of grime corresponded closely with the distribution of the black variety of this moth. It bears its English name of the salt-and-

[1] *Proc. Roy. Soc.*, 99B, pp. 241–63.

[2] It seems, as Haldane has pointed out, that Harrison and Garrett were unlucky in introducing a recessive melanic gene in the heterozygous condition in the wild stock with which they began their experiments, and that their controls did not exclude this possibility. The melanic variety of the moth (which, by the way, was of a different species from the salt-and-pepper moth) was of a kind due to a *recessive* gene and not a *dominant* one as it is in most of the other more typical melanic forms.

[3] H. B. D. Kettlewell, *Heredity*, vol. 9, pp. 323–42, 1955; *Ibid*, vol. 10, pp. 287–301, 1956; *Proc. Royal Society*, Series B, vol. 145, pp. 297–303, 1956.

pepper moth because its wings have the appearance of being dusted irregularly with splashes of these condiments, a coloration which provides an excellent camouflage against the grey, irregular background of the typical lichen-covered tree trunk upon which it rests in the daytime. With its wings outspread, it presents a perfect imitation of the lichen effect. Now, as Kettlewell has shown, the typical lichen will not grow where the soot deposit exceeds a certain figure and here, on the blackened tree trunks, the typical salt-and-pepper coloration is extremely conspicuous, but the black melanic form is almost invisible. In uncontaminated England, where the lichen still thrives, it is the black variety which is conspicuous. The contrast of the two situations is shown in fig. 39 in sketches made from photographs.

For his experiments Kettlewell chose two contrasting scenes: the Cadbury/Bourneville estate, in the well-named " Black Country " near Birmingham, and a completely unpolluted wood in Dorset. First of all he collected large numbers of this moth in the two areas. In the Bourneville area the population was made up of 91 per cent melanic forms and 9 per cent normal type; in the Dorset wood his collection gave only 2 per cent of the black kind with 98 per cent of the typical salt-and-pepper pattern. The latter result shows us that this melanic mutation must be one which is occurring regularly in the wild populations. He now bred large quantities of both the black and normal kinds and marked each individual with a tiny spot of red quick-drying enamel on the underside of a wing, so that it would not be seen when the insect was at rest. He then liberated nearly a thousand on the Bourneville estate, in almost equal numbers of the black and normal types. After a week's time he set up his mercury vapour lamps (lamps which entomologists now use to attract moths for capture in large quantities) and recorded only the moths he caught bearing the little red identity labels showing that they were certainly ones which he had released. Of those he recaptured, 29 were black and only 11 were of the salt-and-pepper form; this clearly showed that the latter were being eliminated almost three times as quickly as the black. The same experiment was made in the Dorset woodland, giving almost exactly the opposite result: with only 5 of the black being recaught as against 16 of the normal type; clearly there is a distinct but opposite differential death rate between the two forms in the two areas.

Next, with the help of Dr. Niko Tinbergen, he took a film showing

39. The salt-and-pepper moth, *Biston betularia*. *a*, the typical form; *b*, the black variety *carbonaria*; *c*, a drawing from a photograph of the two forms at rest on the lichen-covered bark of a tree, each being directly below its portrait above; *d*, the same two forms on the soot-darkened, lichen-free bark of a tree in a smoke polluted area, also drawn from a photograph with the moths in exactly the same positions.

this very act of selection going on. In the Dorset wood they set up their camera in a camouflaged hide and focused it on a tree trunk on which they placed 6 of these moths, 3 black and conspicuous, and 3 normal ones on the lichen background. So they watched and filmed the birds coming to take the moths; again and again in this remarkable record you see birds of several different species picking off the black *carbonaria*, and leaving the typical salt-and-pepper kinds. It is the most striking demonstration of Darwinian natural selection taking place before your eyes. In addition to taking the film, they kept watch in turns and recorded the relative numbers of each kind of moth taken and by the different species of bird. As moths were picked off, fresh specimens were put out on to the tree trunk to keep the numbers 3 of each kind. The visual observations made in the Dorset wood are shown in the accompanying table IV, K and T indicating whether the observer was Kettlewell or Tinbergen: 164 black were taken as against 26 of the typical. In the Birmingham district the birds observed were almost entirely redstarts, and out of 58 such acts of predation they were seen to take 43 of the salt-and-pepper type (here conspicuous on the soot-blackened bark) and only 15 of the black variety.

TABLE IV
Predation of moths (*Biston betularia*) in Dorset Wood

| Bird predator | Observer | Moths taken | |
		Carbonaria	Typical
Spotted flycatcher	T	46 } 81	8 } 9
	K	35	1
Nuthatch	T	22 } 40	8 } 11
	K	18	3
Yellow hammer	T	8 } 20	0
	K	12	0
Robin	T	12	2
Thrush	T	11	4
		164	26

All these results give more significance to the observations of Heslop Harrison on the numbers of dark and light varieties of the November moth (*Oparabia*) he took in the pine and birch woods which I mentioned earlier (p. 116). Harrison attributed the selection to night predators such as owls, nightjars and bats, but almost certainly it must be due to bird predators in the daytime, for these moths, like the salt-and-pepper moth, rest in the daytime on the trunks of trees; these, of course, are dark in the pine wood and light in the other wood of birch.

The spread of industrial melanism, an evolutionary change taking

place over large areas within quite recent times, is here clearly shown
to be produced by the action of natural selection upon the gene
complex changing by mutation. Dr. Kettlewell has now recorded a
number of other refinements of the process of improving the black
colouring in this and other species. Further, this form of selection has
apparently not only controlled the proportions of the colour varieties
in the different populations, but Kettlewell has found that there have
developed in relation to this colour variation differences in the moths'
instinctive behaviour. Just as Dr. Popham had demonstrated with his
differently coloured water-boatmen insects (p. 117), so Kettlewell has
shown[1] that when the moths have a choice of a light or dark background, on which to settle, the dark *carbonaria* variety, more often than
not, tends to settle on the dark background rather than a light one,
whereas for the lighter salt-and-pepper variety it is the opposite.

Similar proof of the force of selection in the field by predators was
obtained by Dr. A. J. Cain and Dr. P. M. Sheppard (now both
Professors) when working at Oxford on the colour variations of the
snail *Cepæa nemoralis*[2] and later by Dr. B. C. Clarke for the allied
species *C. hortensis*[3].

The experimental demonstration of selection is now accumulating
fast. Dr. Tinbergen's school of Animal Behaviour at Oxford has shown
the significance (in quantitative terms of selection) of such camouflage
effects as counter-shading in some species of caterpillars, and the
imitation of twigs in others, or in the frightening qualities of pronounced eye markings on the wings of many moths.[4] In the last-
mentioned experiments we see how birds will leave alone a moth which
suddenly displays the alarming large eye pattern, almost like the eyes
of an owl, whereas when the scales forming the eye pattern have been
brushed off the wings, the moth is attacked and eaten with avidity.
The beautiful eyed hawk-moth provides an excellent demonstration
of this; at rest on a tree trunk it is perfectly camouflaged, but if it
should be pecked at, it at once raises its forewings to display the
terrifying " eyes " beneath.

In addition to the specially designed experiments, there is abundant

[1] *Nature*, vol. 175, p. 943, 1955.

[2] *Heredity*, vol 4, pp. 275–94 (1950); *ibid.*, vol. 6, pp. 217–31 (1952), and *Genetics*,
vol. 39, pp. 89–116 (1954).

[3] *Heredity*, vol. 14, pp. 423–43 (1960); *ibid.*, vol. 17, pp. 319–45 (1962).

[4] The experiments are well summarised in Dr. Tinbergen's most attractive series
of essays: *Curious Naturalists* (1958).

evidence for the action and force of selection in the results of the wide-spread use of various insecticides against crop pests. Again and again it is seen that when some particular chemical has been used, after a time there develops a race of the pest which is resistant to it; the poison has eliminated all but those varieties that can tolerate conditions which have proved fatal for the rest. Various scale-insects, pests of citrous fruits, have now a high degree of genetic resistance to the hydro-cyanic acid gas first used to kill them; this has been developed in at least three different genera: the red scale (*Aonidiella*), the black scale (*Saissetia*) and the citricola scale (*Coccus*). Again, there are strains of the codling moth which have become tolerant of the lead arsenate which for long was used to spray apple trees to prevent infection, and there are the numerous bacterial strains which are now resistant to various antibiotics; all these show the force of the action of selection.

There can no longer, I think, be any doubt that selection acting upon the small random changes in the inherited nuclear material is the main *physical* mechanism of evolutionary change. Looked at just like this, I agree that it appears to be an intensely materialistic process. Here at the end of the fourth lecture it might seem that I was coming down on the side of the mechanists. I have presented the case as I believe it is seen by the majority of biologists of today. I am sure that the main features of the process I have outlined are true, but I am also sure they are not the whole of the process. Undoubtedly the physical environment and the action of predators, as we have just seen, are powerful forces of selection; there is, however, I believe, another equally powerful agent, and whether this can be explained in mechanistic terms I very much doubt. To this aspect of evolution I am leading the discussion, and it is with this that I shall be concerned in the latter half of the present series of lectures. In the next lecture, however, still simply as a neo-Darwinian, I want to discuss further the actual *creative nature* of some of the forces of selection.

THE CREATIVE POWER OF

SELECTION

It has often been suggested by critics of the modern evolution theory that random mutations of the genes and their recombinations acted upon by natural selection could not possibly provide the basis for a truly creative evolution. I want in this lecture to illustrate how surprisingly creative such natural selection can, in fact, be; then later I shall discuss the question as to whether it is the main or, possibly, as some believe, the only creative element in the evolutionary process. Here I shall take examples from adaptive coloration.

It may be thought that the consideration of such colour patterns has now become a somewhat hackneyed theme; they have certainly been dealt with at length by many former authors from Erasmus Darwin onwards. Alfred Russell Wallace was the great pioneer in analysing animal and plant coloration in terms of natural selection in his *Tropical Nature* (1878) and *Darwinism* (1889), closely followed by Edward Poulton in his *The Colours of Animals* (1890); then came the Thayers' (A.H. and G.H.[1]) *Concealing Coloration in the Animal Kingdom* (1909 and new edition 1918) and the magnificent monograph by H. B. Cott on *Adaptive Coloration in Animals* (1940). In spite of all that has been written, the subject has certain elements which have not, I believe, been sufficiently stressed and make it particularly appropriate for our discussion here; it is also one in which I have had a special interest for many years. During the first world war I became a camouflage

---

[1] The main author is G. H. Thayer (the son of A.H.T.) but the book bears as a sub-title: *An exposition of the Laws of Disguise through colour and pattern: being a summary of Abbot H. Thayer's disclosures,* and has both an introductory essay and appendices by A. H. Thayer, who first published his views in 1896 in *The Auk,* vol. 13, pp. 124–9 and 318–20.

officer, and, as a very young man, some 47 years ago, was applying the principles of animal coloration to the arts of war. In one lecture I can, of course, only deal in the merest outline with just some aspects of the subject, and I must make it clear that I am not introducing it for its own sake but essentially as material for our discussion on the powers of selection.

First of all I shall give examples of certain types of animal camouflage, or cryptic colouring as we say in biology, and then touch on the opposite principle of warning coloration (or aposematic coloration, to be more technical). We can classify most animal colour schemes under three main headings: cryptic, aposematic and those which are sometimes called epigamic, being concerned with courtship display and allied behaviour. We must not, or course, assume that *all* natural coloration is of adaptive value. Obviously we could not say that the colour of a ruby or an emerald has any such significance; in the same way some animals may just be coloured by the chance accident of their chemical constitution, such as tubifex worms, which are bright red with their respiratory pigment, hæmoglobin, or some marine worms which are green with other such pigments. On the whole, however, as we learn more about the lives of different animals, we realise that almost every bit of colour does in fact have some adaptive significance; we can certainly say that if any colour variation arose which made an animal more conspicuous to its predators then surely those so adorned would tend to be eliminated by selection, as we saw in the last lecture, unless the effect was accompanied by some other protective factor, as in warning coloration.

It is interesting to compare animal camouflage with man's efforts in the same direction. Nature is incomparably superior to man in this. We see in both fields the same course of development with first of all the adoption of a general background colour, then a picking out of some particular feature in the landscape as a theme for a simple pattern, and finally an exact imitation of parts of the environment under special circumstances. I am speaking metaphorically; the animal itself is not picking out its colour scheme—that is the work of selection. We are all familiar with the general mottled appearance of moorland birds, the sandy colours of desert creatures or the snowy white of many Arctic animals. Man's first realisation of the importance of such protection in war was the adoption of similar general background colours, like our own khaki or the neutral greys of the continental armies. We

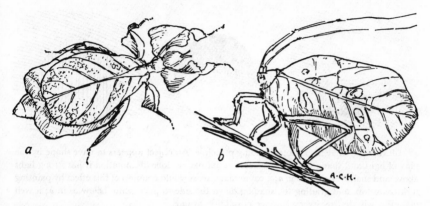

40. Examples of insects in the form of leaves: *a*, the leaf-insect *Phyllium crurifolium* and *b*, the grasshopper *Cycloptera excellens* (which actually reproduces the blotched appearance of a fungus infected leaf). See also the leaf-butterfly in fig. 49a (p. 136).

then see many animals with the main feature patterns: the tiger reproducing the black vertical shadows seen among the bright, sunlit dry bamboos of the jungle, or the leopard with his spotted coat invisible against the dappled sunshine and shadow under forest foliage, or, nearer home, the striped breast and the upward pointing beak of a bittern standing rigidly amongst the reeds when in danger. So man, following the same general course, has begun to develop a blotched battle-dress and mottled tents. Going further the modern soldier conceals some of his fixed positions, observation posts or machine-gun emplacements by painting them to be exact imitations of a bit of hedge, a haystack or some other object of the countryside; in this, however, he is quite out-classed by many animals, particularly insects, which may spend part of the day at rest, as facsimile copies of leaves, twigs and other parts of plants. In fig. 40 I show drawings of two insects masquerading as leaves complete in such details as might be produced by an artist illustrating some botanical work; see also the leaf butterfly in fig. 49a (p. 136). These are the common-place types of adaptive coloration; while perfect of their kind, they are not, to my mind, the most significant of nature's " designs ". The animal world covers the whole range of the artist's subtlety in producing effects by playing with light, shade and tone values. It is to some of these artistic

41. Illustrating Thayer's counter-shading principle. An object appears to have shape by the play of light and shade upon its surfaces; in normal outdoor illumination it has strong light above and shadow below as in *a*; a camouflage artist would counteract this effect by painting it dark on top, and grading the shading down the side to pure white below as in *b*; if well done this will destroy its appearance of solidity, as in *c*.

42. As Thayer first pointed out, the majority of animals living under normal conditions of daylight, unless protected by some other colour principle, tend to have a basic counter-shading coloration similar to *b* in fig. 41.

43. In a natural environment, of highlights and shadows, a counter-shaded animal with no other pattern would be more conspicuous than one with patches of light and dark upon it; such patterns are the general rule.

creations, and I use the words advisedly, that I want to draw your attention. We should note that the successful camouflage officers of the two world wars were artists rather than scientists, or sometimes scientists with artistic inclinations.[1]

Any object appears solid to us very largely by the play of light and shade about its surfaces. In the outdoor daylight world illumination comes mainly from above. We can tell that an object is, say, a sphere, by the highlight on its top, which diminishes over its curved sides to pass with a gradually increasing shade into the deep black shadow of its underneath; but for this shading, we would not know whether the object was spherical or just a disc presented to us. If, as an artist, we wanted to destroy its appearance of solidity, we would paint it dark on the top and gradually merge this into paler shades of increasing lightness as we passed over the sides to a pure white on the underside as in fig. 41b. If we were good enough with our brush we should have made the object look quite flat (fig. 41c). It needed an artist who was also a naturalist, A. H. Thayer,[2] to show us that this counter-shading principle, as he called it, was a general rule in animal coloration (fig. 42). Such a principle destroys the solid reality of the creature but if it were of one colour, however shaded, it would still stand out against its background which is hardly ever uniform; Nature (and I mean, of

---

[1] Perhaps, having said that, I should explain that I was chosen as a camouflage officer in the first world war by Solomon J. Solomon, R.A., under whom I received my training, through, as I learnt afterwards, his mistaking me for another Hardy, a professional artist who had been a pupil at Herkomer's school!

[2] I have already noted Thayer's work on p. 125. Whilst he was the first to realise the great and widespread importance of the counter-shading principle, Poulton had earlier pointed out such an effect in one or two examples of insect coloration. Thayer acknowledges this in his article in *Nature* in 1902 (vol. 65, p. 596) where he writes:

" Since publishing my papers in ' The Auk ' for April and October, 1896, I find that Prof. Poulton perceived years before their appearance the power of a counter-grading of light to make the round surface of a pupa appear flat, and in another case the power of light colour in a depression to make the concavity disappear. In both of these cases he perceived the very *Law of Light-and-Shade* on which the fact of Protective Coloration rests, and recognised the fact itself in these instances."

He then gives the references to Professor Poulton's papers: *Trans. Ent. Soc. Lond.*, 1887, p. 294, and *Ibid.*, 1888, p. 595. Thayer made outstanding contributions to our understanding of both counter-shading and disruptive coloration, but, being carried away in his artistic enthusiasm, sought also to explain many bright colour patterns, both warning and epigamic, in terms of camouflage, and in this he was clearly mistaken.

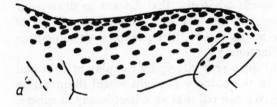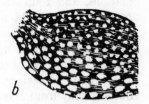

44. The counter-shading effect may be produced by various means other than by simple shading; some particular pattern may be modified to give the same result, for example *a* by black spots being closer together on the back than down the sides as in the cheetah, or *b* by white spots on a dark ground being small on the back and getting larger and larger down the sides to the underneath as in the guinea-fowl (*Munida meleagris coronata*).

course, selection[1]) again steps in and, again as if she were an artist, provides, in addition to the counter-shading, a colour pattern—a composition—which merges it into its surroundings (fig. 43). It has sometimes been suggested that this counter-shading effect is a direct physiological one of greater pigment formation under the influence of light; while this may contribute to the effect in some cases, it is certainly not the whole explanation for often the pattern itself helps in the counter-shading effect. The black spots of the cheetah, for example, are more or less the same size, but are more crowded together on the back and then become progressively further apart down the sides; whereas the shading of the guinea-fowl is seen to be produced by the little white spots which cover its grey plumage becoming larger as they approach the underside (fig. 44). There are interesting examples of animals which pass the daylight hours hanging upside down, such as the caterpillar of the eyed hawk moth, and these are perfectly counter-shaded but in the opposite way to the normal; and there is the Nile catfish, which is similarly coloured and habitually swims belly upwards (fig. 45)!

Apart from its solid form the shape of an object may tell us what it is. In man's camouflage the disruptive colour principle is widely used on objects like tanks, lorries and guns, which are liable to be moved from one site to another. If blotched, with different colours, both light and dark, particularly at its edges, the general outline of an object is destroyed as it comes against the irregular patterns of light and shade

[1] We should remember, however, that it is selection by *perceiving* agents; I discuss this later on p. 151.

45. *a*, the caterpillar of the eyed hawk-moth (*Smerinthus ocellatus*) and *b*, the Nile catfish (*Synodontis batensoda*) are both counter-shaded in the reverse of the normal manner, having light backs and dark undersides. The former feeds at night and rests in the daytime hanging *upside down* as seen in the lower sketch; note how the dark lines along the oblique stripes now appear below them like the shadow of a raised rib on the underside of a leaf. This cat-fish habitually swims *upside down*. *a* is from a photograph and *b* (upper) redrawn from J. R. Norman: *A History of Fishes.*

of a typical landscape background. This is a principle widely developed in the animal kingdom. It is seen among mammals such as anteaters and many antelopes; many snakes have their surfaces broken up by light and dark " designs " which tend to destroy their long cylindrical form against the foliage or dead leaves; and young birds and many moths provide excellent examples. The wings of moths, which habitually rest during the day on exposed surfaces such as old walls and tree trunks, are instructive: note how the *edges* of the wings which would give away their shape are blotched, and so broken up, with contrasting light and dark pigment. Particularly interesting is the " use " of this disruptive principle in helping to hide that most conspicuous feature—the eye; again and again we see frogs, fish, antelopes and other animals, with a dark band of pigment cutting across the tell-tale eye and so reducing its emphasis as a focal point (see figs. 46–48).

More remarkable still are the types of coloration classed under the term of coincident disruptive patterns: bands and patches of colour on

46. Examples of disruptive coloration: *a*, typical gun camouflage; *b*, South American ant-eater, note the typical " gun camouflage " pattern on its long snout; *c*, young woodcock among woodland leaf litter; *d*, the Sargassum weed fish (*Pterophryne*); *e*, the eggs of the lapwing; and *f*, the garden carpet moth (*Xanthorhoë uctuata*) at rest on the lichen covered bark of an elm tree.

different parts of the body which are well separated from one another during active locomotion, but come together, when an animal is at rest, to produce one complete " design ". Such are frequently seen on the undersides of the wings of butterflies which, when at rest, with fore and hind wings together, present some particular camouflage pattern. Some examples of these are shown in fig. 49 including the veining of a leaf reproduced by the tropical leaf butterfly, the dead leaf effect of our own comma butterfly, and the beautiful green and white speckling on the underside of the hind wing of our orange-tip butterfly which at rest covers all but the tip of the fore wing (also green and white); in this last case the curved margin of the hind wing not only exactly fits and masks the bright orange patch, so conspicuous in flight, but merges the insect with the white and green of the cow-parsley flowers on which it so often rests. In the same figure I also include (*d*) the remarkable Central American butterfly *Thecla togarna*, whose coincident stripes suggest that the wings arise from the

47a. A black-and-white sketch from a coloured plate (plate xi) in Thayer's *Concealing Coloration in the Animal Kingdom* showing the typical light and shade pattern in the leaf litter on a forest floor: an ideal background for the concealing of animals by disruptive coloration. If at first glance you have failed to see the quite large creature also portrayed in the picture, turn to fig. 47b overleaf.

other end of the body where a false head, false eye and false antennæ are represented to deflect the attacks of predators from the true head which is largely hidden between the front margins of the wings shown facing to the left. There are several species in this genus with *different* but *equally remarkable* coincident stripes accurately joining up across the fore and hind wings when at rest; *Thecla phaleros* with five instead of six such stripes is the one more usually figured.

Then there are often bands of colour across the limbs and backs of locusts which form one complete design. More exciting still are the series of bands of different colour and thickness to be found on the flanks of some species of frog; these are reversed in their order across the thighs, reversed again on the lower parts of the leg and yet again on the actual feet, so that when the frog is at rest, with its limbs folded up, the bandings fit exactly together to present one whole design (fig. 50). It is just as if an artist had drawn his brush in single strokes of brown, yellow and green right across all four surfaces to distract from their normal anatomical form. It is a miracle of artistry; and incidentally it must be almost a miracle of gene action (under selection) to make the colour bands absolutely continuous when they come together. By this last sentence you may perhaps think I am trying to imply that I doubt whether such gene action can be the physical basis of these patterns; just the opposite, I am sure that all the available evidence points to it and it is just this which makes one realise the *creative power* of selection.

These are surely works as creative as if they had been designed for the animals' concealment. Now here is the point I particularly want to make. All these wonderful effects—combining all the subtleties of the artist's craft as if with an understanding of the significance of light and shade, colour contrast, and tone values—could not possibly have been produced simply by the organisms themselves. They could not be produced, for instance, by any Lamarckian-like principle of the animal trying to make itself more like this or that; the colours and their effect are, of course, unseen by the animal itself. And moreover, they only become significant as camouflage when viewed at *some little distance*

48. Examples of dark bands masking the eyes in a wide range of vertebrate animals: *a*, the common frog (*Rana temporaria*); *b*, the turnstone (*Strepsilus interpres*); *c*, the dotterel (*Endromias morinellus*); *d*, the gemsbok (*Oryx gazella*); *e*, the coral fish *Chætodon*; and the South American boa (*Constrictor constrictor*). *a*, *d* and *f* are drawn from photographs by H. B. Cott in his *Adaptive Coloration in Animals*; *c* and *b* are redrawn from Hudson's *British Birds* and *e* from Portmann's *Animal Forms and Patterns*.

47*b*. This is exactly the same drawing as in fig. 47*a* but with the addition of the white band outlining the copperhead snake which, being both counter-shaded and broken up with a light and dark disruptive pattern, is almost " invisible ". The effect is enhanced by several factors: (1) the light patches of the snake are of the same colour as dried dead leaves so that only occasionally can any outline of its body be detected at such points; (2) the dark shadow patterns are repeated at frequent intervals so that at least once or twice they will coincide with the natural shadows of the background and further deflect the eye from its characteristic shape; and (3) the leaves overlap its edge at several points.

from the animal concerned. In other words, they could only be produced by the gradual selection of better and better imitations of natural objects or better and better optical illusions: *selection by some agent outside them.* This can only be by the action of predators which over long periods of evolutionary time have tended to miss those of their prey which happen to be coloured in such a fashion as to be a little less conspicuous than other members of their species. As the gene complex causes the animal to vary in this way and that, each time such a variation makes its possessor slightly less conspicuous, so will it stand a slightly better chance of surviving. This is why I have stressed this particular type of adaptation. It shows us all the effects—the tricks I might say—of the cunning creative artist; yet they can only have been produced by a form of selection. Whilst it *is* selection, it is well to

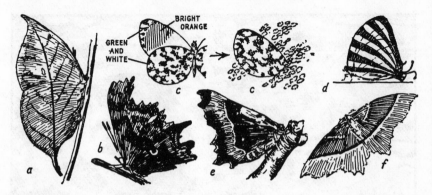

49. Examples of coincident disruptive coloration seen on the wings of butterflies and moths which, when at rest with their wings folded, present a continuous pattern carried on from one wing to the other to produce one complete " design ". *a*, the leaf butterfly (*Kallima paralakta*); *b*, the comma butterfly (*Polygonia c-album*); *c, c'*, the orange-tip butterfly (*Euchlœ cardamines*); *d*, the butterfly *Thecla togarna* Hew (from Columbia); *e*, the purple thorn moth (*Selenia tetralunaria*) and *f*, the light barred moth (*Campæa margaritata*). All drawn from photographs except *d* which was drawn from a specimen in the Hope Department Collection at Oxford.

50. Further examples of coincident disruptive coloration: *a*, across the legs and wings of the grasshopper *Œdipoda cærulescens* and *b* and *c*, across the hind legs of the frogs *Edalorhina buckleyi* and *Bufo valliceps*. *b'* shows how the pattern in *b* will come together when the leg is in the resting position. *b* and *c* from photographs by Cott.

remember at this point that these very subtle forms of adaptation are not those produced by a blind selection as by the inorganic environment, but a selection made by creatures, largely by vertebrate animals endowed with considerable powers of perception—yet actually by this perception being *deceived* by accidental resemblances. I shall return to the significance of this a little later.

Now this form of selection has not only " created " subtleties of colour and form, but at the same time modified the actual behaviour of the animals concerned. We saw in the last lecture that the water-boatmen insects tended to settle on the backgrounds most nearly matching their own colour, and the same was true for the black and grey varieties of the salt-and-pepper moth. Similar observations have also been made on the behaviour of different colour varieties of some birds.[1] We thus see many animals taking up special resting postures which will bring their camouflage pattern into the best relationship with the background upon which they are resting. Here, for example, in fig. 51a, we see a hawk moth which has dark bands upon its wings that reproduce the shadows in the vertical cracks of the bark of a tree; it invariably rests with its head pointing upwards so that the bands reproduce the background. Other kinds, such as some of the geometrid moths, have bandings on their wings going *across from right to left* instead of down from front to back, and these, when at rest, settle with their body *horizontal* (fig. 51b) again bringing the wing pattern into line with the vertical bands on the bark.[2] We see many other more

[1] Mayr in his *Systematics and the Origin of Species* (1942) writes on p. 86: " Niethammer (1940) reviews the literature on cryptically colored larks, and his paper should be consulted for further details. In a series of colored plates, he illustrates the close correlation between soil and coloration of south-west African larks. The most remarkable part of this adaptation is that not only the general tone of color is reproduced accurately in the bird, but also its physical quality. The birds will have a smooth, even coloration, if they live on a fine-grained, dusty, or sandy soil. If, on the other hand, they live on a pebble desert, they will have a coarse disruptive pattern of coloration. Even more remarkable is the fact that the birds become very much attached to the soil to which they are adapted."

And on p. 247 he quotes Niethammer as follows: " It is very striking in south-west Africa that reddish larks are found only on red soil, and dark ones on dark soil, even where two completely different types of soil meet . . ." He then goes on to describe how he tried to drive birds of one colour on to soil of another colour, but each time they at once flew back to their own colour backgrounds.

[2] See J. J. S. Cornes, 1937, Attitude and Concealing Coloration, *Nature*, vol. 140, p. 684.

a   *b*

51. Resting postures of moths on bark showing how instinctive behaviour acts with colour patterns to produce a camouflage effect. *a*, an East African hawk-moth (*Xanthopan m. morgani*) which rests with its head upwards, and *b*, the willow beauty moth (*Boarmia gammaria*) which rests with its body horizontal. Both drawn from photographs by Cott in his *Adaptive Coloration in Animals*.

elaborate behaviour patterns, particularly among some of the insects which mimic others and which I shall be discussing in a moment; for instance spiders, which mimic ants both in body shape and colour, run with their front pair of legs lifted up in an exact imitation of the ant's antennæ.

In all these examples it is certain that the creative element must be outside the organism, continually perfecting the chance patterns that happen to present a camouflage effect, or the chance idiosyncrasies in behaviour which just happen to enhance some particular illusion. I expect most of us at one time or another have looked upon the irregular patterns of the little marble chips let into the tessellated floor of a bathroom and seen among them some groupings that make us say to ourselves " That's a lizard," or " There's a man on horseback," or " a bird in flight "—some outline which at once reminds us of some more or less familiar object. Such chance variations in pattern must be continually occurring by random mutation and recombinations of different genes; whenever these make its possessor look, say, a little more like a leaf, perhaps by stripes which suggest its veins, then such will have a slight selective advantage and tend to escape destruction a little more often than others; such a pattern will gradually spread in the population. A little later perhaps, in another hundred years, another random change will make these striped forms which are now predominant in the population, just a little further like a leaf and so the process goes on through æons of time towards perfection. Some beautiful experimental studies on the reactions of predator birds to camouflaged caterpillars have been made by Dr. L. de Ruiter[1] working under Dr. Tinbergen at Oxford.

Whilst the camouflage or cryptic coloration provides us with such clear examples of a creative element in natural selection, the more specialised phenomena of mimicry show us refinements in the process which would indeed seem incredible were it not for the fact that we see many steps which, whilst not on the direct road to the finest examples, give us every confidence in the theory we believe to underlie the method of their creation. The term " mimicry ", I should explain for those who are not biologists, has for us a special limited meaning. In some books on popular natural history the term may be loosely used in regard to some of the adaptations I have just been speaking of, as when it may be said that a particular insect mimics a leaf or a stick; that is true in plain English, but it has by convention been reserved by biologists for a particular type of coloration. It implies that one animal is mimicking another animal, but we must think of the word " mimicking " in quotes, because what we really mean is that the evolutionary process has produced in one animal an imitation of another without any conscious act of mimicking. Now to explain mimicry I must discuss for a moment that other type of adaptive coloration given the name of " warning " or aposematic coloration.

Warning colours are just the opposite of camouflage; they are in fact advertising colours. Nature uses advertisement to a remarkable extent. All the wonderful bright colours and shapes of flowers are attractive designs, like those on our café or inn signs, saying to the insects " Here be nectar—come and drink ". The bright reds and orange colours of so many fruits and berries are again restaurant advertisements calling birds to come and dine, and in so doing unwittingly distribute the seeds of the plant. We know by experiment that the colour vision of birds is more sensitive to the red and orange, as it is with us, whereas for some insects, particularly bees, blue is a more

---

[1] Some experiments in the camouflage of stick caterpillars. *Behaviour*, vol. 4, pp. 222–32, 1952. Also, Countershading in caterpillars. *Archives Néerlandises de Zoologie*, vol. II, 1955.

significant colour. As you walk down a street of shops, has it struck you that usually the two most colourful and conspicuous kinds of windows are those of the fruiterers with their piles of red apples, oranges, yellow bananas, etc., and the book stalls with their red and orange covered magazines and novels clamouring for attention? They are both concerned with catching the eyes of vertebrates equipped with colour vision. Advertising may be as useful as is camouflage, but for quite different purposes.

The principle of warning coloration is based upon the association of some striking design with some noxious quality, such as possession of a sting, an unpleasant odour or some poison which has been evolved for the protection of the animal concerned. Once such a quality has begun to develop by selection, in that the possessor tends to be left alone by predatory animals, then the advantage of advertisement at once becomes manifest. If any animal, having developed such a noxious quality, should also by a chance mutation become coloured red or orange, it will tend to be left alone more than would otherwise be the case; would-be predators will learn to associate such a striking colour with the unpleasant consequence of the sting or other disagreeable character. A proportion of the population will be destroyed in the process of educating the predators, but the majority of the race will benefit. We are not here, of course, dealing with any altruistic sacrifice on the part of some individuals for the good of the majority; it is just the beneficial result of selection for the species as a whole. The most striking colours employed by nature for this purpose are usually a combination of yellow, orange or red with contrasting bands or spots of black or sometimes white. We know this from experience to be true in regard to warnings for ourselves: railway signals are either red banded with white, or yellow with black, or a crossing gate barrier is usually painted red and white, and a zebra crossing black and white; just so is the body of the wasp black and yellow, the coral snake banded red and black, or the caterpillar of the cinnabar moth similarly banded orange and black. Is this simile just fancy or do we in fact know that such warning colours are effective in the animal world? We do indeed, and again from the brilliant experimental work of the students of animal behaviour. Let me quote two examples dealing with the wasp and the cinnabar moth caterpillar just mentioned. I quote from Dr. Tinbergen's book *Curious Naturalists*, but the references to the scientific papers concerned are given in footnotes.

The problem of whether, and if so why, birds avoid such yellow-and-black prey was tackled seriously by Windecker[1] in Germany. He used the cinnabar moth, *Euchelia (Hypocrita) jacobeæ*, the black-and-red moth that can be seen flying in May and early June in areas where ragwort (especially *Senecio jacobea*) is common. The caterpillars live on this ragwort. They are extremely conspicuous when half- or full-grown, with alternating black and yellow rings, and they live in groups, often defoliating entire plants. Windecker showed that young birds do not hesitate to attack these caterpillars, but that when they take them into their mouth, they reject them with signs of disgust, such as violently wiping their beak. After that they refused them altogether. Windecker applied a simple method to find out what part of a caterpillar is distasteful: he mixed various components (insides, skin) separately with meal-worms and offered these to the birds. He found that mixing finely ground skin with meal-worms spoilt them for the birds. But they did not object to the insides. He then shaved a great number of caterpillars and found that the hairs rather than the skin were responsible. In rejecting the caterpillars after having learnt that they were unpalatable, the birds did not respond to the hairs, but to the colour pattern, for they refused from then on any insect with a similar black-and-yellow pattern.

Comparable results were obtained by Mostler[2] with wasps. Here it is partly the sting, partly the taste of the internal organs of the abdomen that offends the birds. Again, it took very few experiences for many birds to learn to leave wasps alone.

I should not spend more time on emphasising the reality of warning coloration, but I must just mention the delightful experiments made by the late Professor Hale Carpenter[3] in Africa when he gave monkeys the choice of insects to eat, some of which he judged to be camouflaged and some to have warning coloration. From tests made with 244 different species of insects he found that one monkey rejected 84 per cent of the 104 kinds he had classed as having warning coloration, but took 83 per cent of the 101 he considered to be camouflaged; in each

---

[1] W. Windecker, 1939: *Euchelia jacobeæ* L. und das Schutztrachtenproblem. *Zs. Morphol. Œkol. Tiere*, vol. 35, pp. 84–138.

[2] G. Mostler, 1935: Beobachtungen zur Frage der Wespenmimikry. *Zs. Morphol. Œkol., Tierre*, vol. 29, pp. 381–455.

[3] *Trans. Roy. Ent. Soc.*, 1921, pp. 1–105.

case he presented the insects, not against their natural background, but upon a feeding tray where the camouflage effect could not hide the specimens.

Now mimicry I have said is the copy of one animal by another and the essence of the matter is usually that of some quite *palatable* creature gaining protection by displaying the warning colours of another *noxious* species, thereby tending to be avoided by the predators that have learnt to leave such brightly coloured prey alone.[1] This subterfuge, of course, has again been brought about, not by the intentional deceit of the mimic, but by the action of selection. In this country we see a wide variety of harmless insects, such as two-winged flies, some beetles and moths, all mimicking stinging bees and wasps. The reality of such mimicry has again been demonstrated by experiment. Professor Lloyd Morgan in his *Habit and Instinct* of 1896, tells us how he fed young moorhen chicks on bees. Those that were stung refused to eat bees on future occasions and also refused to touch drone flies which mimic bees; other moorhen chicks which had not been given bees, ate the drone flies with avidity. The resemblance of the drone fly to the honey-bee is so close as to deceive even an expert as I was surprised to find when I saw a beekeeper deceived into thinking such a fly was one of his own bees. Similar experiments to that made by Lloyd Morgan have now been carried out by several workers.[2] Fig. 52 shows two examples of ascilid flies mimicking bees, one from South America, the other from Africa.

Now remarkable as are the examples I have just given of flies, beetles and moths mimicking wasps and bees, they do not show us the extraordinary lengths to which mimicry has been carried by many tropical butterflies. Again, of course, I cannot deal with the matter in its own right, with all its fascinating problems, but only use it in the discussion on selection; I must, however, introduce the bare facts of the subject. There are four main groups of these butterflies which have developed noxious odours or unpalatable juices, the Danainæ and the Acræinæ of the old world and the Ithomiinæ and the Heliconinæ of the new world. They are characterised by brilliant contrasting colour

[1] A second kind where two or more noxious species have the same colouring will be mentioned later (p. 144).

[2] G. Mostler, *Loc. cit.*

L. P. Brower, J. V. Z. Brower and P. W. Westcott: *American Naturalist*, vol. 94, pp. 343–56, 1960.

J. V. Z. Brower and L. P. Brower, *Ibid.*, vol. 96, pp. 297–307, 1962.

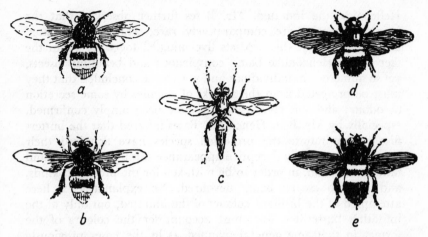

52. Bees mimicked by Ascilid flies. *a*, the South American bee *Euglossa fasciata* mimicked by *b*, the fly *Mallophora fasciipennis*; *c*, an Ascilid fly of typical form, *Andrenosoma vidua*; *d*, the African bee *Xylocopa inconstans* mimicked by *e*, the fly *Hyperechia bifasciata*. Drawn from specimens in the Hope Department collection at Oxford.

patterns, orange and black, black and white, red and black and so on, and these have been mimicked by many butterflies of other families to extraordinary degrees of detail of pattern.

We have now come to realise that there are two distinct types of this imitation, one which is usually known as Batesian because it was first discovered by H. W. Bates, the author of that fascinating classic *The Naturalist on the River Amazon*, and the other known as Müllerian after Fritz Müller, another great naturalist in the South American continent. Bates's discovery could not be summarised in better words than those of Darwin in his *The Descent of Man* (p. 323).

This principle was first made clear in an admirable paper by Mr. Bates, who thus threw a flood of light on many obscure problems. It had previously been observed that certain butterflies in S. America belonging to quite distinct families, resembled the Heliconidæ so closely in every stripe and shade of colour, that they could not be distinguished save by an experienced entomologist. As the Heliconidæ are coloured in their usual manner, whilst the others depart from the usual colouring of the groups to which they belong, it is clear that the latter are the imitators, and the

Heliconidæ the imitated. Mr. Bates further observed that the imitating species are comparatively rare, whilst the imitated abound, and that the two sets live mingled together. From the fact of the Heliconidæ being conspicuous and beautiful insects, yet so numerous in individuals and species, he concluded that they must be protected from the attacks of enemies by some secretion or odour; and this conclusion has now been amply confirmed, especially by Mr. Belt. Hence Mr. Bates inferred that the butterflies which imitate the protected species have acquired their present marvellously deceptive appearance through variation and natural selection, in order to be mistaken for the protected kinds, and thus to escape being devoured. No explanation is here attempted of the brilliant colours of the imitated, but only of the imitating butterflies. We must account for the colours of the former in the same general manner, as in the cases previously discussed in this chapter. Since the publication of Mr. Bates' paper, similar and equally striking facts have been observed by Mr. Wallace in the Malayan region, by Mr. Trimen in South Africa, and by Mr. Riley in the United States.

When Darwin is referring to " cases previously discussed in this chapter ", he is referring to the theory of warning coloration, first given to him by Wallace in relation to brightly coloured caterpillars as mentioned in our chapter II (p. 67).

In 1879 Fritz Müller, collecting in South America, in the footsteps of Bates, also made large collections of butterflies. On more detailed examination of the so-called heliconid butterflies, he found that some of them, which had looked, from the shape and colour of their wings, as if they belonged almost to the same species, were actually, when judged by other characteristics, clearly members of quite a different family; the former Heliconidæ he now found to be made up of two quite distinct families—those that I have previously mentioned (p. 142), the Heliconiinæ and the Ithomiinæ. He went on to show that in different parts of South America there were members of these two families having almost identical colour patterns and, further, that associated with them were often found many other butterflies and even day-flying moths having the same general type of coloration. Now the Heliconiinæ and Ithomiinæ are both characterised by noxious qualities and so avoided by vertebrate predators, birds, monkeys and lizards. Müller spoke of what he called a mimicry ring in which a

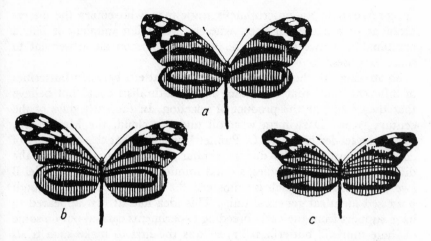

53. Three South American mimetic butterflies each belonging to a quite distinct family: *a*, *Melinæa imitata* (Ithomiinæ); *b*, *Heliconius telchinia* (Heliconiinæ) and *c*, *Dismorphia praxinoe* (Pieridæ). They each have the same colours: black, white and brilliant orange (shown shaded). *a* and *b* are Müllerian mimics and *c* a Batesian one.

number of species, speaking again in metaphor, clubbed together to adopt the same warning pattern, such a ring being made up of a number of noxious kinds, but also a smaller number of harmless ones. The harmless ones are Batesian mimics and the noxious ones are Müllerian mimics; both are illustrated in fig. 53. Natural selection has tended to bring the colour patterns closer and closer together; if there are two species of noxious butterfly and they had quite independent patterns, the predator would have to make two lots of exploratory trials as it learnt to distinguish which butterflies were good to eat and which were not. If two harmful butterfly species came to have the same pattern only half the numbers usually lost by each would now be lost in the course of this " educating " process; the nearer such patterns approached one another the fewer and fewer members of each species would be lost in the course of such testing, thus over long periods of time the patterns would be brought ever closer and closer together by the action of the selection. Then " trading upon this learnt experience of the predators " (speaking metaphorically again) the Batesian mimics, the harmless ones, would " cash in " on the same colour pattern. Poulton expressed it rather nicely by saying " A Batesian mimic may be compared to an unscrupulous tradesman who copies the advertisement of a successful firm, whereas Müllerian mimicry is like a combination between firms who adopt a common advertisement to share expenses."

So striking are the similarities of colour pattern between butterflies of different kinds that for a time many naturalists could not believe that they could be the product of selection. In the early days of the century, when Darwinism was still under a cloud, the Mendelians, under the leadership of R. C. Punnett[1] believed that this similarity of colour pattern must be due to similar genes being present in the different stocks of butterflies, so that mimic A was similar to model B (we call the insect which is mimicked the model) because they both possessed identical genetical units. This idea had at first appeared to have support from the early breeding experiments carried out on some of these mimetic butterflies. Fryer[2] was the first to make such trials with the Asiatic swallowtail butterfly *Papilio polytes* which Wallace had earlier shown to have two different types of female, one mimicking one poisonous form of swallowtail (*P. aristolochiæ*) and the other another species (*P. hector*). It was now seen that these two female forms, "*polytes*" and "*romulus*", of the mimic and another one, "*cyrus*", discovered later, were dependent on an arrangement of *simple* Mendelian factors.[3] Very soon afterwards came a surprising discovery from Africa. Here there are two Danaid butterflies of the genus *Amauris*, one of which, *A. echeria*, is mimicked by a Nymphaline butterfly of the name of *Euralia mima* and the other, *A. dominicanus*, is mimicked by what was thought to be another species of the same Euralia genus, *E. wahlbergi*. Imagine the consternation when it was found that by breeding specimens of *Euralia mima*, specimens of *E. wahlbergi* turned up in the next generation! It was now shown that what were at first thought to be two distinct species were actually simple Mendelian

---

[1] His well-known *Mimicry in Butterflies* was published in 1915.

[2] J. C. F. Fryer (1913): *Phil. Trans. Roy. Soc.*, vol. 204.

[3] It is a form of " sex controlled " inheritance, occurring only in the females because the governing genes only express their *effects* in the gene complex of the female which in butterflies is the heterogenetic sex (*i.e.* having only one x chromosome instead of two as in most animals). The factors concerned are allelomorphs of two genes: PP, Pp or pp, and RR, Rr or rr. The *cyrus* form is pp with any of RR, Rr or rr; the *polytes* form is Pp or PP with rr and *romulus* form is Pp or PP with RR or Rr. In other words the *polytes* and *romulus* forms cannot be produced unless PP or Pp is present, and the latter form only appears if RR or Rr is present.

variations of the same species; "*mima*" being dominant to the "*wahlbergi*" form. It indeed seemed reasonable at that time to say that if the completely different patterns of the two butterflies *mima* and *wahlbergi* could be due to just two forms of the same Mendelian factor (or gene as we should now say), then surely the two exactly similar colour patterns in the two distinct species of the genus *Amauris*, although belonging to quite a different family, must somehow contain these same kind of Mendelian factors. You will remember that in those early days the old idea of single factor producing single character was still in vogue.

It very soon came to be realised, however, that such a hypothesis could no longer be tenable.[1] Dr. E. B. Ford,[2] for example, showed that the pigments producing similar colours in the model and the mimic may be due to entirely different chemicals; this would be most unlikely if they had been due to the effects of the same gene. Again, it is inconceivable that the same genes could be producing mimicry where insects of entirely different orders are concerned, where, for example, flies, beetles or moths may mimic wasps or bees; here we may see the wing cases of a beetle imitating the black and yellow abdomen of the wasp, and surely the same gene could not be responsible for both effects. Apart, however, from such objections, the modern conception of the gene complex, which shows us how the *effect* of any particular gene is altered in different gene complexes, renders it impossible to imagine how the same gene could have the same effect within two quite different families of butterflies.

[1] When Punnett put forward his theory, he did recognise one great difficulty and tried to meet it. He had shown that at least 13 different kinds of insects, some butterflies of different families and some day-flying moths, all took part in what has been called the transparency group, the butterflies and moths concerned all having similar transparent window-like patches on their wings, letting the light through them, giving a most conspicuous contrast with the dark brown of the rest of the wing. Now these transparent areas on the wings of different species are brought about in different ways. In some the scales are reduced in size so that the light passes between them; in other species, the scales may be of normal size but few in number or again may be absent, or in another kind the scales stand up on edge like the slats of a venetian blind and so let the light through, or in yet another, the scales themselves have become quite transparent. Punnett indeed recognised this difficulty, but believed that all these different conditions must be different stages in the manifestation of the activity of the same gene.

[2] *Proceedings of the Royal Entomological Society of London*, vol. 16, pp. 56–90; vol. 17, pp. 87–92.

We are brought to realise that mimicry indeed presents us with the most complete demonstration of the action of natural selection upon small variations, brought about by the varying effects of genes in different gene complexes. While two different mimetic forms of the same butterfly (as in the the two forms of *Euralia* just mentioned) may be shown to be governed by only two different genes or allelomorphs of the same gene, it is not thought that they suddenly appeared by mutation as perfect mimics. It is supposed that, at the beginning, a new mutant had a resemblance just sufficient to give a slight selective advantage; then gradually it would be brought nearer and nearer to the form of the model as the *effect* of the particular gene was altered in different gene complexes, and selection tended to preserve those in which the effect came nearest to that of the model.

It has been shown that the pattern displayed by the mimic is stabilised by the presence of the model; in other words, selection is continually acting to eliminate the less successful copies which may turn up in the regions where the model is providing the education of the predators. Where the mimic happens to extend its range beyond that of its model, it has been shown to become extremely variable. This is interesting in two respects. It shows not only the stabilising control of the model when present, but also shows that those kinds of butterflies which have developed mimicry are just the ones in which great variability of pattern is apt to be the rule. It is these more variable species which by chance have thrown up a similarity to some other form, and so have been seized upon by selection.

I must here explain why it is that usually only the female, and not the male, butterfly has a mimetic pattern; and why the females of some species may have several *alternative* forms each with a pattern mimicking a *different* model. Firstly it seems very likely that it is more important for the female to be protected than it is for the male; the female lays her eggs visiting plant after plant, and spends a considerable time in the process, whereas the male usually carries out fertilisation very soon after emerging. Secondly we know that colour patterns are used as part of the courtship display in butterflies, as in birds, to stimulate the female to yield to the advances of the male; her response remains geared to the original pattern of the race, so that her mate must retain this design whilst she herself can flaunt the false colours of another species. The fact that there are often several female forms of the same species, each mimicking a different model, allows a greater population to exist than would otherwise be the case, for a Batesian mimic must never be more numerous than, nor indeed even approach, the numbers of the model; if it did, the value of the deception would be lost as the predators would now come to associate the particular pattern, more often than not, with something good to eat.

Such, in the barest outline, is the general nature of mimicry. Time will not permit me to go further into the fascinating refinements of the process which has been so well treated by Professor Ford;[1] I must come now to the gist of my argument: the reason why I have introduced the subject in addition to that of camouflage as an illustration of this *creative* power of selection. Both show highly elaborate patterns that must be due to action from *outside* the organism so modified.

There are really two distinct points I want to make about mimicry. Firstly it shows us, even to a greater extent than does cryptic coloration, to what a degree of detail the " effects " of the interplay of genic action can be forced. Whilst we have seen selection reproducing remarkable camouflage resemblances to natural objects such as leaves and twigs they must take second place to these exact mimetic copies involving the most elaborate and diverse patterns imaginable. If we look again at fig. 53, there is no need to discourse on the exactitude of match. In passing I should here just make a general point about mimicry that I have not made before: it is only in the *external visible parts* that mimic and model agree; in their hidden anatomy they are as different as we should expect them to be according to their degree of true taxonomic (*i.e.* classificatory) separation. These almost photographic reproductions of one another are not isolated examples; there are hundreds of them; far more of them, I believe, than those camouflage leaf or twig copies. Let me draw your attention to a few of the refinements of the process. In fig. 54 I have sketched two details of resemblance in butterfly mimicry which were pointed out by the late Sir Ronald Fisher in the colour plates illustrating his *The Genetical Theory of Natural Selection*: the specially enlarged and coloured terminal knobs of the antennæ of the South American butterfly *Methona confusa*, mimicked by the unusual enlargement of the antennæ of a day-flying moth *Castina linus*, and, even more unexpected, the reproduction of the orange coloured palps of the East African ácræine butterfly *Acræa zestes acara* by its mimic, the nymphaline *Pseudoacræa boisdwali trimenii*. As one final

[1] E. B. Ford: The Genetics of Polymorphism in the Lepidoptera. *Advances in Genetics*, vol. 5, pp. 43–87, 1953 and in his recent *Ecological Genetics*, 1964.

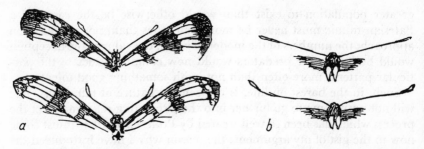

54. Some remarkable refinements of mimetic resemblance pointed out by Sir Ronald Fisher in his *The Genetical Theory of Natural Selection*. *a*, the orange knobbed antennæ of the South American butterfly *Methona confusa* " copied " by a day-flying *moth Castnia linus* below (typical moths lack such knobs); *b*, the head of the East African butterfly *Acræa zetes acara*, seen from in front to show the conspicuous palps which are a bright orange, compared with the head of its mimic, a nymphaline butterfly, *Pseudacræa boidswali tremenii*, placed below it, which has exactly similar orange palps.

example I will refer to that pointed out by Professor Poulton in the case of a day-flying moth and a swallowtail butterfly which fly together in New Guinea; the former, *Alcidis agathyrus*, has a bright orange patch on the abdomen which is reproduced in the mimic, *Papilio lagaizei*, by patches of orange on the inner-margins of the hind wings which come together at rest to give exactly the same effect.[1]

The imitations seen in mimicry indeed drive home to us the fantastic powers of selection. It is amusing to recall that Lull, the author of that one time standard work entitled *Organic Evolution* (1917) was (on his page 246) so astonished at the tropical leaf butterfly *Kallima* that he says it " goes too far, as a much less perfect imitation would be ample for all practical purposes and we cannot conceive of selection taking an adaptation past the point of efficiency." We may *almost* feel like that, but, of course, it is, from what we now know, an impossible view. We cannot get away from the fact that, as in camouflage, the production of mimicry depends upon an agent *outside* the organism so " designed ". But have we fully analysed these outside forces making the selection? I think not.

This brings me to the second point about mimicry, which I shall only most briefly mention here, because it does not really affect my present argument concerning the reality of the power of selection and

[1] E. B. Poulton: *Trans. Entomological Society of London*, vol. 79, pp. 395-8, 1931.

the range of genetic variability; it is a matter I shall return to in a later lecture. I would only point out a difference between the kind of selective action producing camouflage and that producing mimicry. Camouflage is the result of predators *failing* to perceive the cryptically coloured forms; the mimics on the other hand are not imitating natural objects in the usual sense, like leaves or twigs, but are " copying " what are much more like the designs of the abstract artist, brilliant colour patterns of arresting beauty, which have been evolved by the action of the predators themselves, *i.e.* selecting such " designs " as aids to *their* " memory ": striking devices (like warning signals) to enable them to perceive the presence of danger (noxious taste or sting, etc.) before it is too late. I put the word memory, you will note, in quotes; whatever our views are about memory, however, we must recognise that the evolution of the mimics implies a constant *matching* of remarkably detailed patterns by the *perceiving* predators: the " careful " comparison of one design with another which they have *previously* seen and, from their experience, *learnt* to avoid. It can only be this matching with an extraordinarily exact " visual-memory " image which could produce the " photographic " mimetic copies we are dealing with.

Perhaps you will permit me to make a little fanciful digression to add point to my remarks on natural creativeness; I think it likely that there are no finer galleries of abstract art than the cabinet drawers of the tropical butterfly collector. Each " work " is a symbol, if I must not say of emotion, then of vivid life; they are either arresting signs to warn hungry hunting predators, vertebrates like ourselves, of danger, or they are glowing courtship colours flaunted by male insects to attract and coax coy mates to submission. It is often, I believe, the fascination of this abstract colour and design, as much as an interest in biology or a love of nature, that allures the ardent lepidopterist, although all these may be combined; he has his favourite genera and dotes upon his different species of *Vanessa* and *Parnassius*, as the modernist does upon his examples of Matisse or Ben Nicholson. The one-time schoolboy collector will in later life be transfixed with emotion for a moment at the sight of a Camberwell Beauty or a swallowtail— I speak from experience.

After this little harlequinade I should end the present discussion with a more serious summing up. I have chosen to consider adaptive coloration in this lecture because it seems to me to illustrate better than any other form of adaptation these three important points: (1) the almost infinite range of genetic variability that must be available to make possible the photographic-like copies of all manner of patterns and objects; (2) the creative power of the selection that carves out these copies from this mutable, genetic material and (3) the fact that it is certain that all these elaborate adaptations, involving colour, pattern, shape *and behaviour*, and having every appearance of design, could only be the product of some external selective agent and *not* that of any Lamarckian-like mechanism. Whilst we see that the creative element in the forms of selection we have just been discussing is the work of perceiving predators, this does not mean that an entirely " blind " selection cannot also be creative; some of the adaptations of seeds for wind dispersal, embodying striking aerodynamic principles, are just as much creative inventions, but produced entirely by physical forces of the environment.

I must now warn you that I have, in part, been playing Devil's advocate. In addition to demonstrating the creative powers of selection, the examples I have given of selection by exploring perceptive animals, may give us cause for reflection about other possibilities in the mechanism. I believe all that I have said is true, but it is not the whole truth; there are other *selective* forces, equally important, but of quite a different kind, which we shall meet in our next lecture.

BEHAVIOUR AS A SELECTIVE

FORCE

Up to now I have been sketching the development of evolution theory and outlining what I believe to be the generally accepted view as to the mechanism of the process: the action of natural selection upon the inherited variations which are found within any population of animals or plants and which appear to be due to the chance random changes in the chemical constitution of the nuclear material. I come now, in this lecture and the next, to what I regard as the most important part of what I am trying to say in this first series of lectures. I have come to believe, and I hope to convince you, that this present-day view of evolution is inadequate.

As far as it goes, I completely accept this current view, but I do not believe it to be the whole story. There is another part of the process which I consider to be of equal or even greater importance. As to whether this other part is entirely physical, I am doubtful, for reasons which later lectures will explain; it is clear, however, that it must be closely linked with the physical process. I am very grateful for the opportunity that these lectures give me for developing my argument. The ideas I am now presenting have not been arrived at in any hurry. It gives me some satisfaction to be elaborating them here, because it was actually in this lecture theatre, in the spring of 1942, that I first openly expressed my doubts about the validity of modern evolutionary theory and pointed in the direction from whence I believed a change of view would come. I will ask you to allow me to quote the closing paragraphs of the inaugural address which I gave here as Regius Professor of Natural History on April 28th of that year and which was published under the title of *Natural History Old and New*.[1] The words still stand as

[1] As the first part of my address was concerned with marine research, especially in

a good introduction to my theme, so let me use the *end* of that lecture to form the *beginning* of this one, but please remember that when I refer to the " last quarter of a century " I was speaking nearly that length of time ago.

For the last quarter of a century evolutionary research has been largely the study of cultures of a little fly kept in bottles. This brilliant chapter in biology has given us the great concepts of the gene and the gene complex. But now is the time to leave the laboratory for a bit of fresh air—to bring these concepts to the test in the living world outside. We want more and more research into the working of natural selection in the wild. Dr. Gordon of this department has already made a beginning in his studies of *Drosophila* populations in the open country and his observations on the action of natural selection upon a mutant form liberated in the open. Dr. Ford, of Oxford, is pressing forward his genetical-ecological investigations. The doors of the laboratory have been opened at last.

But are natural selection and the gene complex the only factors? Important they must be—but are they all-important? Frankly we do not know, and I for one doubt it.

Plants, rooted to one spot, are certainly at the mercy of their environment; but animals which can move about have an opportunity to choose their habitat. In the evolution of motile animals there are two opposing selections at work. In the words of Mr. Charles Elton[1] who has most forcibly brought this conception forward, there is " the selection of the environment by the animal as opposed to the natural selection of the animal by the environment."

There is a pressing need for the objective study of animal behaviour in the field: of an animal's power of choice. It would seem that choice must be governed in part by the gene complex, but is it entirely? Have we in this quarter of a century discovered the whole or the real essence of the evolutionary mechanism? I think it unlikely. The hypothesis of racial habit has for the time

---

relation to the fishing industry, the whole address was printed in a May issue of *The Fishing News* and also sold as a separate publication at their office at 20 Broad Street, Aberdeen.

[1] *Animal Ecology and Evolution*, Oxford, 1930.

being been eclipsed by the brilliance of gene analysis and by inherent difficulties in putting it to the test of experiment. We must recognise that a test of this hypothesis of the development of racial habit can only be valid if carried on for a long period of time.

I go on in two more paragraphs to urge the need of long-term evolutionary studies in the field; whilst still valid I need not stress the matter further at this point. Some who heard me, or read my lecture, may not perhaps have grasped what I really meant by the term " racial habit ". All I wanted to imply was the idea of habit developed and handed on in a continuing population, in a particular race of a species, other than by being fixed, as an instinct, as part of the inheritance governed by the gene complex: in fact handed on by copying or by " tradition " as we might say today.

I am now going to say a good deal about change of habit or behaviour. Change of habit as a factor in evolution was of course the great contribution made to biological theory by Lamarck: a contribution which, as we have seen, has been largely rejected or neglected. In stressing this factor Lamarck was, I believe, absolutely right. In saying this I must explain that I am not a Lamarckian in the generally accepted sense of the term; I do *not* believe that change of habit can influence evolution through a supposed inheritance of changes in bodily structure brought about *directly* by a greater use of some organs and a lesser use of others. I certainly feel, however, that Lamarck deserves much more credit, than he gets at present, for discerning the great importance of the behavioural side in the working of animal evolution. I have little doubt that he will get this credit in time.

Before I go on to explain just how I believe change of habit affects the course of evolution I would like as a Darwinian and a Mendelian, if it does not sound too paradoxical, to do homage to Lamarck and try to undo some of the misunderstanding that has grown up about his ideas. I specially wish to do so at this juncture because in the last lecture I gave so many examples of adaptation which I said could never be explained on any Lamarckian principle. It has been the recognition of the failure to demonstrate the inheritance of acquired characters by the means he suggested that has, I believe, blinded so many biologists to the real greatness of the conception he was trying to introduce.

There can be no doubt that the whole concept of Lamarckism is fraught with emotion in spite of the fact that Lamarck himself, contrary to opinions often expressed, declared himself to be a materialist.[1] It is particularly important for us to recognise the existence of this emotive element which may so easily distort the clarity of our thinking and vision when dealing with these problems. We must always be on our guard against having a biased view which may blind us to what others see as reasonable. A degree of prejudice occurs, of almost equal intensity I believe, on *each side* of the Lamarckian argument.

It is not difficult to see why emotion plays such a part in this question. On one side there are those who are so shocked by the materialism of the Darwinian conception that with all their finer feelings they cannot bring themselves to believe that it is the real mechanism of our creation; for them Lamarckism with the inheritance of acquired characters may seem the only alternative. They have this deep felt wish to believe Lamarck to be right. Again and again faulty conclusions have been reached in research because the worker has been unwittingly influenced by an ardent desire for particular results. On the other side are those who feel that Lamarckism is nothing but a superstition.

Some people, thoughtless people, imagine that all scientific research must be conducted with a cold impartiality. That is the ideal, but it is often, I would say usually, impossible; and we must recognise it. If what we are testing concerns only the physical world we may achieve such an aloofness; even here, however, if we have invented a pet hypothesis, which by intuition we feel must be true, we are in danger of falsely imagining ourselves to be getting the results we expect. The scientist who has vision, who has fertile ideas, is not unlike the artist in having a certain, perhaps misplaced, affection for the children of his creative thoughts. He devises experiments to see if they will survive tests of validity; although he may pretend not to care one way or the other, yet, secretly, he hopes they will live. Just because of this his experiments may later be found to have been unconsciously biased in their design. How much more likely is such a bias to creep in when the very ideas to be tested are concerned with ourselves as living beings and related to our deeper feelings and our philosophy of life.

[1] See footnote (1) on p. 58.

Certainly we must recognise this danger. How real it is is well illustrated in perhaps the most famous Lamarckian experiment of the century: the tests made by the late Professor William McDougall to see if there was an inheritance of acquired experience. I am sure the case is well known, but I will just briefly outline its character for those who are not biologists. He trained rats to escape from a tank of water by swimming to one and not the other of two alternate sloping ramps. The ramp they were taught to use was only dimly lit; the other was brightly lighted and connected to an electric battery so that a rat on touching it received a slight shock and eventually, after many trials, learnt always to use the dimmer exit. He bred from the rats so taught, and generation after generation repeated the same training; after a long series of experiments he thought he had found that the descendants of those rats so trained, as the generations went on, learnt to escape by the correct exit with a smaller and smaller number of lessons, compared with a line of controls. This, indeed, at first appeared like a noteworthy Lamarckian success; many faded hopes were revived. McDougall in describing his results, made a remarkable and, I think, courageous acknowledgement of the kind of bias I have just been discussing. In his account in the *British Journal of Psychology*[1] for 1927, which bore the title of " An experiment for the testing of the hypothesis of Lamarck," he wrote as follows:

In this connection it is necessary to avow that, during the course of the experiment, there grew up in all of us a keen interest in, I think I must in fairness say, a strong desire for, positive results. From the first it was obvious that a positive result would be more striking, would excite more interest in the biological world, than a negative one. And, when indications of a positive result began to appear, it was but human nature to desire that this result should appear as clearly cut and positive as possible. Further, on my own part, there was a feeling that a clear-cut positive result would go far to render tenable a theory of organic evolution, while a negative result would leave us in the Cimmerian darkness in which Neo-Darwinism finds itself.

I was conscious, therefore, of a strong bias in favour of a positive result; and throughout I was consciously struggling against the temptation to condone or pass over any detail of procedure that might unduly favour a positive result. Such details are encountered

[1] vol. 17, pp. 268–304.

at every point, more especially in the breeding of the animals. To have disguised from oneself this bias, to have pretended that we were superior to such human weakness, would have been dangerous in the extreme; the only safeguards against its influence were the frank avowal of it and unremitting watchfulness against it. I can conceive of no task that could make greater demands upon the scientific honesty of the worker; and it is in part this demand for unremitting watchfulness that renders the work peculiarly exhausting. I can only say that I believe we have succeeded in standing upright; and in fact, for myself, I am disposed to believe that I have leaned over backwards, as we say in America. Whether we have really succeeded in this, the most difficult part of our task, can only be proved when other workers shall have undertaken similar experiments. If our results are not valid, the flaw, which has escaped our penetration hitherto, must, I think, be due to some subtle influence of this bias.

How right he was. Several other workers did indeed repeat the experiments but failed to get similar results. Crewe,[1] for example, found in experiments he made at Edinburgh that there were different genetical strains of rats, some being quicker learners than others and some reacting more to light than others; McDougall had not considered this nor the possibility that he might in the course of the experiments have been unconsciously selecting and breeding from those which were genetically "quicker in the uptake". Agar, Drummond, Tiegs and Gunson[2] in Melbourne made a most prolonged trial with such experiments over a period of some 15 years; excitement rose when they began to get trends of improvement in learning rate very like McDougall's, but unfortunately this quicker learning also showed in their control stocks using animals of untrained ancestry. Statistical analysis of the data revealed that the "condition" of the rats markedly affected their speed of learning; there were progressive changes in learning rate over a succession of generations and these were shown to be connected with the health of the laboratory colony as a whole which, for some unknown reason, was subject to periods of

[1] F. A. E. Crewe: "A repetition of McDougall's Lamarckian experiment." *Journal of Genetics*, vol. 33, p. 61, 1936.

[2] W. E. Agar, F. H. Drummond, O. W. Tiegs and M. M. Gunson: "Fourth (final) report on a test of McDougall's Lamarckian experiment on the training of rats." *Journal of Experimental Biology*, vol. 31, pp. 307-21, 1954.

decline and recovery. There was no demonstrable inheritance of acquired learning. The hopes of the Lamarckians were dashed again, just as they had been a few years earlier when a similar but even more remarkable result had been announced as coming from the Pavlov school in Russia. This supposed discovery was at once incorporated, without checking, by that enthusiastic Lamarckian, MacBride, into perhaps the most biased of all books, An Introduction to the Study of Heredity[1] (see his p. 107); then almost as quickly it was declared by Pavlov to be an entirely misleading interpretation of some faulty experiments made by an assistant.

The story of the Lamarckians has, I think, been a particularly sad one. By intuition they feel certain that changes in behaviour have played a much greater part in evolution than their colleagues will admit. In this I am sure they are right, but they have failed to provide a convincing argument to support their case.

Now if we look at the opposition party we shall, I think, find some of them just as biased and blind for another emotional reason. They also, with an almost religious passion, are fighting to stamp out the last vestiges of the " superstition " that they feel to be lurking in the minds of some who call themselves scientists. I will give only one example, that of a friend and colleague who is one of the most outspoken of the so-called " anti-Lamarckians "; I hope he will forgive me for taking the liberty, and I think he will for two reasons. He knows I have an unbounded admiration for his great contribution to our knowledge of the mechanism of evolution, to which I referred in lecture IV; and also I am heart and soul with him in his scathing attack on what he calls " Lamarckism ". I refer to Professor Darlington. We have all greatly enjoyed his lively thrusts at those who harbour in their minds thoughts like Jacob's belief, that striped hazel rods held before conceiving sheep would make them have striped offspring, or who accept the ideas of Michurin and Lysenko in Russia. If he were right in regarding these ideas as Lamarckian I should agree with him when he refers to " the disreputable theory of Lamarck ";[2] but is he right? I venture to think that, in his commendable anti-superstitious fervour, he, like so many other leading biologists, has not only been blind to the more

[1] This volume in the Home University Library was happily replaced in 1938 by a little classic, The Study of Heredity, by Dr. (now Professor) E. B. Ford.

[2] In Professor Darlington's foreword to a reprint of the first edition of Darwin's Origin of Species issued by Watts, of London, 1950.

important part of what Lamarck was trying to say, but has imagined him to have proclaimed what he *never* said.

Let me compare the writings of the two: Darlington and Lamarck. In his *The Facts of Life* (second edition, 1956) in a chapter entitled " The Evergreen Superstition " with a sub-title " The Resurrection of Lamarck ", Darlington, after discussing the amazing affair in Russia, wihch he has described (p. 231) as " the fusion between Lysenko's ordinary Lamarckism and the specialised Lamarckism of Michurin's mentors ", writes two pages later:

> In this series of revelations the name of Lamarck is not used by Lysenko: his name is mentioned only five years later. But Lysenko's theory is in the authentic Lamarckian succession following Kammerer and MacBride and the less articulate Michurin. The environment, at least the Soviet environment, is supreme. This environment changes heredity to suit it.

Now let me quote from Lamarck, from chapter 7 of his *Philosophie Zoologique* (Paris, 1873 edition), vol. 1, p. 223:

> Ici, il devient nécessaire de m'expliquer sur le sens que j'attache à ces expressions: *Les circonstances influent sur la forme et l'organisation des animaux*, c'est-à-dire qu'en devenant très-differentes, elles changent, avec le temps, et cette forme et l'organisation elle-même par des modifications proportionnées.
>
> Assurément, si l'on prenait ces expressions à la lettre, on m'attribuerait une erreur; car quelles que puissent être les circonstances, elle n'opèrent directement sur la forme et sur l'organisation des animaux aucune modification quelconque.

I do not think I am misrepresenting Lamarck by summarising this passage as follows: " circumstances influence the form of animals, but I must not be taken literally, for the environment can effect no direct changes whatever upon the organisation of animals."

Again and again Lamarck made the point that changes in the environment can bring about changes in the habits of animals and that it is these *changes of habit* which can be so important in bringing about evolutionary modifications. I hope to show that there is good evidence that this is so, although not in the way that Lamarck thought; indeed that it is a cardinal part of the evolution process.

It may be said that the term " Lamarckism " is now generally accepted by the majority of biologists to signify belief in the inheritance of acquired characters; that may be so, but I would say that the majority are quite wrong in attaching Lamarck's name to any doctrine which supposes a *direct* effect of the environment.

The late Professor Graham Cannon in two books[1] made vigorous attempts to overcome the prejudices of his colleagues against Lamarck. Unfortunately he did not really discuss the crucial issue of how changes of habit can affect the course of evolution beyond saying that Lamarck's idea of the inheritance of the effects of use and disuse, which he agreed might be wrong, was only of secondary importance; he further misunderstood, and so misrepresented, most of the modern genetical work. He was right, however, in pointing out that many people had been mistaken in translating Lamarck's word "*besoins*" as meaning "desires" or "wishes" when a more correct interpretation would be "needs"; new habits create new needs and it is these new requirements, not desires, which Lamarck stressed as being so important.

Now, after praising Lamarck's vision, let me return to the development of the views I wish to advocate. Of course, I too may well be biased, especially as a Theist, although I claim my theism to be an empirical one based, as I hope to show in my second series of lectures, upon the natural history and experience of Man. We are all part of the living stream, and few of us can be disinterested in an understanding of its ultimate nature; and we are all inclined to have our intuitions. We are all "religious" in one way or another; few sights have given me a stronger impression of religious passion than the anti-God posters that came from Russia in the thirties.

How, in fact, do I believe that changes in behaviour alter the course of evolution? Quite simply by a form of Darwinian *selection*.

My ideas are, I believe, a development of those first put forward by Baldwin in America and Lloyd Morgan in this country at the end of the last century under the name of organic selection; some people, however, with whom I have discussed the matter insist that I am saying something rather different. At any rate I wish at the outset to acknowledge that my ideas spring from them and that I was directed to them by that wonderful mine of evolutionary knowledge and reference: Sir Julian Huxley's *Evolution, the Modern Synthesis*. The few biologists who have seriously considered Baldwin and Lloyd Morgan's Organic Selection as a factor in evolution have mostly done so in relation to

[1] *The Evolution of Living Things* (1958) and *Lamarck and Modern Genetics* (1959), both at the Manchester University Press.

habitat selection.[1] I am concerned to show that it is a principle which may profoundly influence the evolution of the structure of animals.

Huxley in his *Evolution, the Modern Synthesis* discusses this Organic Selection at two points (apart from three other very brief references directing readers to the two passages I am quoting). In the first (his p. 304) he discusses it in relation to the remarkable experiments carried out by Dr. Thorpe[2] demonstrating the establishment of an olfactory conditioning in insects in relation to their particular sources of food: parasitic ichnemon flies conditioned to the chemical nature of their hosts or the fruit fly *Drosophila* conditioned to lay its eggs in a peppermint scented medium after having been reared in such an essence during early larval life. He writes as follows:

We have here a beautiful special case of the principle of organic selection, as enunciated by Baldwin (1896, 1902) and Lloyd Morgan (1900), according to which modifications repeated for a number of generations may serve as the first step in evolutionary change, not by becoming impressed upon the germ-plasm, but by holding the strain in an environment where mutations tending in the same direction will be selected and incorporated into the constitution. The process simulates Lamarckism but actually consists in the replacement of modifications by mutations (see also Osborn, 1897).

His second discussion of it (his p. 523) is in relation to restrictions on selection and in particular to what he calls " historical restrictions " due to the previous evolutionary history of the stock concerned. He writes:

. . . once adaptive specialisation has begun in one direction it must become progressively harder, on the basis of the known facts of mutation, for selection to switch the trend onto another direction. . . . Subsidiary (or consequential) historical restrictions simply make it easier for selection to act in certain ways than in others, while leaving the adaptive direction to be guided by selection.

A special case of subsidiary historical restriction is provided by the Baldwin and Lloyd Morgan principle of Organic Selection,

[1] See especially W. H. Thorpe, The Evolutionary Significance of Habitat Selection. *The Journal of Animal Ecology*, vol. 14, pp. 67–70, 1945.

[2] *Proc. Roy. Soc.* Series B, vol. 124 (p. 56), 1937; vol. 126 (p. 370), 1938; vol. 127 (p. 424), 1939.

according to which an organism may in the first instance become adapted to an ecological niche merely by behaviour (whether genetic or purely habitual) and any consequent non-heritable modifications, after which mutations for the kind of structural change suitable to the particular mode of life will have a better chance of being selected. Where the modifications are extensive, the process of their replacements by mutations may closely simulate Lamarckism. The principle is an important one which would appear to have been unduly neglected by recent evolutionists.

Now Huxley does refer here to *structural change*. Let me repeat the significant sentence:

after which mutations for the kind of structural change suitable to the particular mode of life will have a better chance of being selected.

That is the essence of my thesis; only I would say, as I am sure Huxley also means, not only by mutation but also by reassortment and combination of existing genes. I am saying nothing original. But what I am doing, which I believe *is* new, is to say, jointly with Dr. R. F. Ewer (see p. 185), that this is not just a slight subsidiary effect but is indeed one of the major factors in the evolutionary process: by this means the changing habits of animals become, at any rate in the higher groups, the dominant factor in the process. I am sure Huxley cannot have intended to imply this because the two paragraphs I have quoted are all he says on the subject in the whole of his text of 578 pages. I think he was right when he said " it would appear to have been unduly neglected." He does not refer to the matter in the new Introduction to the recently published (1963) new edition of his book, although he does refer to Waddington's principle of genetic assimilation. About the latter he says: "Waddington has made a notable contribution to evolutionary theory by his discovery that Lamarckian inheritance may be simulated by a purely neo-Darwinian mechanism." Whilst I recognise that Waddington's principle has great merit in that he has now demonstrated it experimentally several times, we should recognise that Lloyd Morgan and Baldwin with their Organic Selection first showed how such a Darwinian simulation of a Lamarckian effect could be possible.

Waddington, and most other biologists with whom I have discussed the matter, think that his theory is different from that of Organic Selection, or the Baldwin Effect as so many prefer to call it. In his *The*

Strategy of Genes (1957) he gives what he believes is a diagrammatic demonstration of the difference; to me, however, what *he* calls Organic Selection seems to be only a shadow of all that was implied in the concept as originally put forward and particularly as enunciated by Lloyd Morgan. I have to admit that I cannot really see any difference between Waddington's theory and the earlier one, that is if the earlier theory is given in reasonable completeness. Let us go back to Lloyd Morgan, Mark Baldwin and Fairfield Osborn; their pioneer contributions should be remembered. Huxley, as you will see in the first quotation, gives the reference dates of 1896 and 1902 to Baldwin, 1900 to Lloyd Morgan and 1897 to Osborn; these are important references, but they suggest that Baldwin published the idea four years before Lloyd Morgan, whereas the latter was, I believe, the first to make public his views. It seems that they all three came to their ideas quite independently; Baldwin and Osborn briefly put forward their views in a discussion which *followed* a lecture given by Lloyd Morgan to the New York Academy of Sciences on January 31st, 1896, and then, later in the year, published papers on them. A résumé of Lloyd Morgan's views, to which I shall refer in a moment, was then published in America, also in 1896. There was a most illuminating series of articles discussing the whole conception of Organic Selection in the American journals *Science* and *The American Naturalist* for 1896 and '97;[1] from a study of these it is seen that the germ of the idea was also present in

[1] J. M. Baldwin. Heredity and Instinct: Discussion (revised) following Professor C. Lloyd Morgan before the New York Academy of Sciences, January 31, 1876. *Science*, N.S. vol. 3, pp. 438–41 and 558–61, 1896.

——. A New Factor in Evolution. *The American Naturalist*, vol. 30, pp. 354–451 and 536–53, 1896.

——. On Criticisms of Organic Selection. *Science*, N.S. vol 4, pp. 724–7, 1896.

——. Organic Selection, *Nature*, April 15, 1897. See also Appendix to *The Play of Animals* quoted on p. 165.

C. Lloyd Morgan. On Heredity and Variation. *Science*, N.S. vol. 4, pp. 733–40, 1896.

——. *Habit and Instinct*, Arnold, London, 1896.

——. *Animal Behaviour*, Arnold, London, 1900.

H. F. Osborn. A mode of evolution requiring neither natural selection nor the inheritance of acquired characters. *Trans. New York Acad. Sci.*, vol. 15, pp. 141–2 and 148, 1896.

——. Ontogenic and Phylogenic Variation. *Science*, N.S. vol. 4, pp. 786–9, 1896.

——. The Limits of Organic Selection. *The American Naturalist*, vol. 31, pp. 941–51, 1897.

some of the writings of both Weismann and Alfred Russell Wallace. I will also mention here a general review article on the " Baldwin Effect " by G. G. Simpson in *Evolution* (vol. 7, 1952) giving a valuable discussion, with references, on the views of more recent authors concerning its validity; the latter, however, really add nothing to the original concept and hardly discuss the habit and behaviour aspect which I am concerned with here. Simpson puts his finger on the reason for the neglect of these ideas: they were put forward " shortly before the rediscovery of Mendelism gave a radically different turn to biological thought."

The whole of the early discussion between the three originators of the idea was summarised by a statement drawn up by Professor Baldwin " in consultation with Principal Morgan and Professor Osborn." It appears as an Appendix to a translation of a book by Professor Karl Groos edited by Professor Baldwin and published under the title of *The Play of Animals: a study of Animal Life and Instinct* by Chapman and Hall of London in 1898. It is actually a slightly revised version of a similar summary which appeared in *Nature* (April 15, 1897) and reads as follows:

In certain recent publications an hypothesis has been presented which seems in some degree to mediate between the two current theories of heredity. The point of view taken in these publications is briefly this: Assuming the operation of natural selection as currently held, and assuming also that individual organisms through adaptation acquire modifications or new characters, then the latter will exercise a directive influence on the former quite independently of any direct inheritance of acquired characters. For organisms which survive through adaptive modification will hand on to the next generation any " coincident variations " (*i.e.* congenital variations in the same direction as adaptive modifications) which they may chance to have, and also allow further variations in the same direction. In any given series of generations, the individuals of which survive through their susceptibility to modification, there will be a gradual and cumulative development of coincident variations under the action of natural selection. The adaptive modification acts, in short, as a screen to perpetuate and develop congenital variations and correlated groups of these. Time is thus given to the species to develop by coincident variation characters indistinguishable from those which were due to acquired modification, and the evolution of the race will proceed in the lines marked out by private and individual adaptations. It will appear as if the modifications were directly inherited, whereas in reality they have acted as the fostering nurses of congenital variations.

It follows also that the likelihood of the occurrence of coincident variations will be greatly increased with each generation, under this " screening " influence of modification; for the mean of the congenital variations will be shifted in the direction of the adaptive modification, seeing that under the operation of natural selection upon each preceding generation variations which are not co-incident tend to be eliminated.

Furthermore, it has recently been shown that, independently of physical heredity, there is among the animals a process by which there is secured a continuity of social environment, so that those organisms which are born into a social community, such as the animal family, accommodate themselves to the ways and habits of that community. Prof. Lloyd Morgan, following Weis-mann and Hudson, has employed the term " tradition " for the handing on of that which has been acquired by preceding genera-tions; and I have used the phrase " social heredity " for the accommodation of the individuals of each generation to the social environment, whereby the continuity of tradition is secured.

I have thought it well to give this joint summary as prepared by Baldwin, but to my mind a much clearer statement is that by Lloyd Morgan in his earlier article in the American journal *Science* for November 1896 (p. 740).[1] For those readers who are not familiar with biological terms I should explain that, in the summary just given and in one I am just about to quote, *modifications* mean non-inherited changes (*i.e.* those due to the effects of the environment) and *variations* mean inherited genetic changes; it is interesting to remember that the authors were writing some fifteen years before Johannsen established the distinction experimentally in 1909,[2] as also, of course, they were writing before the dawn of Mendelism. Lloyd Morgan in the article I have just referred to summarises his argument under a series of points; I need only begin quoting at his eighth point for the earlier ones are not especially relevant:

[1] Actually a preview of a chapter from his *Habit and Instinct* published later.
[2] See p. 90.

8. Let us suppose, however, that a group of organisms belonging to a plastic species is placed under new conditions of environment.

9. Those whose innate somatic plasticity is equal to the occasion survive. They are modified. Those whose innate plasticity is not equal to the occasion are eliminated.

10. Such modification takes place generation after generation, but, as such, is not inherited. There is no transmission of the effects of modification to the germinal substance.

11. But variations in the same direction as the somatic modification are now no longer repressed and are allowed full scope.

12. Any congenital variations antagonistic in direction to these modifications will tend to thwart them and to render the organism in which they occur liable to elimination.

13. Any congenital variations similar in direction to these modifications will tend to support them and to favour the individuals in which they occur.

14. Thus will arise a congenital predisposition to the modifications in question.

15. The longer this process continues, the more marked will be the predisposition and the greater the tendency of the congenital variations to conform in all respects to the persistent plastic modifications; while

16. The plasticity continuing the operation, the modifications become yet further adaptive.

17. Thus plastic modification leads and germinal variation follows; the one paves the way for the other.

18. Natural selection will tend to foster variability in given advantageous lines when once initiated, for (a) the constant elimination of variations leads to the survival of the relatively invariable; but (b) the perpetuation of variations in any given direction leads to the survival of the variable in that direction.

Surely this *is* Waddington's genetic assimilation expressed in pre-Mendelian terms. Waddington introduced his idea in 1942,[1] presented the first experimental proof of it in 1952[2] and discussed it at greater length in his *Strategy of the Genes* (1957). For comparison with the statements of Baldwin and Lloyd Morgan I will quote from the brief and particularly clear expression of his concept which he gives in his book *The Nature of Life* (1961):

[1] *Nature*, vol. 150, p. 943.   [2] *ibid.*, vol. 169, p. 278.

There is also [he writes on p. 91] a second cyclical system which has to be considered in relation to evolution. The environment influences the nature of the adult organisms which grow up within it. When organisms reproduce and leave offspring, the characters which enable some to be more successful than others depend only in part on their hereditary constitution, but in part also on the environmental circumstances under which they develop. The older discussions of the Lamarckian problem of " the inheritance of acquired characters " usually missed the point that all characters of all organisms are to some extent acquired, in that the environment has played some part—possibly only permissive, but often also to some extent directive—in their formation, and that equally all characters are to some extent inherited, since an organism cannot form any structure for which it does not have the hereditary potentialities. The question we need to ask is not whether acquired characters are inherited, but whether, as we should expect, the ability to acquire the character differs hereditarily in different individuals in a population, and so what will be the effect of natural selection on the potentialities of later generations. Once the problem has been formulated in this way it is easy to carry out experiments which will give us at least the first answers in this field.

Whenever a population has been tested for the ability of its members to acquire characters during their lifetime under the influence of abnormal environments, it is found that different individuals differ in their hereditary potentialities in this respect. The consequence of this is that if selection, either natural or artificial, operates on the population the hereditary potentialities of the next generation for acquiring the character will be changed.

He then goes on to give some further account of his experimental demonstrations of the working of this principle. These clear proofs of its action are indeed a great contribution to our knowledge of the evolutionary process, but the principle is really the same, or so I think, as that contained in Organic Selection. If, however, some subtle distinction escapes me and they are in fact different, then both may be working to bring about the kind of evolutionary change I am discussing. Waddington, however, it should be noted, is mainly discussing the effects of the environment, physical effects such as temperature and salinity, which, as I have already pointed out, were not those entertained by Lamarck, although sometimes they are referred to by present-day biologists as examples of an assimilation of a Lamarckian effect. It is with the effect of habit, the true Lamarckian influence, and its incorporation into evolution by organic selection (and genetic assimilation if it is different) that I am particularly concerned with.

When I was President of the Zoology Section of the British Association at their meeting in Newcastle-upon-Tyne in 1949 I took as the subject of my address " Zoology outside the Laboratory ". After discussing several lines of field work I went on as follows:

A still more important contribution that field zoology can make to evolutionary theory is to throw more light on the part played by Organic Selection. The gene combinations which are best suited to the *habits* of the animal may tend to survive in preference to those which do not give such full scope to the animal's pattern of behaviour. This idea of Organic Selection, which was put forward independently by Baldwin and Lloyd Morgan at the turn of the century, has been almost forgotten until quite recently. This possible selection of structural variations by habit as opposed to the selection of other variations by the environment may indeed be a factor of importance. It is in effect similar to that postulated by Lamarck but brought about on Darwinian lines. External Natural Selection must of course be important, but if Organic Selection can be shown to be a really significant factor, it may well alter our way of looking at evolution as a whole. The relative importance of the two forms of selection must be the subject both of experiment and of more research into the habits and behaviour of animals in nature.

I had thought that I might have started a discussion on the relative potencies of these two forms of selection; but I was disappointed. It has taken me some time to realise that there appears to be a curious, I might almost say psychological, block preventing the majority of biologists with whom I have discussed the matter from really appreciating the point I have been trying to make, or even being interested in what they quickly dismiss as the " Baldwin Effect: a principle of only minor importance." In part no doubt it has been my lack of explanatory skill, but I think now that there have been two other reasons for their failure to grasp the possible significance of selection by change of behaviour. One I have already dealt with: the imagined bogy of

Lamarckism; the other is that so many people still think of evolution in terms of individuals rather than of populations. Of course the process is mediated by the variations in the gene complexes of the individuals and a differential mortality among them; but it is the populations which are evolving not the individuals. The effect I am discussing is essentially a population effect.

When I have previously discussed the matter I have, I think, usually been misunderstood. I would therefore ask you to excuse me if I appear perhaps to be needlessly over-labouring one or two points. I want to be quite certain of making clear a distinction which some people evidently seem to find a somewhat subtle and almost unreal one; it is one which to me, however, appears to be of paramount importance.

I will first of all state the proposition in the simplest terms. If a population of animals should change their habits (no doubt often on account of changes in their surroundings such as food supply, breeding sites, etc., but also sometimes due to their exploratory curiosity discovering new ways of life, such as new sources of food or new methods of exploitation) then, sooner or later, variations in the gene complex will turn up in the population to produce small alterations in the animal's structure which will make them more efficient in relation to their new behaviour pattern; these more efficient individuals will tend to survive rather than the less efficient, and so the composition of the population will gradually change. This evolutionary change is one caused *initially* by a change in behaviour.

As an illustration of what I mean let me use the example I gave when I discussed the matter at a meeting of the Linnean Society in 1956.[1] If birds of a particular species, originally feeding on insects from the surface of the bark of trees, found, in a time of shortage, that they could get more prey by probing into or under the bark, then they might develop a change of habit which, by being copied by other members of the species, could gradually spread through the whole population. In recent years we have seen two examples of such new habits spreading across the country: firstly the opening of milk bottles —first the cardboard tops, then the metal tops—spreading, apparently by copying right through the tit populations of Europe,[2] and secondly the spread across England of the attack on *Daphne* seeds by green-

[1] *Proc. Linn. Soc. Lond.*, vol. 168, pp. 85–7, 1957.
[2] Hinde, R. A., and Fisher, J., *British Birds*, vol. 44, pp. 393–6, 1952.

finches.[1] Now to return to our birds probing into the bark for insects; if this new habit became well established and more profitable to the bird than mere pecking off the surface, then any members of the population with a gene complex giving a beak slightly better adapted to such probing would have a better chance of survival than those less well equipped. A new shape of beak would be evolved as a result of a change of habit. I went on to say (*loc. cit.*): " The same will apply to any other changes of habit as when an animal turns to digging for its food, diving into the water for fish and so on; in any population those gene complexes which modify particular organs to give a better expression to the new habit, will, in the long run, supplant those which produced organs less efficient in satisfying its needs."

Now most people with whom I discuss this say that I am talking about pure Darwinism and seem to imply that I am just making a fuss about nothing. This is where I disagree and insist that there is a real if somewhat subtle difference: a difference which it is essential that we should understand if we are to appreciate the true nature of the living stream—the evolutionary process. To try and make clear this point I must return for a moment to the different kinds of selection.

We can classify the forms of selection in various ways; most people when thinking of Darwinism think of two main types: selection by other organisms, including both predators and competitors, and selection by the inanimate environment. The first kind is usually sub-divided into inter- and intra-specific selection, *i.e.* one of competition and combat between different species and the other of rivalry between members of the same species. In the last lecture we saw examples of the powers of predator selection. Examples of the second kind of selection, that of the physical environment, are obvious, such as species of mammals with thicker fur being selected by survival in colder regions or races of wingless flies left surviving on small oceanic islands because those with normal wings are blown away to destruction. Undoubtedly these kinds of selection account for a great deal of adaptation and evolutionary change. I would, however, make another kind of division between the forms of selection. I would distinguish all the foregoing kinds under a super heading of *external* selective agencies, meaning those acting from outside the organisms concerned, *i.e.* the selective forces acting from both the animate and inanimate environments; and in contrast to these I would place an *internal* selective

[1] Max Pettersen, *Nature*, vol. 184, p. 649, 1959.

force due to the behaviour and habits of the animal itself. Much of behaviour—all instinctive behaviour—is, of course, governed by the gene complex; in addition however there are the kind of changes in behaviour to which I have just referred: new modes of action which spread through the population and are maintained in higher vertebrates by tradition before they become converted by assimilation into instinctive action. I think it likely that most instinctive behaviour has developed in this way, but that will be discussed later (p. 195).

Now because a change of habit is usually occasioned by changes in the environment, it is generally supposed, I think, that any selection due to such a habit change is one differing only in degree, but not in kind, from the other forms of selection just discussed. This for me is the crux of the whole issue; I think they are radically different. I realise, of course, that it is the differential mortality in the population which brings about the survival of the more efficient type of beak, for example, and this is obviously mediated by factors in the external world killing off a higher proportion of the less efficient forms; nevertheless the real initiating agent in the process is the new behaviour pattern, the *new habit*. I believe the case for regarding this " behavioural " type of selection as different in kind from the rest can be maintained. A new habit, as Lamarck said, is frequently the result of some environmental change and this may make this kind of selection seem similar to the other kinds. But among vertebrates, it must often be the restless, exploring and perceiving animal that discovers new ways of living, new sources of food, just as the tits have discovered the value of the milk bottles. The restless, exploratory type of behaviour has no doubt been fostered and developed by selection just because it pays dividends; this is well illustrated in the quotation from Dr. Ewer's letter on p. 193.

Dr. Thorpe in his penetrating survey of the different kinds of animal learning in his *Learning and Instinct in Animals* (Second Edition, 1963) follows Agar[1] and Whitehead[2] in regarding the animal as an essentially perceiving organism. He suggests " that the concept of perception includes an actively organising, possibly a purposive, element; and that perception is a basic characteristic of the drive of the living animal." It is impossible in just part of a lecture to do justice to the ideas he presents. I will only give one or two quotations to show

[1] *The Theory of the Living Organism*, Melbourne University Press, 1943.
[2] *Process and Reality*, Cambridge, 1929.

how very differently the modern student of animal behaviour regards his animals compared with the members of the old so-called "Behaviourist" school.

Regarding trial-and-error learning he writes:

For trial-and-error learning, then, one must have appetitive motivation (e.g. the drive of the pecking response), often appearing as if governed by "curiosity" relating to the external world; and so we see that trial-and-error learning is especially characteristic of the unrestrained animal in something like its normal environment actively performing one of its normal activities. It is, taking the animal kingdom as a whole, infinitely the most important learning process involved in adjusting the "voluntary" actions to the environment. It enters into every positive example of individual adaptation of motor behaviour, and there is no instance of adaptive modification of actions, however "insightful" and "intelligent" it may appear, that does not comprise trial-and-error learning in at least some degree.

Further, in discussing latent learning, he says:

Actually what we have here amounts to much the same thing as exploration for its own sake—generalised exploratory appetitive behaviour (Thorpe, 1944).[1] We may say that "the animal tends to explore its surroundings: that it has a tendency to investigate its environment."

Then there follows the problem of insight.

Here, *he writes*, it is important to make a clear distinction between insight itself and insight-learning. As a practical and convenient definition, I consider insight to be primarily a matter of the organisation of perceptions and to mean *the apprehension of relations*. Insight-learning, on the other hand, includes, as an essential element, the appropriate organisation of effector response, and can, I suggest, be defined as *the sudden production of a new adaptive response not arrived at by trial behaviour* or as *the solution of a problem by the sudden adaptive reorganisation of experience*.

Insight learning has certainly been demonstrated in mammals and most likely also occurs in birds.

Evolution theory can no longer afford to neglect the experimental evidence of the modern ethologists as to the way animals really behave.

Let me now continue with the subject of beaks. Darwin writing in

[1] *Proceedings of the Linnean Society of London*, vol. 156, pp. 70–83.

The Voyage of the Beagle (chapter XVII) of the finches of the Galapagos Islands says:

> The most curious fact is the perfect gradation in the size of the beaks in the different species of Geospiza, from one as large as that of a hawfinch to that of a chaffinch, and (if Mr. Gould is right in including his sub-group, Certhidea, in the main group) even to that of a warbler. . . . The beak of Cactornis is somewhat like that of a starling; and that of the fourth sub-group, Camarhynchus, is slightly parrot-shaped.

Dr. David Lack, in his evolutionary study *Darwin's Finches* (Cambridge, 1947) based upon his studies in the Galapagos, places the above quotation at the head of his chapter dealing with beak differences and food; I now give the following quotations from his study:

> The chief way in which the various species of Darwin's finches differ from each other is in their beaks. Indeed, the beak differences are so pronounced that systematists have at various times used as many as seven different generic names for the birds. In this book the genera are reduced to four, but it is convenient to retain the other generic names as subgenera, since they emphasise the adaptive radiation of the finches. . . .

He then goes on to give details of the feeding habits of the different sub-genera in relation to shapes of beak, and sums up as follows:

> To summarise, the beak differences between most of the genera and subgenera of Darwin's finches are clearly correlated with differences in feeding methods. This is well borne out by the heavy, finch-like beak of the seed-eating *Geospiza*, the long beak of the flower-probing *Cactornis*, the somewhat parrot-like beak of the leaf-, bud- and fruit-eating *Platyspiza*, the woodpecker-like beak of the woodboring *Cactospiza*, and the warbler-like beaks of the insect-eating *Certhidea* and *Pinaroloxias*. Only in one group, namely the insectivorous tree-finches of the sub-genus *Camarhynchus (sens. strict.)* is the beak not particularly suggestive of the feeding habits; these birds, though feeding primarily on insects, may be regarded as moderately unspecialised in both diet and beak.

The differences in the beaks are illustrated in fig. 55.

Which is the more reasonable explanation of these adaptations: that chance mutations, first occurring in a few members of the population, caused these birds to alter their habits and seek new food supplies

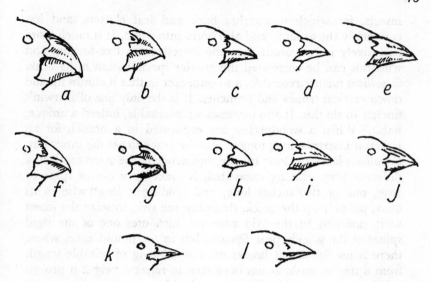

55. Beak differences in Darwin's finches on the central islands of Galapagos, all ⅔ natural size redrawn from Lack (after Swarth): *top row,* the genus *Geospiza, a, G. magnirostris; b, G. fortis; c, G. fuliginosa; d, G. difficilis debilirostris; e, G. scandeus; middle row,* the genus *Camarhynchus, f, C. crassirostris; g, C. psittacula; h, C. pavulus; i, C. pallidus; j, C. heliobates; bottom row,* k. *Certhidea olivacæ,* and *l, Pinaroloxias inornata.*

more suitable to their beaks and so become a more successful and surviving race, or did the birds, forced by competition, adopt new feeding habits which spread in the population so that chance changes in beak form giving greater efficiency came gradually to be preserved by organic selection?

Differences of habit clearly play a great part in the ways of life of these different species. Can we really doubt which of the two explanations just suggested is the more likely to be true? It is among these finches that we meet with one of the most remarkable examples of the exploring perceptive behaviour of animals. I quote again from Lack, from the same chapter:

The woodpecker-finch *Camarhynchus pallidus* has a stout, straight beak, with obvious affinities to that of the insectivorous tree-finches, but more elongated, and modified in the direction of that of a woodpecker or nuthatch. It feeds on beetles and similar insects, for which it searches bark and leaf clusters, and less commonly the ground, and also bores into wood. It is much more exclusively insectivorous than the insectivorous tree-finches, and with this can be correlated the greater specialisation of its beak. *C. pallidus* further resembles a woodpecker in that it climbs up and down vertical trunks and branches. It is the only one of Darwin's finches to do this. It also possesses a remarkable, indeed a unique, habit.[1] When a woodpecker has excavated in a branch for an insect, it inserts its long tongue into the crack to get the insect out. *C. pallidus* lacks the long tongue, but achieves the same result in a different way. Having excavated, it picks up a cactus spine or twig, one or two inches long, and holding it lengthwise in its beak, pokes it up the crack, dropping the twig to seize the insect as it emerges. In the arid zone the bird uses one of the rigid spines of the prickly pear *Opuntia*, but in the humid zone, where there is no *Opuntia*, it breaks off a small twig of suitable length from a tree or bush. It has been seen to reject a twig if it proved too short or too pliable. Sometimes the bird carries a spine or twig about with it, poking it into cracks and crannies as it searches one tree after another. This remarkable habit, first reported by Gifford (1919) and fully confirmed first by W. H. Thompson and later by the writer, is one of the few recorded uses of tools in birds. The nearest parallel is the use of fruits by the bower-bird *Ptilonorhynchus violaceus* for staining the stems of its bower.

To return to the structural differences in these finches in general let me quote again from Dr. Lack (*loc. cit.*, p. 148):

I consider that adaptive radiation of Darwin's finches can have come about only through the repeated differentiation of geographical forms, which later met and became established in the same region, that this in turn led to subdivision of the food supply and habitats, and then to an increased restriction in ecology and specialisation in structure of each form. On Cocos, where conditions are unsuitable for species-formation, there has likewise been no adaptive radiation among the land birds.

Such subdivision of the food supply and habitats clearly implies the development of different behaviour patterns.

[1] Since going to press another member of the same genus, *C. heliobates*, has been shown by E. Curio and P. Kramer (*Z. Tierpsychol.*, vol. 21, pp. 223–34, 1964) to have a similar habit.

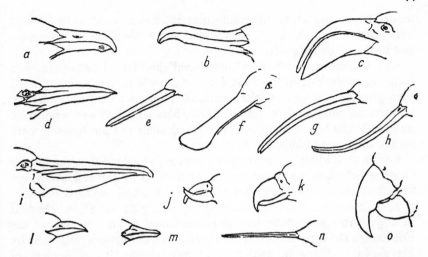

56. A selection of beaks of birds of various habits: *a*, herring gull; *b*, frigate bird; *c*, flamingo; *d*, gannet; *e*, snipe; *f*, spoonbill; *g*, curlew; *h*, avocet; *i*, pelican; *j*, cross-bill; *k*, **eagle**; *l*, swallow; *m*, spotted flycatcher; *n*, humming-bird; *o*, parrot.

Now in fig. 56 let us look at the diversity of beaks among birds in general. Can it really be maintained that it is *more likely* that random mutations forced these different groups of birds to their different modes of life, rather than that they developed different habits and that such differences in feeding led gradually to beaks better and better adapted to their ways of life? Surely it must be admitted that it is change of habit which is the dominating factor influencing such selection. Now if we had been looking at a chart showing not the forms of beaks but the legs and feet of these birds would we not have come to a similar conclusion?

When I had mentioned my hypothetical birds pecking at insects on the bark of trees in the 1956 discussion at the Linnean Society already referred to, and then talked of tits opening milk bottles, someone half jokingly said " and eventually I suppose we shall have a race of tits with beaks like tin-openers! " Exactly. If milk bottles were some curious hard-covered organic objects and a species of tit specialised on them for food, then if " the bottles " with the thicker " caps " tended to survive, who could doubt that in time there would be evolved both thicker and thicker " caps " and more specialised tin-opener-like beaks for dealing with them?

In this lecture I have only introduced the idea of behaviour as a factor in evolution; in the next I will discuss it further, when I shall then give some account of the important paper, which I have already referred to, published in 1960 by Dr. (Mrs.) R. F. Ewer who quite independently has come to the same conclusions as I am stressing here on the influence of habit on structure.

I am now adding to this lecture a postcript to show that the idea of Organic Selection was actually first formulated by James Hutton, the founder of modern geology, in a manuscript of a book entitled *Principles of Agriculture* upon which he was working during his last illness. He died in 1797 and the unpublished work remained in the custody of the Edinburgh Geological Society until extracts from it were published by Sir Edward Bailey in an address given to the Royal Society of Edinburgh in 1947.[1] My attention was kindly drawn to this after my lecture by Dr. W. P. D. Wightman, Reader in the History and Philosophy of Science at Aberdeen. Hutton, after discussing " a general law or rule of seminal variation, by which the form of the animal should constantly be changing, more or less, by the influence of external causes, but with no particular attention . . .", he goes on to discuss " a beautiful contrivance for preserving the perfection of animal form in the variety of the species ". I now quote a remarkable passage:

> To see this beautiful system of animal life (which is also applicable to vegetables) we are to consider, that in the infinite variation of the breed, that form best adapted to the exercise of those instinctive arts, by which the species is to live, will be most certainly continued in the propagation of this animal, and will be always tending more and more to perfect itself by the natural variation which is continually taking place. Thus, for example, where dogs are to live by the swiftness of their feet and the sharpness of their sight, the form best adapted to that end will be the most certain of remaining, while those forms that are least adapted to this manner of chase will be the first to perish; and the same will hold with regard to all the other forms and facilities of the species, by which

1. *Proceedings of the Royal Society of Edinburgh*, Series B, Vol. 63, pp. 357-368 (see especially p. 361) 1948-49.

the instinctive arts of procuring its means of subsistence may be pursued.

This was written a hundred years before Lloyd Morgan and Baldwin put forward their versions of the theory; and it was written eleven years before Charles Darwin was born and twelve years before Lamarck first published his evolutionary views. We should note, however, that he refers to variation *within* a species and not to the evolutionary origin of species.

ADDENDUM

Since going to press my attention has been drawn to a book *The Method of Evolution* published in 1900 by Professor H. W. Conn and quoted in an appendix to Mark Baldwin's book *Development and Evolution* 1902. He holds very similar views to mine and likewise derives them from those of Lloyd Morgan and Baldwin. I will quote a brief extract:

' Perhaps a concrete case may make this somewhat obscure theory a little clearer. Imagine, for example, that some change in conditions forced an early monkey-like animal, that lived on the ground, to escape from its enemies by climbing trees*. This aboreal habit was so useful to him that he continued it during his life, and his offspring, being from birth kept in the trees, aquired the same habit. Now it would be sure to follow that the new method of using their muscles would soon adapt them more closely to the duty of climbing. . . . All this would take place without any necessity for a congenital variation or the inheritance of any character which especially adapted the monkey for life in the trees.

" But, in the monkeys thus preserved, congenital variations would be ever appearing in all directions. It would be sure to follow that after a time there might be some congenital variation that affected the shape of the hands and feet. These would not be produced as the result of the use of the organs or as aquired variations, but simply from variations in the germ plasm."

He also considers consciousness as a factor in evolution in the same way that I do in my final lecture: ' This conception of the action of selection evidently makes consciousness a factor in evolution. It has always been claimed by the Lamarckian school that consciousness aids in the process of descent. It has sometimes been supposed that by this claim is meant that by conscious efforts an animal can modify its structure; but such a conception has certainly not been held by scientists in recent years. Consciousness may, however, lead to the use of organs or to the adoption of the new habits, and, if the view we are now considering be sound, such use of organs, or such habits, leads to the development of aquired characters which enable the individual to live in new conditions more successfully, until after a time congenital variations take their place. Consciousness thus becomes an indirect factor in evolution."

---

* We now know that the primate stock came from earlier arboreal animals like the tree-shrews, but his argument on the original adaptations to a climbing life is valid.

HABIT IN RELATION TO BODILY

STRUCTURE

A large part of the late Dr. E. S. Russell's *Form and Function* (1916) is a penetrating historical review of the two opposing schools of thought regarding the relations of structure and function. He writes (on p. 78):

The contrast between the teleological attitude, with its insistence upon the priority of function to structure, and the morphological attitude, with its conviction of the priority of structure to function, is one of the most fundamental in biology.

Cuvier and Geoffroy are the greatest representatives of these opposing views. Which of them is right? . . .

The problem as Geoffroy and Cuvier understood it was not an evolutionary one. But the problem exists unchanged for the evolutionist, and evolution-theory is essentially an attempt to solve it in the one direction or the other. Theories such as Darwin's, which assume a random variation which is not primarily a response to environmental changes, answer the problem in Geoffroy's sense. Theories such as Lamarck's, which postulate an active responsive self-adaptation of the organism, are essentially a continuation and completion of Cuvier's thought.

It is somewhat ironical that there should be this connection between the thoughts of Lamarck and Cuvier when we know how the latter ridiculed the evolutionary views of the former. Russell ends his book with the following words:

What the future course of morphology will be no one can say. But one may hazard the opinion that the present century will see a return to a simpler and more humble attitude towards the great and unsolved problems of animal form. Dogmatic materialism and dogmatic theories of evolution have in the past tended to blind us to the complexity and mysteriousness of vital phenomena. We need to look at living things with new eyes and a truer sympathy. We shall then see them as active, living, passionate beings like ourselves, and we shall seek in our morphology to interpret as far as may be their form in terms of their activity.

This is what Aristotle tried to do, and a succession of masterminds after him. We shall do well to get all the help from them we can.

You will, I am sure, have little doubt, from what I said in my last lecture. that my sympathies are entirely with Russell in that final statement. Yet when he says, as he does in the earlier quotation, that evolution theory is essentially an attempt to solve the problem as to whether structure or function has priority, I think he is wrong to suggest that the process must be brought about by one, and one only, of these two alternative principles. In the same way I think the controversy, which he so ably reviews and which for so long dominated zoological thought, dividing mechanists from vitalists, is largely an unreal one. I believe that both principles are true, and that sometimes structural changes come first and sometimes functional ones; and further that many animals are the result of a mosaic and interaction of the two methods.

Thorpe in the opening chapter of his *Instinct and Learning in Animals*, to which I referred in my last lecture, quotes one of my favourite passages from the introductory chapter to that classic by Sir D'Arcy Thompson *On Growth and Form*; it is very relevant here, for he has just been discussing these two approaches: " Still, all the while, like warp and woof, mechanism and teleology are interwoven together, and we must not cleave to the one nor despise the other; for their union is rooted in the very nature of totality."

Now there is much else in this profound chapter of D'Arcy Thompson's that bears upon our discussion and I cannot resist two further quotations:

Nevertheless, when philosophy bids us hearken and obey the lessons both of mechanical and of teleological interpretation, the precept is hard to follow; so that oftentimes it has come to pass, just as in Bacon's day, that a leaning to the side of the final cause " hath intercepted the severe and diligent enquiry of all real and physical causes," and has brought it about that " the search of the physical cause hath been neglected and passed in silence." So

long and so far as " fortuitous variation "[1] and the " survival of
the fittest " remain engrained as fundamental and satisfactory
hypotheses in the philosophy of biology, so long will these " satisfactory and specious causes " tend to stay " severe and diligent
enquiry . . . to the great arrest and prejudice of future discovery."
Long before the great Lord Keeper wrote these words, Roger
Bacon had shewn how easy it is, and how vain, to survey the
operations of Nature and idly refer her wondrous works to chance
or accident, or to the immediate interposition of God.

I would particularly call attention to his footnote and would remind
the reader that by natural selection he almost certainly was thinking
only of what I have called the external type of selection.

A little later he writes:

Often and often it happens that our physical knowledge is
inadequate to explain the mechanical working of the organism;
the phenomena are superlatively complex, the procedure is
involved and entangled, and the investigation has occupied but a
few short lives of men. When physical science falls short of explaining the order which reigns throughout these manifold phenomena
—an order more characteristic in its totality than any of its
phenomena in themselves—men hasten to invoke a guiding
principle, an entelechy, or call it what you will. But all the while
no physical law, any more than gravity itself, not even among the
puzzles of stereo-chemistry or of physiological surface-action and
osmosis, is known to be transgressed by the bodily mechanism. . . .

My sole purpose is to correlate with mathematical statement
and physical law certain of the simpler outward phenomena of
organic growth and structure or form, while all the while regarding
the fabric of the organism, *ex hypothesi*, as a material and mechanical
configuration. This is my purpose here. But I would not for the
world be thought to believe that this is the only story which Life
and her Children have to tell. One does not come by studying
living things for a lifetime to suppose that physics and chemistry
can account for them all.[2] [His footnote is again given below.]

[1] D'Arcy Thompson's footnote: " The reader will understand that I speak, not
of the ' severe and diligent enquiry ' of variation or of fortuity, but merely of the easy
assumption that these phenomena are a sufficient basis on which to rest, with the
all-powerful help of natural selection, a theory of definite and progressive evolution."

[2] D'Arcy Thompson's footnote: " That mechanism has its share in the scheme of

Structure has priority to function when selection is of the external type; the reverse is true when selection is of what I have called the internal (or behavioural) type. I now want to say a little more about these two kinds of selection and to show how at times there appears to be an interplay between the two.

No one can doubt that in the adaptation of seeds to aerial dispersal, mentioned in an earlier lecture, structural changes govern function. Mutations that provided seeds with hairy coats would give them a better chance of being carried a little further by the wind than other seeds not so endowed and this would also give them a better chance of spreading the species on to new and favourable ground; thus by successive chance mutations the beautiful thistle-down parachutes of the Compositæ were evolved to ride far and wide on the summer convection currents. Similarly the remarkable gliding seeds of the pine tree *Pithecoctenium echinatum* were gradually improved or the spinning autogyro-like seeds of the sycamore. Here there can be no behavioural habit selecting the mutations better suited to it. Now if such external selection can modify plant structure to create such a series of " inventions ", then surely it can do the same in animal structure as well; and at once we see that this must be so in the similar devices— parachute-like spines, buoyancy chambers, etc.—evolved for keeping plankton animals afloat.

Among the fascinating adaptations of many of the marine larvæ to a pelagic life we see, as the late Professor Walter Garstang pointed out, a balance or compromise between two rival selective advantages: on the one hand to grow up as soon as possible so as to reproduce the species, and on the other to remain floating for as long as possible in order to distribute the species over the largest area. He showed clearly how the larval stages are as much adapted for dispersal as are the seeds or fruits of plants; he also showed how, with all manner of devices in different groups, these two rival " needs " are met.[1]

Just as the form of an animal may be moulded by two or more such

---

nature no philosopher has denied. Aristotle (or whosoever wrote the *De Mundo*) goes so far as to assert that in the most mechanical operation of nature we behold some of the divinest attributes of God."

[1] I have discussed Garstang's views at some length in *The Open Sea: Part 1, The World of Plankton*. Collins, New Naturalist Series, London, 1956.

rival selective forces, none of which are of the behavioural pattern, so, I believe, we may get structures which are the result of different selective agents, some external but others of the behavioural and habit kind that I discussed in the last lecture.

Since I have just mentioned the aerodynamic seeds as examples of nature's " inventions " I should, in passing, say that these are by no means her most remarkable " technological " wonders. Professor Pringle[1] has shown us how the halteres, those little knobbed structures of the Diptera, or two-winged flies, which take the place of the hind-wings of the more typical insects, serve as gyroscopic stabilisers; the two, one on either side, each vibrating through a half-circle, produce an effect which is equivalent to a spinning gyroscope. Nature has never managed to evolve a freely rotating wheel, but here she does it almost as well " by halves ". As I was actually preparing this lecture there came the announcement of the discovery of an organ in the metathorax of certain moths which can generate ultrasonic signals; the authors[2] in describing the organ, after cautiously saying that it is not possible to be certain of the function of the sounds produced, go on to point out that " nevertheless, it is curious that strong components of the sound sweep rapidly and continuously over the whole of the frequency band used by bats for echo-location." Here apparently has been evolved a system for jamming the bats' sonar (sound " radar ") hunting apparatus!

The development of gliding flight, as seen in the flying fish, would seem to give us an example of the two factors I am discussing working together. The fish must first develop the behaviour of leaping through the surface in escape from predators, itself no doubt a habit produced by the survival of those which perhaps in the first place shot through the surface " by accident " in the panic of escape. Then they would develop the habit of keeping themselves out of harm's way for as long as possible; and they would do this by skimming along the surface using the pectoral fins for support with the lower lobe of the tail vibrating in the water for propulsion, as does that close relative of the flying fish *Scomberesox saurus* which is sometimes called the skipper. Once this habit became well developed a series of chance mutations giving larger and larger pectoral fins and a larger lower lobe to the

[1] *Philosophical Transactions of the Royal Society*, Ser. B, vol. 233, pp. 347–84, 1941.
[2] A. D. Blest, T. S. Collett and J. D. Pye, *Proc. Roy. Soc.* Series B, vol. 158, pp. 196–207, 1963.

tail would gradually lead to a flying-fish whose wing-like fins can carry it soaring from the surface to rise and fall in a long graceful glide. Habit and random mutation must continually be working together to produce the forms of the animals we know—habit fostering a form of selection.

Now before I go further I must make more mention of the illuminating paper by Dr. (Mrs.) R. F. Ewer entitled " Natural Selection and Neoteny " published in the *Acta Biotheoretica*[1], Leiden, in 1960, to which I briefly referred in the last lecture. We are both making the same points independently; she had been unaware of my short discussion of the subject in the *Proceedings of the Linnean Society* in 1957 or at the British Association in 1949 and I had not been aware of her paper until these present lectures were well developed. I would like to include some fairly lengthy quotations from her paper because her views fit so perfectly with my own. I am not, of course, in any way implying that she follows me in my more philosophical arguments based upon such concepts. My first quotation comes from a passage where she had just been discussing the reaction against the oversimplified teleology of an earlier unwarranted anthropomorphic attitude; she writes:

The reaction against teleology was both natural and necessary but the trouble was, it went too far. In rejecting simple teleology it rejected teleology altogether; and in pointing out that no evidence was forthcoming for the inherited effects of the animal's own activity it concluded that the latter was an irrelevancy in evolutionary studies. In this it threw away two of the most powerful weapons in our theoretical armoury, and provides a classical example of what I would like to christen " bath-waterism ". The concept of selective advantage is based on a consideration of " ends ", although it does not place them inside the consciousness either of a creator or of the evolving animal and, as will become clear later, activities are very far from being irrelevant.

The legitimate use of teleology, following this exaggerated avoiding reaction, has gradually come to be, if not exactly enthusiastically appreciated, at least accorded toleration. Thus, although we would no longer say that the birds evolved wings in order to fly, only a few would object to the formulation that in the avian lineage a positive survival value was associated with increasing

[1] vol. 13, pp. 161–84, 1960.

ability to fly and mutations tending to convert the fore limbs to wings were therefore preserved and accumulated. Similarly, in behaviour studies it is now perfectly respectable to consider the adaptive significance of any particular piece of behaviour.

This somewhat grudging use of the concept of survival value is, however, not sufficient. It leaves out the live animal and concentrates too much on what it is, too little on what it does. It would appear to be glaringly obvious that what an animal does, or tries to do, can determine what characters are of survival value, *i.e.* can decide the direction of natural selection—and yet even today this indirect action is frequently ignored and the only possible effect of an animal's activity which receives consideration is the direct Lamarckian one: for example, Carter (1958) writes that " the effects of activity can only influence the evolution of the race if they are inherited and passed on to the next generation." If evolution results from natural selection conferring direction on a non-directional process of genetic mutation, it should be clear that factors which affect selection rather than mutation are the ones which determine the *direction* of evolution: factors affecting mutation rate may speed up, or slow down, but will not change the direction of the process, except indirectly. Moreover, if we wish to decide whether something has an effect on evolution we must ask the two questions: (i) does it affect the genetic mechanism? (ii) does it affect the selective forces impinging on the organism? To return to the question of birds' wings: had the ancestors of the birds used their fore limbs only for terrestrial locomotion, what hope of preservation would there have been for any mutations tending to convert them into wings?

The importance of the activities and behaviour of the animal in determining its evolutionary fate is most obvious in cases where the animal is in a position to make direct use of a structure in a number of different ways—for example, to use its limbs for climbing, running, digging or swimming—but even physiological characters will also be affected. A change of diet will alter the selective value of digestive enzymes: a higher level of activity or a tendency to explore environments poor in oxygen will alter the selective value of changes in concentration or loading tension of blood pigments. . . .

Changes in sensory equipment, or in effector organs will, of course, affect behaviour, but progressive change involves mutations affecting the structure and mode of action of the directing central nervous system—and these will follow the same pattern as those concerned in the evolution of any other functional organ. The relationship between activity and anatomy will, however, be asymmetrical for two sorts of reasons. There is firstly the one already mentioned, which can be summarised by saying that while a genetic change causing an animal to take to swimming will result in accumulation of genes making for webbing of the digits, a mutation causing slight webbing in a non-swimmer will not cause accumulation of genes making for the habit of swimming. Secondly, it must be borne in mind that an evolutionary change does not have to "wait for the right mutations to turn up": the first advance will always be made on the basis of changes in frequency and recombination of genes already present in the population[1] with new mutations bringing up the rear by continually replenishing the pool of variability.

This evolutionary plasticity at the level of the population applies to all characteristics, both structural and behavioural. Behaviour, however, generally has much more plasticity at the level of the individual than has structure. The adaptability of behaviour to varying environmental conditions gives it a "factor of safety" allowing an immediate behavioural response to be made at once to a changed situation, without the necessity of waiting for appropriate changes in the genetical structure of the population. Thus behaviour will tend to be always one jump ahead of structure, and so to play a decisive role in the evolutionary process.

Then, after saying "that since behaviour does not fossilise it will rarely, if ever, be possible to demonstrate that changes in habit did, in any particular instance, precede structural change" she goes on to show that there are indeed examples of where such an assumption would appear to provide the simplest explanation; she presents a study of the feeding habits of two of the living African Suidæ (i.e. members of the pig family), the bushpig and the warthog, as an introduction to considering the fossil forms:

The Warthog chews with a specialised sideways grinding move-

---

[1] Waddington's (1956) demonstration of the "genetic assimilation" of the bithorax phenotype shows how very great a departure from the norm is capable of being produced in this manner.

ment. This statement is based on personal observations, but might have been inferred from the details of the skull architecture in relation to the jaw muscles and from the direction of the wear marks on the canines made as the lowers move across the uppers. In addition, a peculiar polish on the outer surface of the lower canine results from the way in which the Warthog moves its head as it selects out the grass tips which form its favourite food from amongst the weeds (see Ewer, 1958 for details). I have not been able to watch Bushpig chewing, but the skull structure, muscle arrangement and the wear on the canines indicate that there is no highly developed grinding action. Many of the South African fossil pigs, belonging to a number of different lineages, show stages in the evolution of complex grinding teeth, like those of the Warthog, from an ordinary unspecialised condition not unlike that occurring in the Bushpig. On the hypothesis of " habit a jump ahead of structure " the sequence of events would be expected to be as follows. First a change of habit, so that grass starts to become a more important component of the diet. This will confer selective advantage on any mutations converting the unspecialised cheek teeth into more effective grinders, and such mutations will now be preserved and accumulated. Once this process has advanced to a significant degree, but not before, there will be selective advantage in a more effective grinding with the jaws as the food is chewed. Once this habit develops, but not before, there will be selective advantage in alterations in skull architecture facilitating a grinding jaw action—but until the animals do the best they can to grind with the equipment they have there will be no tendency to preserve " favourable " (actually only potentially favourable) mutations. One would therefore expect that in the fossil pigs the teeth should be " ahead " of the skull architecture.

She now gives a good illustration of this from a study of the fossil remains of two extinct pigs: *Potamochœroides shawi* and *Potamochœrus antiquus*.

Another author who quite independently developed the idea of behaviour influencing selection is the late Professor Erwin Schrödinger, but he does so with a difference which should be noted; he gave considerable space to the idea in his Tarner Lectures, delivered at Trinity College, Cambridge, in 1956 and published (Cambridge U.P.)

under the title of *Mind and Matter* in 1959. He, as I did, came to Organic Selection through Huxley's *Evolution, the Modern Synthesis* as he explains on his p. 20; he believes, however, that structural change comes first and is then developed by the selective action of behaviour:

Without changing anything in the basic assumptions of Darwinism we can see that the behaviour of the individual, the way it makes use of its innate faculties, plays a relevant part, nay, plays the most relevant part in evolution. There is a very true kernel in Lamarck's view, namely that there is an irrescindable causal connection between the functioning, the actually being put to profitable use of a character—an organ, any property or ability or bodily feature—and its being developed in the course of generations, and gradually improved for the purposes for which it is profitably used. ... Lamarck thought that the organ (a) is used, (b) is thus improved, and (c) the improvement is transmitted to the offspring. This is wrong. We have to think that the organ (a) undergoes chance variations, (b) the profitably used ones are accumulated or at least accentuated by selection, (c) this continues from generation to generation, the selected mutations constituting a lasting improvement.

You will see that there is an important difference between his conception of the matter and that of Dr. Ewer and myself; he stresses that the genetical change must come first and that this triggers off the change of behaviour which then develops it. Sometimes, no doubt, the course of events suggested by Schrödinger may well take place; we believe, however, and I have had a recent letter from Dr. Ewer on the subject, that far more often it is the change of behaviour that came first. I shall return to this point a little later.

In the last lecture I briefly discussed Waddington's theory of genetic assimilation and stated that I found it difficult to distinguish it from part of the original idea expressed in Lloyd Morgan's and Baldwin's concept of Organic Selection. However that may be—and I realise that some subtle distinction may have escaped me—I do believe that in his later book, *The Nature of Life* (1961), unless I misunderstand him, he is approaching the position that Dr. Ewer and I have taken up. I quote as follows:

The time has come to ask this question about evolution. Mayr felt that simply proceeding from the consideration of single genes to that of systems of genes, was a step important enough to be dignified by the name of the " genetic theory of relativity ". We need now, however, to go to a much more far-reaching relativistic theory which brings into the system not merely organised groups of genes but the environment as well.

As soon as we try to do this we find ourselves passing out of the sphere of atomistic theories, whether they deal in simple deterministic causation or probabilistic causation, into the domain of organismic or cybernetic thinking. The first point that confronts us, for instance, is that before an organism's environment can exert natural selection on it, the organism must select the environment to live in. If we release a rabbit and hare—animals which look rather like one another—in the middle of any ordinary piece of country, the rabbit will run to a hedge or bank and take refuge in it, while the hare will set up house somewhere in the middle of an open field. Even within a single species different individuals differ hereditarily in their behaviour; for instance, in their choice, out of a number of alternatives of an environment to live in, or a member of the opposite sex to mate with. Thus the animal's hereditary constitution influences the type of natural selective pressure to which it will be subjected. And then, of course, the natural selection influences the type of heredity which is passed on to the next generation. We are dealing with a feed-back or cybernetic system in which there is nothing that is simply cause or simply effect.

If you compare this with the quotation from my Aberdeen 1942 Inaugural Address with which I introduced my last lecture (p. 154) and where I stated the genesis of my thoughts on this subject, I think you will agree we are very close in our approach to our respective themes; and I should say that I don't suppose for a moment that he ever saw a copy of my lecture which was largely concerned with marine ecology. He then goes on to approach our position still more closely:

We have considerable grounds for believing, then, that mentality in the broad sense, or at least behaviour (biologists tend to be very timid about mentioning the mind), is a factor of importance in evolution. Lamarck's insistence on the " Will " is not wholly unjustified. But it is not necessary to suppose, as he seems to have thought, that an Act of Will brings into being an appropriate hereditary variation. The situation is that existing modes of behaviour (themselves controlled, with greater or lesser latitude, by heredity) combine with external circumstances to determine the nature of the effective environment.

From this Waddington leads up to the account of his idea of genetic assimilation which I quoted in my last lecture (p. 168). In an article in *Nature*[1] on " Evolutionary Systems—Animal and Human " in 1959, after discussing genetic assimilation, he goes on to distinguish *external* from *internal* selective forces:

To obtain a complete picture of the evolutionary system, we need to take into account one further set of factors. These may be spoken of as the exploitive system. Animals—and the following considerations do not apply so directly to plants—are usually surrounded by a much wider range of environmental conditions than they are willing to inhabit. They live in a highly heterogeneous " ambience ", from which they themselves select the particular habitat in which their life will be passed. Thus the animal by its behaviour contributes in a most important way to determining the nature and intensity of selective pressures which will be exerted on it. Natural selection is very far from being as external a force as the conventional picture might lead us to believe.

The problems which arise in this field have as yet been rather little studied, even in the biological field, where the relations are likely to be relatively simple. This idea of study is, however, likely to be of particular importance for eugenics, since human behaviour is incomparably more elaborate than that of the majority of animals, and in particular the behaviour associated with choice and the seeking of particular goals is much more fully developed.

Professor J. M. Thoday, in the course of discussing[2] the disruptive selection he has demonstrated, emphasises the great variability of wild populations upon which selection can act; clearly this is important in relation to the influence of new habits on the course of evolution. He writes as follows:

It is a fact that has become more and more clearly and strikingly established in recent years that in natural populations genetic variety is ubiquitous. Much of the most striking evidence comes from studies of flies, but there is quite sufficient evidence from

[1] *Nature*, vol. 183, pp. 1634–8, June, 1959.
[2] Causes and Functions of Genetic Variety. *The Eugenics Review*, vol. 54, pp. 195–200.

other organisms, including man, for us to generalise. Any natural population of an outbreeding species contains an enormous variety of genetically different individuals.

Much of this variety is fairly readily detected, but much more is variety not readily discernible as affecting the variety of observed characteristics of contemporary individuals: it is what we call cryptic, or concealed, genetic variety and its demonstration depends on relatively sophisticated experiments, or techniques.

More recently Sir Julian Huxley has stressed the same point in a review[1] of Ernst Mayr's *Animal Species and Evolution*. " One of the most surprising evolution discoveries of recent years," he writes, " is that wild species, far from being genetically uniform, contain a vast reservoir of variability, some overt, some concealed or stored but capable of being released in response to selective pressures." He goes on in the same review to say: ". . . the key problem of trans-specific evolution is the steady rise in level of organisation seen during the entire process, and especially the increased organisation and quantitative differentiation of ' mind ' and awareness—the mental or psychological properties of organisms."

This great variability provides ample opportunity for the working of the kind of behavioural selection we are considering. I want to stress again that I am not in any way belittling the force of the external type of selection; to show this I deliberately devoted a whole lecture (lecture v) to the amazing creative power of such selection. We must always remember that both may be taking part together, but I would suggest that the behavioural influence, particularly in the higher groups, may often be the more fundamental in determining the animal's make-up; the effects of external selection are generally more limiting, pruning the organism to fit its surroundings or supplying it with the better means of escaping from its enemies. It is adaptations which are due to the animal's behaviour, to its restless exploration of its surroundings, to its initiative in seeking new sources of food when its normal supply fails or becomes scarce through competition, that distinguish the main diverging lines of evolution; it is these dynamic qualities which lead to the different rôles of life that open up to a newly emerging group of animals in that phase of their expansion technically known as adaptive radiation. What *are* the main features that do in fact distinguish the different diverging lines of evolution to

[1] *Nature*, Aug. 31st, 1963.

be found both in the outbursts of the reptiles in the mesozoic age and of the mammals in the tertiary period? They are behavioural differences associated with their newly exploited environments; the development of new habits giving us the lines of runners, climbers, burrowers, swimmers and conquerors of the air. It cannot have been a new mutation or reassortment of genes that made an animal long used to terrestrial life begin to take to the water for its food. Again and again in the long history of the terrestrial vertebrates we have seen different forms, particularly among reptiles and mammals, but also, of course, among birds (and the more terrestrial lines of amphibia) turning to the water for their food. Some, of course, have become completely aquatic like the extinct Icthyosaurus and modern whales which show such a wonderful convergence in evolution between reptiles and mammals, towards a fish-like form.

Dr. Ewer in a recent exchange of letters, since we realised our views were so much the same, writes regarding how she thinks such an aquatic adaptation might first arise; it is exactly what I believe. With her kind permission I quote her letter (we have been discussing Schrödinger's view):

I cannot see chance structural modification as the first step (at least — not as a general rule, although there might be exceptional cases) for I think if the behaviour were not already suited to it, such structural change would just be weeded out most of the time. I see the answer as lying in the plasticity of behaviour. Many patterns are very rigid, but no whole animal is. The animal has *some* ability to modify *some* of its behaviour to suit changing circumstances. Suppose, for instance, there is a small carnivore living on small terrestrial things like mice and lizards and these become very scarce. It will almost certainly be able to change to frogs, if these become abundant—to *learn* that these can be found near water and even to follow them into shallow water. Here is the first stage—ever-present modicum of modifiability and learning. Then comes selection—selection for those who learn most quickly how to catch frogs and elimination of any that simply cannot respond to a frog as food. Then comes Waddington's genetical assimilation—gradually building up the efficiency of the response—until in the end a genotype results in which the environmental " treatment " (=learning here) is no longer required and we find a built-in innate response to frogs. And *pari passu* with this—but following from the changed behaviour—will have gone selection for any structural changes making for better frog-catching.

As I see it, what usually starts the process is some external change—in this example a scarcity of the previously adequate normal food—I do not imagine the animal changing its behaviour in a random or arbitrary manner, for no reason. Moreover, the normal plasticity of behaviour which makes the change possible is, of course, itself a product of selection, so that the system as a whole shows " Waddingtonian " feed-back characteristics. It is true that in formal logical terms a feed-back loop may have neither beginning nor end—but in practice the situation is that a species in a certain place and time is faced with changing circumstances and the problem is, " what is going to be the evolutionary result? " I believe that very frequently the answer is of the type I have just outlined in my imaginary example.

Again within the major adaptive lines we see mainly feeding *habits* distinguishing the lesser categories: herbivores and carnivores among the land animals, plankton filter feeders and sharp-toothed predators among the whales. Then among both herbivores and carnivores it is habit that is mainly determining structure as Dr. Ewer has so well shown in regard to living and fossil pigs.

Professor D. M. S. Watson in his Hooker Lecture to the Linnean Society on " The Mechanism of Evolution "[1] has much to say about the influence of the persistence of habit on evolution, although he appears to be mainly concerned with habits which are instinctive, *i.e.* genetically controlled. (I shall discuss in a moment how instinctive behaviour in turn must almost certainly have been derived from newly acquired habits by the process of organic selection (or genetic assimilation).) He is first discussing the gradual changes observed in the fossil series of sea urchins (*Micraster*) in the chalk and says " such a change would depend, I think, on the persistence of definite ecological conditions throughout the series, and also of habit in the animals considered."

He continues:

This matter of the persistence of habit is, I feel, of great importance and has perhaps been inadequately considered. It is clear that in some cases habit, as represented by instinctive behaviour,

[1] *Proceedings of the Linnean Society*, vol. 160, pp. 75–84, 1949.

is as dependent as are morphological qualities on the hereditary mechanism. . . .

An example may conveniently be found among the Plesiosaurs. These are large marine reptiles found in shallow seas all over the world continuously from the Lower Lias to the Upper Cretaceous. At all these horizons several types occur which fall, not very accurately, into two groups—the small-headed, very long-necked form and the large-headed, short-necked one. . . . [After describing details of structure, including dentition, he continues] . . . An analysis of the shoulder girdles and pectoral limbs of these forms suggested to my mind that the series of structural changes, which take place between the beginning and the end of the story, are of such a kind that the speed of movement of the long-necked forms directly through the water must have been reduced, whilst that of the short-necked forms increased, and that the long-necked forms developed a power of swinging the head laterally through a large arc and rapidly, whilst the neck of the large-headed forms becomes less and less flexible, and no provision is made for rapid lateral movements of the head. The implication is that the long-necked forms caught their relatively small and rapidly moving prey by guile, by rapid lateral flicks of the head, whilst the members of the other group ran down the large animals on which they fed by sheer speed, capturing them in their enormous mouth when they had overtaken them. It is evident that these changes are adaptive, but that they are adaptations to feeding habits selected from a very much greater range of possibilities, and that these habits must have persisted from the beginning to end of the whole history of the two stocks, for only so can the changes of structure, which have every appearance of arising under the influence of natural selection, have been brought about. Thus we have, I think, a clear illustration that habits may be as persistent as any morphological quality.

Having just mentioned instinctive behaviour, this may be a good place to interpose a brief reference to the possible method of its evolution. Surely it is more likely that genetical changes may have been selected to give, by new nerve-cell associations, a built-in inherited behaviour pattern to replace that of a learned habit, than that a chance change in the nervous mechanism (by mutation) may have produced a new form of behaviour which can be used with advantage by the animal. Each method may no doubt occur at times but, I think, the first may be considered the more usual and both Dr. Ewer[1] (1956) and Professor J. B. S. Haldane[2] (1959) have shown how this can come about by genetic assimilation. They have both made their suggestions following Waddington's experimental demonstration of the assimilation into the heredity of the stock of a character induced in the fruit-fly *Drosophila* by an environmental (temperature) change: the character of *not* having the typical cross-vein in the wing, a condition referred to as " cross-veinless ". Dr. Ewer writes:

In the evolution of a fully innate behaviour pattern evoked by a releaser, it seems possible that a similar process may have occurred. It is difficult to imagine that the process could begin otherwise than with the making of an appropriate response, probably imperfectly performed and subject to trial and error, and with learning of a simple conditioning type involved in the determination of the situation in which the response is made. From this stage there will be rapid selection, on one hand for more perfect performance of the motor response, and on the other for the shortening of the conditioning period, provided the environmental stimulus (or some special part of the total stimulus situation) remains constant. As in the case of cross-veinless, this should result in the building up of a genotype giving the motor response in more and more perfect form with the learning period more and more curtailed. The final result will be the innate pattern evoked by its releaser. But may not imprinting represent a penultimate stage on this route, a stage in which the motor response has been perfected and the learning period has become vestigial but has not yet disappeared?

Haldane now writes, three years later (he does not seem to have seen Dr. Ewer's contribution):

If we substitute learning for " not developing a cross-vein " we have a possible parallel with the development of an instinct. I take a hypothetical example. In area A a particular volatile substance is produced by a nutritious plant, in area B by a poisonous plant. In area A those insects of a certain species which learn most readily to recognise this odour and associate it with food are at an advantage. As the features in the nervous system which favour

[1] *Nature*, vol. 177, pp. 227–8, 1956.
[2] On p. 149 in *Darwin's Biological Work*, ed. P. R. Bell, Cambridge, 1959.

such learning are accentuated, a few insects appear to whom the odour is attractive without learning, as the odour of sheep appears to be attractive to sheep-dog puppies. They are at a double advantage, and after some time all members of the insect species are attracted by the odour without any learning. Similarly, in area B a race evolves which finds the odour repulsive. We know that there is in fact " raw material " on which selection can act from a study of our own species, where there are considerable differences in the capacity for detecting smells and tastes, and in judgment as to whether they are attractive or repulsive. Some at least of these differences are genetically determined.

Both Dr. Ewer's and Professor Haldane's ideas carry us back to those of Lloyd Morgan; I quote from his *Animal Behaviour* (1900), p. 115:

Thus any hereditary variations which coincide in direction with modifications of behaviour due to acquired habit would be favoured and fostered; while such variations as occurred on other and divergent lines would tend to be weeded out. Professor Mark Baldwin, who has independently suggested such relation between modification and variation, has applied to the process the term " Organic Selection "; but it may also be described as the natural selection of coincident variations.

It may be urged, therefore, that if natural selection be accepted as a potent factor in organic evolution, and unless good cases can be adduced in which natural selection can play no part and yet habit has become instinctive, we may adopt some such view as the foregoing. While still believing that there is some connection between habit and instinct, we may regard the connection as indirect and permissive rather than direct and transmissive. We may look upon some habits as the acquired modifications which foster those variations which are coincident in direction, and which go to the making of instinct.

Surely Lloyd Morgan, Ewer and Haldane are right. There are indeed many instincts which can much more easily be thought of in this fashion than to suppose that chance nerve connections due to mutation initiated new habits. There are, for example, species of ants,[1] such as *Œcophylla smaragdina*, which practise a method of weaving leaves together; as they themselves are incapable of secreting thread, they weave with the help of the spinning glands of their larvæ which they

[1] Described by Katz in his *Animals and Men, Studies in Comparative Psychology*, 1937.

hold in their mandibles and use as a tool, much as one might hold and squeeze a tube of quick-setting liquid glue. Then there are the remarkable Australian trapdoor spiders[1] which make a prey-indicator of long and slender eucalyptus leaves radiating, like the points of a compass, round their burrows; each leaf, being attached to the rim of the burrow, indicates by its vibration any prey walking over it and the spider rushes out in the required direction—north-east, or south-south-west as the case may be. Surely these and many other examples of elaborate instinctive patterns must in the first place have arisen by new habits being subsequently passed into the instinctive equipment by organic selection or genetic assimilation—whichever term you prefer.

Are not " fixed-action patterns " of behaviour, e.g. inherited releasing mechanisms, often as specifically constant as anatomical features? Such must surely have come about in this kind of way.

After this digression on the evolution of instinct let me return to the so-called adaptive radiation we were discussing: i.e. the outburst of new evolutionary lines adapted in different directions to new modes of life. Many authors have been both struck and puzzled at the rapidity with which the different orders of the placental mammals were evolved—so clearly shown in fig. 4 (p. 24). Almost equally striking is the similar outburst exhibited by the reptiles in the earlier Mesozoic age if in fig. 3 (p. 23) we remember that the wide band labelled " archosaurian reptiles " should really be shown as eight distinct radiating adaptive orders each as important as the other major lines included in the chart. G. G. Simpson discusses this problem in his *Tempo and Mode in Evolution* (1944), particularly the mammalian outburst and explains it by supposing that at the time of such adaptive radiation the primitive mammals were split up into a large number of very small populations which would undergo more rapid evolution under the influence of " genetic drift ".[2] For such " drift " to operate, however, the populations would have to be *exceedingly* small. Normal selection, of course, would be more likely to produce many different lines if the mammalian stock were split up into small isolated populations, each being selected to suit the slightly different environments. I would suggest, however, that behavioural changes working through organic selection would give the more likely solution to the problem. As the reptiles declined the small mammals multiplied and competed

---

[1] *Aganippe raphiduca*.   [2] The principle enumerated by Sewell Wright.

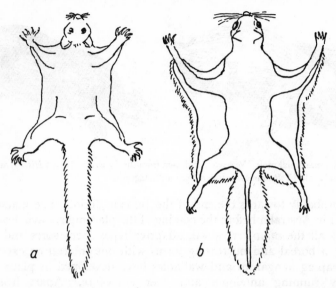

57. *a*, a marsupial flying phalanger (*Petaurus sciureus*) and *b*, a placental flying squirrel (*Sciuropterus volucella*), both redrawn from Lull's *Organic Evolution*.

for the available food; with their exploratory behaviour they took to a great variety of new methods of obtaining a living: climbing, burrowing, swimming and flying. Mutation did not accelerate, but selection acted far more quickly as the changing habits developed; with keen competition in the new environments, behavioural selection quickly moulded the body forms of the different pioneering groups into the main new adaptive types. Once these were produced they remained characteristic of their particular modes of life and further modifications could only be of a minor kind.

It is a commonplace of evolutionary discussion to compare the similar adaptive radiation of the marsupial mammals isolated in Australia to that of the later and more typical placental mammals in the rest of the world which we have just discussed; and particularly to point to the striking similarity in form of many of the corresponding types. For those who are not zoologists I should stress that the marsupials are not only an entirely separate evolutionary stock from the placental mammals; they are also more primitive, having diverged from early mammalian ancestors (the Pantotheria) in the Mesozoic

58. *a*, the marsupial mole (*Notoryctes*), redrawn from the *Cambridge Natural History*, and *b*, the placental mole (*Talpa europæa*) drawn from a photograph.

era, probably towards the end of the Jurassic period. The marsupials, cut off in Australia before the coming of the placentals, have developed nearly all the main terrestrial, adaptive types: herbivores and carnivores, arboreal and burrowing forms with one interesting exception: the leaping kangaroos and wallabies have developed in place of the swiftly running antelopes and deer elsewhere.[1] Apart from the kangaroos, the similarity of the types of the marsupial and placental mammals is indeed remarkable. Let us remind ourselves of this convergence of structure by comparing in illustration four pairs of these parallel forms: the flying phalanger (*Petaurus*, etc.) and the flying squirrel in fig. 57; the marsupial mole (*Notoryctes*) and the true mole (fig. 58); the Tasmanian wolf (*Thylacinus*) and the true wolf (fig. 59); and the marsupial jerboa (*Antechinomys*) and the true jerboa (fig. 60).

I think it must be admitted, when we look, for example, at the details and proportions of the skulls of *Thylacinus* and the true wolf shown in fig. 59, that the similarities are almost as striking as those of mimic and model discussed in lecture v. They are no doubt just as much produced by the creative power of selection; but what are the selective forces here? Are they simply those of similar environments or are they those of organic selection by similar behaviour patterns of animals obtaining the same kind of food and living in a similar fashion? I think it must be conceded that the latter is the more reasonable. Among the fossil South American mammals we find another

[1] Probably in relation to the more sandy nature of the terrain which makes leaping a more effective means of locomotion than running on the often insecure surface.

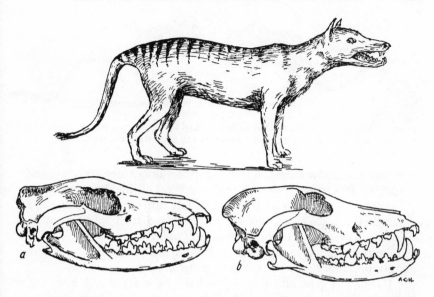

59. The marsupial Tasmanian wolf, *Thylacinus cynocephalus*, with below, *a*, its skull compared with *b*, that of the placental wolf *Canis lupus*, drawn to the same scale, all from specimens in the Oxford University Museum.

carnivorous marsupial which is an almost exact independent reproduction of *Thylacinus*; and here also those extinct, noto-ungulate, placental mammals of the Litopterna group show us a remarkable parallel to the evolution of the one-toed horses.

There is another noteworthy example of such parallel adaptive radiations to be found among the Cumacea: a group of small shrimp-like crustaceans. Comparatively recently in geological time the Caspian Sea was cut off from the wide ocean and separated with it were members of only one genus of these little shrimps. Just as the marsupial mammals underwent an adaptive radiation, cut off from the rest of the world in Australia, so did these Cumaceans in the Caspian Sea and they produced forms remarkably similar to members of *quite different families* in the larger world outside. The late Dr. Calman writes:[1]

The thirteen species known from the Caspian Sea all belong to the family Pseudocumidæ, and were originally referred to the

[1] *Crustacea* (Volume of Lankester's *Treatise on Zoology*), 1909, p. 188.

60. *a*, the marsupial jerboa (*Antechinomys laninger*) and *b*, the placental jerboa (*Dipus hirtipes*) redrawn respectively from Troughton's *Furred Animals of Australia* and the *Cambridge Natural History*.

single genus *Pseudocuma*, which comprises only three truly marine species. It is interesting to note that several of the Caspian species " mimic " in their general aspect widely different genera of other families, and have on this account received such specific names as *diastyloides*, *eudorelloides* and *campylaspoides*.

Like the original mammalian radiation this production of different adaptational forms within this one genus has been exceedingly rapid; the Caspian is generally thought to have been separated from wider seas sometime in the Pliocene or even, as some authorities believe, as late as the early Pleistocene. We can have little doubt that these parallel forms also have parallel habits.

This last consideration brings us to the invertebrate animals which through the splendid series of researches of Dr. Sidnie Manton on the locomotion of members of all the different groups of Arthropod animals (centipedes, millipedes, insects, etc.) provide us with perhaps the best examples of the relation of habits to bodily structure. The extent and detail of her work is monumental, I will only quote two passages from her more general statements:

The changes in structure which occurred during the evolution of Arthropoda from annelidan ancestors, and in the subsequent divergence of the several arthropodan groups, are not adaptations to particular environments or circumstances. Indeed, animals of widely different form and locomotory mechanism, such as Peripatus, centipedes and millipedes, live in exactly similar habitats. It is the locomotory habits of the animals which differ. Peripatus stands up on its short legs and walks, or squeezes its flexible body through narrow cracks; centipedes run swiftly round obstacles, either for escape or for catching prey; millipedes push their way through loose materials. One type of animal may move about in a comparatively inflexible manner, another may be able to use a variety of gaits, its capabilities depending upon its morphology. In each case there appears to be some predominant habit of fundamental importance to the animal's well being which has been associated with the evolution of the body form.[1] And then concerning habit reversals she writes:

The search for the functions of morphological characteristics of animals is often greatly helped by comparisons between different groups. Some arthropods, like humans, appear to have become " dissatisfied " with what they have achieved and have embarked upon opposite habits. Such reversals are correlated with structural modifications and superimposed upon an earlier morphology associated with the opposite type of habit. The most significant habit concerned with the evolution of Diplopoda is that of obtaining cover and food by pushing into the substratum. Subsequent changes in the exact method of pushing and in the perfection of secondary accomplishments appear to be associated with the morphology of the various orders. The Lysiopetaloidea, however, have abandoned their basic pushing habit in favour of fleetness and carnivorous feeding. The angle of swing of the leg has been increased at the expense of the strength of the coxa-body articulation; the appearance of long extrinsic limb muscles gives increased displacement at the leg joints, while the normal short extrinsic muscles usually supplying strength are reduced; long intrinsic muscles traversing many segments replace the typical diplopod series of short muscles, and many convergencies towards the morphology of the fast-running centipedes are seen in the muscle topography. The study of animals such as the Lysiopetaloidea provides additional evidence as to the significance of muscle and joint morphology in typical pushing diplopods and in fast-running chilopods, besides giving clear indications as to the phylogeny and changing habits of the Lysiopetaloidea themselves.[2]

As we have seen in the beaks of birds and the dentition of mammals, the structures evolved for the collection or capture of food are, as one would expect, closely related to the feeding habits of the animals concerned; this is equally well shown to be so in the great phylum of

[1] *Symposia of the Society for Experimental Biology*, no. VIII. *Evolution*, pp. 339–76, 1953.
[2] *Journal of the Linnean Society of London, Zoology*, vol. 44, p. 67, 1958.

the Arthropoda, particularly by the mouth parts of insects which present such a range of diversity from the stiletto-cum-pipette of the blood or plant-juice suckers to the savage jaws of the dragon-fly. Who can doubt that we also have here the behavioural pattern selecting, *within the population*, the products of the gene complex most suited to its proper performance. Dr. Sidnie Manton has told me that she has for some time been engaged upon a study of the feeding mechanisms of the arthropods in general in relation to their evolution, similar to that which she has made upon their organs of locomotion; and that again she can demonstrate the over-riding influence of habit.[1]

In discussing the evolution of structural differences in relation to differences in behaviour Dr. Ewer in the paper already cited says that the clearest example known to her is a " particularly elegant analysis of the evolution of different stridulatory mechanisms in related species of scorpions by Alexander (1960)."[2] This is indeed a beautiful illustration of the result of behavioural selection. One species of the genus *Heterometrus* in a " threat situation " would adopt an aggressive attitude with the claws (the pedipalps) thrust forward in a clasping attitude, whereas another species, of the genus *Pandinus*, made more defensive movements with the claws pulled in to cover the front of the animal. They both produce a threat sound, a rasping stridulation, by the development of " keyboard " bristles, but on the *pedipalp* of *Pandinus* and on the *first leg* of *Heterometrus*. They have been developed from the unspecialised bristles in the two areas entirely in relation to the differences in the movements in the two kinds of threat behaviour.

It may be felt by some that it is difficult to conceive how changes in behaviour could spread through a widely distributed population of invertebrate animals if they have not some means of learning from one another as is seen in what has been termed " tradition " among vertebrates. We have clearly much to find out about this problem. Given, however, that there is a similar degree of variability in behaviour, as there is in structure, and that such differences may be selected, and, by assimilation, built into the genetical system as suggested by Dr. Ewer and Professor Haldane (see pp. 196–198), then I do not think the part played by habit and behaviour in the

[1] Her magnificent study has now been published in the *Phil. Trans. Roy. Soc.*, *Series B*, Vol. 247. pp. 1-183, 1964.

[2] Anne J. Alexander, *Proceedings of the Zoological Society of London*, vol. 133, pp. 391-8, 1960.

evolution of invertebrates need be more difficult to understand than would be that of a supposed spread through a population of a structural change which was *not associated with* or *appropriate to* the animal's behaviour pattern.

It is especially interesting that some physiologists are now coming, on *physiological grounds*, to realize the great importance of an animal's behaviour and its choice of a mode of life as factors in evolution. I particularly have in mind the recent paper by Dr. J. W. L. Beament on " The Role of Physiology in Adaptation and Competition between Animals ".[1] He writes concerning what he calls the " possessive environment " as follows:

Since the range of environment in which the unimpeded animal can survive is so great—so great that the ecologist must make out an extremely detailed case before he dare appeal to physiological factors to explain anything but large differences—there quite obviously must be some mechanism or property which directs animals into their own environments and whereby different species do not compete. The short answer to this is that an animal's environment is that which it selects through its behaviour mechanisms, for an animal's behaviour tends to limit it to an environment far narrower than that in which it can survive. Indeed, there are even indications that such behaviour may lead it away from what, physiologically, might be regarded as optimal conditions. For example, corixids [aquatic insects commonly called " water-boatmen "] choose to lay their eggs in circumstances clearly different from those which physiological studies would suggest are optimal for development. But one has only to compare the food and conditions on which laboratory animals will thrive with those to which they restrict themselves in nature to know how true is this statement. There can be no doubt whatever that the result of interspecific competition during evolution has been an extraordinary multiplicity of habit and through this interspecific competition is limited and virtually prevented. It is true that the behaviour of an animal may be regarded as a part of its " physiology " and that its behaviour is integrated with its physiological systems. Nevertheless, in the present state of knowledge, we would be wrong to attribute its

[1] *Symposia of the Society for Experimental Biology*, vol. xv, *Mechanisms in Biological Competition*, pp. 62–71, 1961.

choice of environment merely to simple factors such as the limitations of its sense organs. *Choice of environment is a result of integrated action within the central nervous system.*

Finally he sums up his paper with the following conclusions: Considered from a physiological viewpoint, inter- and intraspecific competition are entirely different things; they involve processes which, in the course of evolution, have had entirely different effects on the present state of the animal kingdom. Interspecific competition has possibly played the major rôle in the development of those behavioural characteristics which largely eliminate such competition; by comparison it has probably had very little effect on the general physiology of animals, which appears to be very unspecialised. It would appear that we greatly underestimate the rôle which behaviour has played in evolution and that we have very much more to learn in this respect. By comparison, it may reasonably be claimed that intraspecific competition, in the particular sense of one lion chasing two zebras or of an expanding population which forces individuals to the limits of their environmental tolerance, has had something to do with the physiological efficiency and physiological range which we find in animals today. It is, however, very doubtful if we may argue justifiably in the reverse direction and attribute to physiology the outcome of successful competition in any particular case.

Let me now draw attention to one of the main differences between the plant and animal kingdoms. The plant division of organic life was evidently separated from the animal division in evolution before the development of behaviour patterns such as we know in animals; or indeed we might better say they were left behind by such a nervous development linked with the hunting for organic food which is the hallmark of the animal. The greater part of the plant's structure is mainly, although perhaps not entirely, the result of the external selective forces, for example, those of the physical environment, of competition with neighbours, and of the browsing of herbivorous animals. Now animals are subject to as many such external forces of selection as are plants, as we saw in an earlier lecture, but in addition, they have this " internal " behavioural selection—the effects of habits developed by active, exploring, inquisitive, initiating creatures; this makes the vital difference. It is instructive to note that the more dramatic adaptations of plants are those of flower structure and whilst

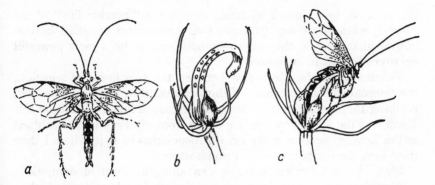

61. *a*, the male ichneumon fly *Lissopimpla semipunctata*; *b*, a flower of the Australian orchid *Cryptosylia leptochila* which bears a resemblance to the spotted abdomen of the female fly and evidently has the odour of the female, for the males are attracted to the flowers and attempt copulation as shown in *c*. The fly leaves with pollen attached to the tip of its abdomen and so pollinates the next flower it visits. Redrawn from Coleman (see footnote below).

they are produced by an external selection, it is one made by the *behavioural patterns* of the pollinating insects. The elaboration and the beauty of the flowers, which give man such satisfaction, are the products of animal perception and reaction, just as are the colour patterns on the wings of butterflies. Not quite all, however, are beautiful to our eyes. There are some kinds of orchids with flowers which mimic, in colour, shape and smell, the female form of certain insects and so offer sexual attraction to the males of these insect species; the excited spouses who come for the creative act, unwittingly, by carrying pollen, complete, instead, the sexual process for the flower! There are now a number of examples known; I illustrate in fig. 61 the first one to be discovered, observed again and again, and described in detail by Mrs. Edith Coleman.[1] Here, without doubt, we see the sexual behaviour of an *animal* selecting the shape, scent, etc., produced by the gene complex of a *plant* to convert it into a passable representation of another *animal*—its opposite sex. If animal behaviour can so modify the body of such a different kind of organism, how much more may its behaviour be expected to play upon the products of the gene complex within the population of its *own* species.

I think we can say, from the many different lines of argument, that

[1] *Transactions of the Entomological Society of London*, 1928, pp. 533–8 (and several earlier papers in the *Victoria Naturalist*).

the internal, behavioural selection, due to the " psychic life " of the animal, *whatever we may think about its nature*—and we shall be discussing that later in the course—is now seen to be a most powerful creative element in evolution.

The reality of the distinction between the two forms of selection, the external and the internal, is I think evident if we examine ourselves, realising that we are part of this great stream of life. To illustrate this I will end the lecture by quoting again from my Presidential Address to the Zoology Section of the British Association in 1949 where I then tried to make the point without much success.

Man by his selective breeding can alter the form of domestic animals to suit, within limits, his own desires; he selects those which better suit his needs. I am now going to say something which might easily be misunderstood, and, perhaps, is dangerous to say. I am saying it only for the sake of argument, and not advocating something I necessarily think desirable. What I want to say is this. No modern biologist would doubt that if we knew as much about the genetics of man as we do about the genetics of some animals, then if mankind wished to control marriages by law, he could, by permitting some and prohibiting others, gradually in the course of long periods of time, alter the human race. Modern biology points to that, not as something desirable or undesirable, but as a theoretical possibility. If that is in fact a logical deduction from the present biological position, you will see where it must lead us. Evolution would no longer be guided from outside the species by natural selection, but by a directive activity from within the organism itself. We would see an organism directing its own evolution towards a goal in the future, whatever that might be decided to be. [The perceiving, exploring, initiating animal again.] . . . although man would be carrying out conscious organic selection, he would still be subject to natural selection by external agencies; for example the elimination of certain gene combinations less resistant than others to the attacks of pathogenic organisms. There would be an interplay between the two selections: natural and directive. We have seen that in nature there is probably a similar interplay between natural selection from without and organic selection from within.

The only alteration I should make, fourteen years later, would be to replace " probably " by " certainly " in the last sentence.

SOME PROBLEMS FOR CURRENT

EVOLUTION THEORY

In this lecture I want to discuss a number of problems which seem to me to present some difficulties for the generally accepted present-day theory of the mechanism whereby the process of evolution is effected. I must say at once that I am not wishing to suggest for a moment that any of these matters will be found to lie outside the process; I just mean that I think it likely that our theory may have to be modified to give an adequate explanation of at any rate some of them. I have two reasons for discussing a number of these rather diverse topics in this one lecture; my first is to show that the assumption, often expressed, that all the major difficulties of the theory have now been solved, is, in my view, far from being true.

I am not alone in this feeling. Professor Medawar, in his 1959 Reith Lectures on *The Future of Man* (published in book form in 1960), says in discussing genetics in relation to Man, "There is indeed an immense amount we cannot be sure about," and then a little later (on p. 62) he continues:

> The same goes for our understanding of evolution. Twenty years ago it all seemed easy: with mutation as a source of diversity, with selection to pick and choose, and with a mainly homozygous make-up to be aimed at, all we were left to wonder about was why on earth evolution should be so slow. But we know now that natural populations are obstinately diverse in their genetic make-up, and that the devices which make them so are bound to make them rather resistant to evolutionary change. Our former complacency can be traced, I suppose, to an understandable fault of temperament: scientists tend not to ask themselves questions until they can see the rudiments of an answer in their minds.

Embarrassing questions tend to remain unasked or, if asked, to be answered rudely. That is why I thought it important, in a previous lecture, to put an innocent question about the causes of evolutionary advancement. And here is another: why does so much of evolution lend itself to a belief in the inheritance of acquired characters? As I shall explain in my final lecture, belief in Lamarckism—in the idea that the environment can somehow issue genetic instructions to living organisms—is founded upon a misconception far wider than merely concerns genetics; but the question I put—how comes it that a Lamarckian style of inheritance should be so astutely imitated?—must still be asked, though I shall not have time at present to explain how an answer has been taking shape.

[At this point he gives a reference to a note at the end of the book: C. H. Waddington expounds his important concept of *genetic assimilation* in *The Strategy of the Genes* (London, Allen & Unwin, 1957), and explains the Darwinian basis of ostensibly Lamarckian patterns of inheritance.]

The puzzle of how it comes about that " a Lamarckian style of inheritance should be so astutely imitated " is I am sure largely to be explained in terms of this principle which is the one I have discussed in the last two lectures under the terms of the organic selection of Lloyd Morgan and Baldwin and of the genetic assimilation of Waddington; these, as I have explained, I believe to be one and the same process. I think it possible, however, that there may be another element involved: one which I shall discuss in the next lecture—one which I realise is very speculative. Medawar, in the passage I have quoted, refers to a further discussion on Lamarckism to come in his final lecture; I shall quote from this also in my own last lecture (on p. 277).

In this lecture I too want to ask some innocent questions. I fear that some may feel that my topics are too specifically biological to be included here; I will do my best to avoid being unduly technical. My main reason for introducing them at this point is that I think it *just possible* that some of them may be indirectly related to the subject I shall discuss in the next lecture.

My first topic is one I briefly mentioned in lecture II when considering early history: that of homology. You will remember that the idea behind the conception, when first thought of, was not an evolutionary one at all; it was thought by the German Transcendentalists, and later by our great anatomist, Richard Owen, to indicate the Deity's plan of creation. I will just remind you that Owen defined homology as " the same organ in different animals under every variety of form and function." This is really very simple when we explain it with diagrams, as in fig. 15 (p. 51) where we see sketches of the skeletons of the fore limbs of several vertebrate animals—a man, a porpoise, a bird, and a bat. In each case we see a similar general arrangement of bones which correspond in the different animals: humerus (h), radius (r), ulna (u), carpals (c), metacarpals (m), and phalanges (p); throughout the vertebrates with limbs we see the *same* organs (in this case, these various bones) under a great variety of form and function, *i.e.* here shaped as a flipper and used for swimming, there shaped as a wing and used for flying, etc. These *same organs* Owen called homologous structures.[1]

As soon as the evolution doctrine was accepted the term took on a new significance: homologous structures were now defined as those derived from the same single structure in a common ancestor, however much that structure may have been modified by subsequent variation in evolution. All the humerus bones of the terrestrial vertebrates, for instance, are thought to be derived by modification over millions and millions of years from the bones of the primitive limb-like fins of the first fish-like amphibia that pioneered the conquest of the land from the water. In the same way, the hearts, the nerve cords, the eyes and so on are said to be homologous, derived by gradual modification from the original ancestral type. This seemed very simple at one time and is still spoken of by most zoologists as if it were; the fact is, however, that today the idea of homology is not quite so easy to understand.

It is a curious paradox that this concept of homology is absolutely fundamental to what we are talking about when we speak of evolution, yet in truth I believe we cannot explain it at all in terms of present-day biological theory *except* by assuming one postulate which seems to me to stretch speculative credulity too far.

When I was an undergraduate student just after the First World War, and indeed when I was a professor in the '30's, it all seemed so obvious. The same homologous structures must clearly be due to the same hereditary factors handed on generation after generation from

[1] For the earlier history of the term see p. 49.

the early ancestor with occasional changes by mutation; the wide variety of form seen in different animal groups being due to natural selection acting upon these factors or genes which were handed on, with mutational changes, from the original ancestral form. We saw in lecture III how, with the development of experimental genetics, the old idea of one factor or gene governing one particular body character has been replaced by that of the gene-complex whereby all the genes are interacting to have their united effect upon the various structures. In truth we can no longer say that homologous structures are always due to the same—homologous—genes, however modified by mutation, handed on in the process of descent. Any animal structure we are looking at is produced by the combined effects of a particular gene-complex and the influence of the environment in which the animal develops; and we now find that what we have been calling homologous structures are often produced by the action of *quite different* genes.

T. H. Morgan was perhaps the first to demonstrate this surprising fact in 1929;[1] although its importance was not recognised until a number of other examples came to light particularly those discovered by S. C. Harland[2] among plants. In the fruit fly *Drosophila* there is a particular gene which governs the formation of the eyes and there is an allelomorph (a mutant alternative) of this gene which in the homozygous state produces an eyeless condition. Now Morgan showed that, if a pure homozygous eyeless stock is inbred, the other genes in the gene complex, by reassortment, may come to be recombined in such a way that they will deputise for the missing normal eye-forming allelomorph, and lo and behold flies appear in the " eyeless " stock with eyes as good as ever! These eyes must surely be regarded as homologous with the eyes of normal flies, yet their production is not controlled by the same genes. Homologous structures need not be produced under the influence of homologous genes. Rather similar results were obtained by Gordon and Sang[3] with a stock of *Drosophila* lacking antennæ; in a culture of such antennaless flies they were able by inbreeding, and so reshuffling the gene-complex, to produce flies which had either only one antenna or the normal pair. Several other curious effects in the little fly *Drosophila* were shown by Mohr;[4] one of these concerned the

---

[1] Morgan, T. H. (1929), *Publ. Carnegie Inst. Wash.*, vol. 399, pp. 139–68.
[2] Harland, S. C. (1936), *Biol. Rev.*, vol. 11, p. 83.
[3] Gordon, C. and Sang, J. H. (1941), *Proc. Roy. Soc. B.*, vol. 130, pp. 151–84.
[4] Mohr, C. (1929), *Z. 8 ind. Abst.*, vol. 50, pp. 113–200.

interaction of two mutant genes known as oblique and vortex, both recessive. " Oblique " has the effect of shortening the tip of the wing in an oblique fashion and " vortex " produces whorls of bristles on the thorax, yet a combination of the two genes gives a perfectly normal looking fly. Again, as Fisher showed,[1] structural characters controlled by identical genes need not be homologous; in wild type poultry he showed that a particular gene acted as a dominant when producing a crest of feathers but as a recessive in respect to a condition called cerebral hernia in which the frontal and parietal bones of the skull fail to close so that the brain bulges out through the gap. In certain breeds of poultry other genes in the complex completely suppress the hernia effect but allow the crest of feathers to appear. Then indeed all Waddington's experimental genetic assimilation effects such as cross-veinless and others show us how apparently identical characters may be brought about by quite different assortments of genes.

The concept of homology in terms of similar genes handed on from a common ancestor has broken down. Perhaps homologous structures are always formed from the same corresponding set of *cells* in development? No, this also fails; the lenses of the vertebrate eyes must surely be regarded as homologous, yet in experiments on frogs and newts they may be formed from epidermal cells at all sorts of places on the body surface if part of the eye (the optic cup) is grafted in below the skin. The optic cup is then said to act as an " organiser ". It was thought then that homologous structures might be due to the handing on from ancestors of similar " organisers "; this hypothesis, however, also collapses. For instance, in one species of frog (*Rana fusca*) the lens of the eye can only be induced by the presence of the optic cup; in another species (*Rana esculenta*) while it can be induced by the optic cup, it is also formed in its proper place if the optic cup is removed—formed apparently in relation to the developing whole animal. This subject has been well discussed by de Beer,[2] but he does not, I think, experience my difficulties.

For the present we appear to be forced into the position of saying that the only explanation of homology that the latest generally accepted views on evolution can offer is that *selection by the environment* is governing the maintenance of all the internal spatial relationships of the

[1] Fisher, R. A. (1935), *Phil. Trans. Roy. Soc. B.*, vol. 225, 195–236.
[2] de Beer, G. R. (1938), " Embryology and Evolution," in *Evolution*, ed. de Beer, Oxford.

animal; *i.e.* all the multitude of homologous parts which make up complex creatures such as, say, a hedgehog, a chaffinch and a frog. We must recognise that within relatively short periods of time there is a good interchange of genes (gene flow as it is called) throughout the range of an interbreeding population and this helps to keep the race comparatively uniform; is it not, however, stretching the concept of *external* selection a bit far to suppose that it alone, by controlling the effects of an ever-changing gene complex, is maintaining the stability of structure in a species over vast areas of different types of country— and over long periods of time? Can the whole complicated *internal* structure of our chaffinch, for instance, really be maintained—or rather slowly evolved—entirely under the influence of its multifarious *external* surroundings and nothing else? I could understand natural selection by the environment controlling the evolution of the whole intricate organ system if there were, associated with the homologous structures, some actual homologous units which varied and were handed on to be selected. But no, the homologous structures now appear to be governed by the *effects* of a whole multitude of units which are continually being reassorted. According to modern mechanistic biology the only " plan " for the intricate homologous " machinery " —for instance, the vertebrate, the arthropod or the molluscan plan— would seem to have been laid down by the variable environment outside. I am perfectly prepared to accept the proposition that the genetic code is handing on from generation to generation the specification for the plan of development of the animal body as determined by an act of selection of one sort or another; I am doubting, however, whether the plan itself is entirely the product of the environment. To my way of thinking, and remembering the great variety of environments which a single species may encounter and the variety of different kinds of animals which may live in the same habitat, such a conclusion seems almost a *reductio ad absurdum*. I may be unduly sceptical but I cannot help wondering if there is not something else concerned with the evolution process that we do not yet understand in addition to what I have discussed in the last two lectures.

I shall not attempt in this lecture to suggest what the missing factor may be, that will come later; I am here collecting together a number of problems which I feel require further explanation. My next is related to the last one; in fact it is a particular aspect of homology. I don't think anyone would deny that the limbs of the tetrapod vertebrate animals, *i.e.* of the amphibians,[1] reptiles, birds and mammals, are homologous yet there is a very extraordinary fact about them which very few zoologists discuss today. All the vertebrate animals are, as we say, " metamerically segmented "; by this we mean that the vertebrate body is divided into a large number of segments along its longitudinal axis from head to tail. As we eat a whiting or a herring we see clearly that both the muscles (the flesh we are eating) and the parts of the skeleton, the vertebræ of the backbone with its spines and ribs, are repeated as units of structure down the body; if we were zoologists we would know that other features, for example the nerves coming from the spinal cord, are also similarly repeated. The more ancestral the vertebrate the more complete is this " segmentation "; in some primitive forms like the lamprey we find the kidney tubules similarly arranged in series right down the body. With the higher vertebrates, however, like the mammals and birds, we find it difficult to see this segmentation in the adult animal until we examine the vertebral column and the central nervous system; in the embryo, however, all the incipient muscles are arranged in repeating units as they are in a fish. This segmental system, so admirable for producing the undulating motion of a swimming fish, has been drastically modified by evolution for locomotion with limbs on land. Now in the course of the development of each individual we see that each of these limbs is formed by the fusion of *several segmental elements*: muscle segments and their accompanying segmental nerves. We can number the segments, for reference, down the body from head to tail; and we can note (from the study of its development) that the fore limb of the Salamander, for example, is made up of segments 2 to 5 and its hind leg of segments 16 to 18. It then comes as a bit of a surprise to find when we similarly study the lizard that the corresponding, *homologous*, limbs are made up of segments 6 to 9 and 25 to 30 respectively, or in a bird like the swift the wing is formed from segments 10 to 14 and the leg from segments 20 to 27. A diagrammatic comparison of the segmental make-up of the limbs of six different vertebrates is shown in fig. 62. We note that not only do the position of the limbs vary, but also the actual number of segments involved; for example in the two birds shown the wings are made of five and four segments respectively,

[1] Among the early fossil amphibia there is the possibility, according to some workers in this field, that one stock was independently derived from the crossopterygian fish and so their limbs may not be strictly homologous with other amphibia.

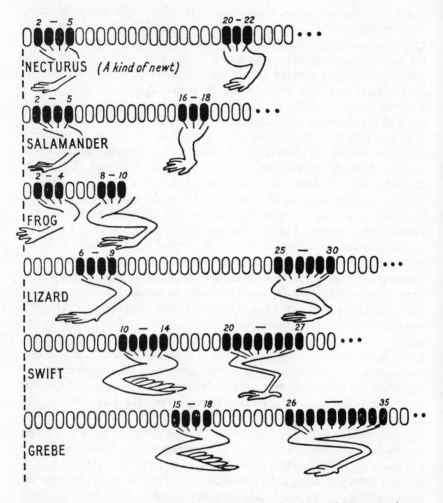

62. A diagram illustrating the variation in the number and positions of the metameric segments making up the limbs of different vertebrates. For further explanation see text.

while their corresponding legs arise from eight and ten segments.

The whole system of bones, muscles, nerves and blood vessels, all according to the same "homologous" plan, have been shifted in position; this means that the actual individual muscle segments and nerves concerned are *not* strictly homologous in the true sense: they are *not* the same segments as in the ancestral limb. Yet no one can doubt that the leg of a bird has been evolved from that of a reptile and that in turn from an amphibian ancestor; it is at the heart of all we are talking about in evolution. The same general *plan* of the limb is being handed on in all its details with gradually evolving changes, but its position along the body is altered: not by migration but by being built up of quite different segments. I cannot go into the several early theories which had been put forward to try and explain this; they were fully dealt with and dismissed in a classical paper by Goodrich[1] in 1913 when he made a most important contribution to the solution of the problem from his study of the development of the fins of fish.

Goodrich showed that in the more primitive adult fish, as also in the very young stages of any fish, there is a continuous fin along the back; in the development of most fish this gives rise to two or three separate fins which are formed from various numbers of segments in different species. The same is true of the paired fins. In the rays and skates, which have huge wing-like fins to support the body in the water like an aeroplane in the air, they are made up of many segments; in more typical fish they are made up of comparatively few segments, and, like the limbs of the terrestrial vertebrates we have been considering, may be formed at different points down the metameric series. Their relative positions, as Goodrich said, are *transposed* up and down the segmental series.[2] He showed that the same was true of the limbs of these higher forms; in the course of evolution their positions have been transposed. Now it may well be said, and may indeed be true, that this whole complex of the limb is formed in the course of development under the influence of some organising centre whose position is changed during the course of evolution; it must be realised, however, that the form of the whole body will have to be altered to fit the new design (speaking metaphorically). It is as if there is a plan which is being modified in the course of evolution. Again I have little doubt that the almost infinitely varying gene-complex, the changing code specification of the DNA molecules, is providing the groundwork for

[1] *Quarterly Journal of Microscopical Science*, vol. 59, pp. 227–48, 1913.

[2] In addition to this fundamental method of formation, there has been in some groups of fish a subsequent migration of fins as in the cod family; here the hind paired (pelvic) fins have moved up in later evolution to a secondary position *in front* of the typical anterior paired (pectoral) fins to act as braking organs. But this is something quite different; we can tell they have in fact migrated by seeing the nerves to the muscles coming from their original segmental position further down the body.

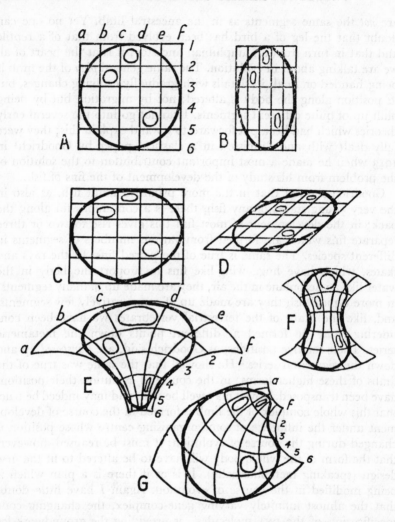

63. Diagrams to illustrate Sir D'Arcy Thompson's principle of transformations. The circle (A) is changed into various other shapes by replotting in relation to Cartesian co-ordinates which are modified according to different mathematical formulæ. Small circles have been added to show the distortion of a more detailed pattern.

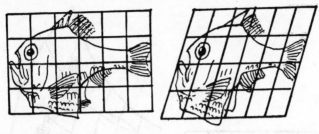

64. Outlines of two closely related species of deepwater fish: *Argyropelecus olfersi* (left) and *Sternoptyx diaphana* (right); the oblique co-ordinates on the latter fish bear the same relations to its anatomy as do those on *Argyropelecus*. After D'Arcy Thompson.

selection to act upon, but again I want to ask if it is just the *environment* that is modifying the plan in this way?

Now for another puzzle: that of the theory of Transformations propounded by D'Arcy Thompson in his great book *On Growth and Form*, first published in 1917. If you draw a squared lattice over any geometrical design, as in fig. 63a, you can of course describe all the points on its curved lines in terms of measurements along these vertical and horizontal co-ordinates, as Descartes showed us long ago. Now, if you redraw the co-ordinates in different ways so that their relationships are varied according to definite mathematical laws—e.g. spaces between vertical lines half that of spaces between horizontal ones (63b), or spaces between horizontal lines increasing according to a logarithmic scale (63c), or with the lines skewed, curved, etc. (63d–g) —then you may redraw your original design within each system so that the points on its curves again bear the same relations to the co-ordinates as before; if you do this you will find its shape modified in all manner of ways—each according to a particular mathematical equation. If we add circular spots to our original design, as in fig. 63, we see their size and relationship also altered accordingly. Now D'Arcy Thompson found that if he placed such Cartesian co-ordinates over the shape of one animal and then examined the shapes of others belonging to the same zoological group, he usually found that it was possible to show that the form of one species could be transformed into that of another by such a relatively simple mathematical distortion of the plan. For example, in figs. 64 and 65, redrawn from D'Arcy Thompson, we see in each case two different but closely allied species of fish, that on the

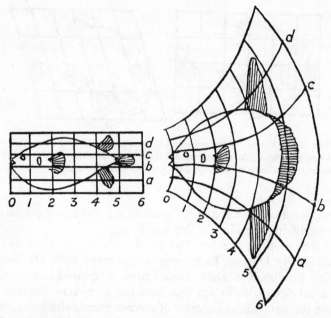

65. Outlines of two other closely related fish: *Diodon* and the sun-fish *Orthagoriscus*; the co-ordinates on the latter fish bear the same relations to its anatomy as do those on *Diodon*. After D'Arcy Thompson.

right with a lattice drawn to have the same relation to the parts of the fish as has the lattice drawn over the one on the left. Again and again he shows such regular mathematical transformations within different groups.

Professor P. B. Medawar has since shown that there is just the same type of transformation occurring in individual human development.[1] Of course, it will be understood that D'Arcy Thompson's transformations between adult and adult must be brought about by *changes in successive developments* during evolution, as shown in fig. 66. Let us follow Medawar and draw an outline of a human fœtus, aged 5 months, and place it within a frame having equidistant horizontal lines drawn across behind it as in fig. 67; now for comparison, let us draw an adult human and draw similar horizontal lines at the same *anatomical levels* as those on the fœtus. If we do this Medawar shows that we shall find

[1] " Size, Shape and Age " in *Essays on Growth and Form* (Oxford, 1945).

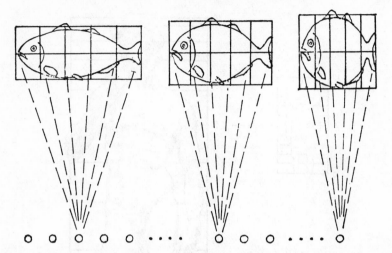

66. The geometrical transformations of adult form must be brought about by a gradual modification of development over a vast number of generations.

that the lines on the adult occur further and further apart in a regular progression from head to toe. It is for all the world as if a drawing of the fœtus had been made upon a rubber sheet which was thicker at the head end and tapered evenly towards the feet, and that, to represent growth, it was then stretched so that the general form of the body now shows this regular increase in extension from the head downwards.

How are we to explain these remarkable transformations? It is customary, following Sir Julian Huxley in his *Problems of Relative Growth* (1932), to speak about varying differential growth rates, or to discuss the regular diffusion of growth stimulating or inhibiting hormones and the like. Medawar has shown that it is possible to produce simple analogies with tissue culture. If a small piece of living spleen is grown on a culture medium it will send out mesenchyme cells around it to form an expanding circle of new tissue; now if we introduce into the culture medium a slightly toxic substance which will slowly diffuse through it we can inhibit this new growth in various ways depending on how we put the substance in. The circle of growth will be distorted into slightly different shapes according to whether, for example, we inject the toxin at a single point or along a line at one edge. I find it very hard, however, to imagine how the various organs of different

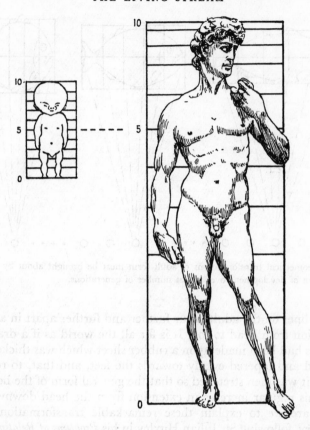

67. Drawings of a five-months' old fœtus and an adult. The frame of horizontal lines shown behind the adult are drawn in relation to the same anatomical points as are the *equidistant* lines drawn behind the fœtus. Note how the distance between the lines shows a regular increase down the body from head to feet with growth. Drawn from Professor Medawar's data. The size of the fœtus is somewhat enlarged in relation to the adult.

textures with their complicated blood and nervous supplies, can all be distorted in just the right proportions all together, as are, for example, the circular spots in our diagrams in fig. 63. The effect is just as if the whole body were seen through some distorting lens. Surely no growth promoting or inhibiting substance could, during development, diffuse evenly in this fashion through all the different kinds of tissues, and if it was carried, like a hormone, in the bloodstream it again could not produce such an even effect. I find it still more difficult to imagine how such a mathematical plan of growth could have been evolved, and then subsequently modified according to regular mathematical laws, entirely under the selective influence of a very heterogeneous environment.

I now want to turn again to Dr. Medawar and add to my collection of puzzles another problem which he raises. I am referring to a most valuable study of some aspects of adaptation which he contributed to *New Biology* (vol. 11, pp. 10–26) in 1951. I introduce this especially for the attention of biologists and I am afraid for the moment I may have to be a little more technical. In this article he discusses two types of adaptation, A and B, and gives examples of each concerning skin and bone. He gives a list as follows:

BONE

(A) The air-spaces that lighten the bones of birds and elephants.

(B) The patterns of the articulations of long bones at their joints.

(B) The organisation of cancellar bone in relation to strains and stresses.

(A) The possession of antlers, which presumably serve the purposes of aggression or defence.

SKIN

(A) The peculiar transparency of the epidermal cells and dermal fibres that form the cornea.

(B) The peculiar thickness of the epidermis on the heel of the foot.

(A) The modification of certain epidermal cells to secrete sweat.

(B) The structural modification of the dermis of the skin to form the flexure lines of the palm of the hand.

(B) The callosities that form on (what are functionally) the " knees " of the forelegs of the African wart-hog.

He discusses the nature of these adaptations and points out that they are all, both A and B, inborn, inherited characters " laid on " by development; at birth a baby has a complete pattern of dermal flexure lines and the sole of a guinea-pig's foot has a much thicker epidermis than is found on the rest of the body. And a little later he goes on:

What then *is* the difference between class A and class B adaptations?

It is this: adaptations of class B are such that even if they were *not*

" laid on " by development, they could be acquired in an individual's own lifetime merely by habit of use. In genetical language, they are inborn adaptations of a type of which very exact phenocopies can be made. If we were born without flexure lines, we should very soon acquire them, just as older people do on the face or forehead if they habitually grin or frown. If the skin on the plantar surface of the foot were as thin at birth as it is on the upper surface, a few weeks barefoot walking would soon make it thicker than gardener's palms. The same thing, *mutatis mutandis*, no doubt applies to the knees of an African wart-hog. As to joints, we can be sure that a perfectly functional joint with cartilaginous linings, capsule, complementary articulations and synovial fluid, would develop *de novo* at any two apposed and mobile bony surfaces, for in the accidental formation of so-called " pseudo-arthroses " just such a thing occurs.

On the other hand [now referring to class A], no amount of peering through an opaque or merely translucent epidermis would make it in any degree more transparent, and no attempts to fly could be supposed to introduce air spaces into the bones.

I must refer the reader to his full discussion of these interesting problems; I mention them here because the class B adaptations are in general those which are most likely to have been formed by the method of organic selection (or genetic assimilation if you prefer it); *however*, Medawar points out a difficulty which has to be faced. As he says:

... the selective forces are *sometimes* relatively obvious: if it is advantageous to have thickened feet at all, it will be advantageous to have them ready made when the foot is first put to ground. With other adaptations the selective advantage is much less obvious. What can be the value of genetically prefabricated flexure lines on the hand?

What indeed? I borrow this question as another in my list of the difficult problems evolutionary theory has to meet.

I will next turn to some rather different problems concerned with explaining the activities within primitive organisms of certain cells which appear to display elaborate instinctive behaviour patterns and yet are not linked to a nervous system such as would in higher forms be thought necessary for the control of such innate actions. My first example is one to which Dr. Thorpe drew attention in his Riddell

Memorial Lectures of 1961;[1] he gives an excellent summary of the complex series of events described by Kepner and his co-workers in America.[2] It concerns a little free-living freshwater flatworm called *Microstomum* which has only a very simple nervous system. It stores in the surface layer of its body the nematocysts or stinging-capsules which have been produced by cells in the body of the polyp *Hydra* upon which it feeds simply in order to obtain weapons to use for its own defence. When *Microstomum* has sufficient nematocysts it will no longer attack *Hydra* even if it is starving. When the hydra tissues have been digested, the nematocysts which so remarkably have not been discharged, are picked up by cells lining the stomach, the endoderm, and passed through to cells of the inner tissue, the so-called parenchyma; these cells, like wandering amœbæ, now carry the nematocysts to the outer skin, the epidermis, where they are arranged and turned into position ready to fire the stinging threads like so many guns mounted ready to counter any attack. The following is a brief quotation from the original paper by Kepner and his co-workers:

Cells of the parenchyma are responsible for the transportation of these stinging nematocysts to the epidermis. The cell that engulfs and transports one or more nematocysts becomes changed in a striking manner by the time it has carried its load to the epidermis. A second parenchymal cell forms with its cytoplasm a capsule about the transporting cell as the latter becomes orientated. The epidermis takes part also in the manipulation of the stinging nematocysts . . .

Thus it becomes evident that the endoderm, parachyma and epidermis of *Microstomum* co-operate in the manipulation of *Hydra's* nematocysts.

Thorpe, in the lecture to which I have just referred, discusses this work as follows:

Here, then, is a specific drive or appetite satisfied only by a very indirect series of activities, the recognition and selection of a specific object, recognition of the undischarged stinging cells by the wandering tissue-cells, and some sort of " perception " of its form so that it may be aimed. The uniform distribution of the

[1] Published under the title of *Biology and the Nature of Man* by the Oxford University Press, 1962.

[2] Kepner, A. W., Gregory, W. C., and Porter, R. J., *Zool.*, *Anz.*, vol. 121, p. 141, 1938.

nematocysts over the surface suggests a *gestalt*. So striking are these facts that Kepner was driven to postulate a group mind amongst the cells of the body to account for the internal behaviour of the *Microstomum*. Such a conclusion seems to us absurd: but it is to be remembered that behaviour such as this, while striking the ethologist with amazement, is a commonplace of embryology— though the embryologist has no better theory for explaining it than has the ethologist.

There is indeed point in what Thorpe says.

Let us pass down the scale of life a little further to those most rudimentary of all many-celled animals, the sponges. They have no nervous system at all. It is generally accepted that they have been derived from the protozoan animals—the single-celled animals—by a separate line of evolution to that of all the rest of the multicellular stock (the Metazoa). Many of them build the most beautiful skeletal structures of fine spicules (needle-like crystalline structures of various shapes), either of lime or glass-like silica, which are formed by a secretion from special wandering cells; frequently in the calcareous sponges, which have been more studied than the siliceous ones, two or three or more cells co-operate to secrete and build between them one spicule.[1] Such spicules, in different kinds of sponges, may have three, four or six radiating needle-like spikes; some are of great length in the siliceous sponges. In the hexactinellid siliceous sponge *Euplectella*, Ijima[2] in Japan first showed that six-rayed spicules were formed by large cells having many nuclei; this was later confirmed by Woodland[3] and Okada[4] for other kinds of hexactinellid sponges. A multitude of such large cells working together build structures far more complicated than any assembled by a party of workmen putting up a scaffolding against a building. How do they work to such a plan? That indeed is a problem. Such a structure was beautifully described by Professor Pantin in his Presidential Address to the Zoology Section of the British Association at their meeting in 1951; the title of his address was " Organic Design ". I cannot resist quoting him:

I should like to give you an example of this apparent design from

[1] W. Woodland, *Quarterly Journal of Microscopical Science*, vol. 49, pp. 231–82, 1906.
[2] I. Ijima, *Journal of the College of Science of Tokyo*, vol. 15, pp. 1–299, 1901.
[3] W. Woodland, *Quarterly Journal of Microscopical Science*, vol. 52, pp. 139–57, 1908.
[4] Y. Okada, *Journal of the Faculty of Science, University of Tokyo*, sec. IV, vol. 2, pp. 1–27, 1928.

amongst the simplest of the cellular animals. In the sponges, the body consists essentially of a porous cylinder of loosely organised cells. Through these pores are swept the fine planktonic organisms upon which the animal feeds. Certain cells construct a skeleton which may be of protein or of calcium carbonate or of silica. Among the siliceous hexactinellid sponges there is one of singular beauty, *Euplectella aspergillum* of Owen. Its skeleton is a hollow cylindrical framework of siliceous spicules. These are arranged in the form of longitudinal struts running the length of the cylinder, which are braced by lighter hoops at right angles to them at regular intervals. These simple components of themselves confer great mechanical rigidity on this seemingly delicate structure. They can evidently withstand compression in the same way as in the steel framework of a building. By itself such a structure would have little power to resist a twisting force. Mechanically such torsion can be met by the insertion of ties running obliquely through the rectilinear network of struts. In *Euplectella* we find this very thing. We find that in addition to the firm system of a rectilinear siliceous scaffold there is a network of thinner siliceous ties running in spiral geodetics through the framework. In fact we arrive in this skeleton at a marvellous combination of rigidity and lightness which recalls the geodetic construction familiar to aeroplane designers.

I give a sketch of the skeleton of *Euplectella* in fig. 68, as well as some microscopic views of the spicule-building cells. How *do* they work together to build the complete structure?

Now let us come to the simplest of animals: the Protozoa. The proverbial amœba is popularly spoken of as the simplest form of life; that, of course, is far from true, but it is certainly a relatively simple single-celled animal. Its cytoplasm, *i.e.* the living cell material outside the nucleus, is continually passing from one colloidal state to another —from the more fluid " sol " to the more gelatinous " gel " condition and back to the " sol " again—to carry out its characteristic flowing locomotion. The typical amœba sends out such flowing plasmic processes, called pseudopodia, for the capture and ingestion of its prey. In the sea there are relatives of amœba which typically secrete calcareous shells perforated with tiny holes to allow their exceedingly fine pseudopodia to extend in all directions; on account of these fine holes, they are called Foraminifera. They feed upon

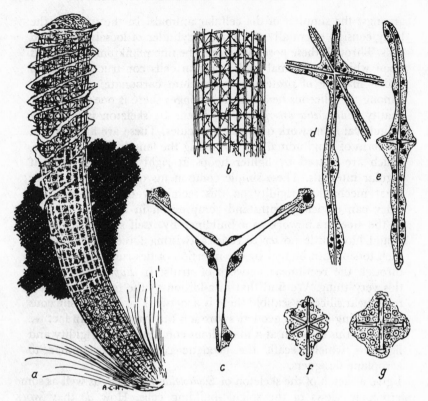

68. *a*, the Venus's flower-basket sponge, *Euplectella aspergillium*, one of the hexactinellid sponges, with skeleton made of spicules of silica (about ⅓ natural size); *b*, a more detailed drawing of the " girder " construction of the skeleton; *c, d, e, f* and *g*, highly magnified studies of spicule formation seen through a powerful microscope: *c*, separated cells (scleroblasts) taking part in the construction, by secretion, of a single tri-radiate spicule in a calcareous sponge (*Sycon cornata*), redrawn from Woodland (1906); *d* and *e*, large multinucleate cells forming siliceous hexactine spicules in the hexactinellid sponge *Rosella*, from Woodland (1908); *f* and *g*, similar multinucleate cells in the early stages of spicule formation in *Euplectella*, redrawn from Ijima (1901).

smaller organisms which they catch in a network of these branching and anastomosing protoplasmic strands; they are web and spider all in one, for, on capturing any prey, the meshes close about it, digest it *outside* the shell and the dissolved food then flows inwards to the main body within.

Most kinds of the Foraminifera secrete calcareous shells of many chambers which, in different species, take on almost every imaginable design and arrangement. Others, however, instead of producing their own shell by secreting lime, build around themselves grains of sand or other particles, to form a shelter like those houses constructed by the aquatic larvæ of caddis-flies. Many make just a rough covering of sand, but some—and to these I particularly want to call attention—build houses which are little short of marvels of engineering and constructional skill. I use the word " skill " advisedly. With the late Dr. E. Heron-Allen who made a special study of these forms, I share the view that the building of these devices cannot be simply a matter of physico-chemical mechanism alone.

Let us briefly consider the " houses " built by just one or two different species of these remarkable microscopic animals. *Technitella legumen* constructs a long cylindrical case entirely of sponge-spicules it has picked up from the sea-bed (fig. 69); Heron-Allen and Earland[1] described it as follows:

The shell wall consists of two distinct layers of spicules: an outer layer, in which the spicules are all laid with their long axes parallel to the long axis of the test; and an inner layer of spicules laid with their long axes at right angles to the outer layer. We thus get as close an approximation to " woof and warp " as is possible with a rigid, non-flexile material, and it is obvious that the strength of the test must be enormously increased by the crossing of the two layers, as resistance to tensile strain is given in two directions instead of one.

Next let us take *Psammosphæra rustica* which builds a polyhedral but almost spherical chamber, again of sponge spicules, as also illustrated in fig. 69. I will again quote the same authors:

Hardly any two specimens exhibit an identical shape or external appearance. This diversity is due to the methods of construction and the material employed. The apparent mode of construction is to select a number of long slender spicules often 2 or 3 mm. or more in length. These are placed like tent poles at various angles about 0·5 mm. apart, forming a rough open-work figure enclosing a central space between the points of intersection of the poles. The open spaces in the wall are then filled in with shorter fragments of spicules carefully selected for length, so as just to fill the required

[1] *Journal of the Royal Microscopical Society*, 1912, pp. 382–9.

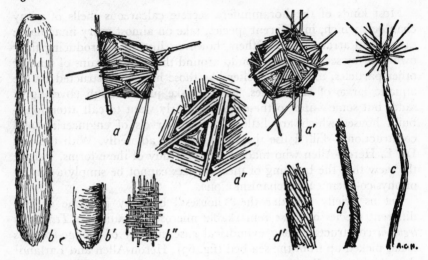

69. " Houses " of microscopic size built of sponge spicules picked up by arenaceous foraminifera (Protozoa) ×35. *a, a'*, examples made by *Psammosphæra rustica*, with *a"* giving the
detail of a small part to show the fitting into place of spicules of different size. *b*, external and
b' internal view of a house of *Technitella legumen* with a small part, *b"*, highly magnified to
show spicule arrangement. *c*, that of *Marsipella cylindrica* and *d*, of *M. spiralis* with a portion
d' further enlarged. All except *a"* drawn from specimens collected by the late Mr. E. Heron-
Allen and now in the British Museum (Natural History); *a"* is redrawn from Heron-Allen
and Earland (1912).

space. The animal thus secures the nearest possible approach to a
spherical chamber obtainable with the material employed, the
salient angles being the points where two or more of the " tent-
poles " join. The long spicules employed as " tent-poles " project
irregularly all over the surface of the test in perfect specimens,
and probably serve a secondary purpose as catamaran spars in
supporting the animal in the surface layer of ooze. They are,
however, very fragile, and are frequently more or less damaged, if
not destroyed, in the process of cleaning the dredged material.

Marsipella spiralis makes a long cylindrical case, but here the sponge-
spicules, in a single layer, are always built into the wall in a spiral,
giving added strength to the structure. To my mind these various
astrorhizid Foraminifera present one of the greatest challenges to the

exponents of a purely mechanistic view of life. Here are minute animals, apparently as simple in nature as amœba, without definite sense-organs such as eyes, and appearing as mere flowing masses of proto-plasm, yet endowed with extraordinary powers; not only do they *select* and pick up one type of object from all the jumble of fragments of other sorts on the sea-bed, but they build them into a design involv-ing a comparison of size. They build as if to a plan. Here is another mystery worth looking into. There must be an instinct of how to build and some sort of " memory " as to how far they have filled in the spaces and what sizes of spicules remain to be picked up to complete a section. Of course the whole activity of the animal is performed according to the physics and chemistry of the living material; we may be sure that none of these laws are broken, but are we so sure that this intricate physico-chemical machine has not been evolved as much by a selection of variations made by the animal's behavioural pattern as by the environment? The mystery surely concerns the relation of this " psychic " life of the animal to its mechanical body, and indeed is just as much a mystery as our own body-mind relationship.

I will end the lecture with a puzzle of a different kind. The problem was propounded by Alfred Russell Wallace in his *Tropical Nature*.[1] He was criticising that part of Darwin's theory of sexual selection con-cerned with females selecting the more brightly coloured males as mates. He objected that it implied not merely an æsthetic sense in the female, of which there was no evidence, but more than this, it implied that this sense was of the same uniform standard in all the females of the species. They must have shown an unfaltering preference for one particular type of coloration, refusing to mate with any birds that did not come up to this exact pattern. I quote from his chapter on the Colours of Animals:

We now come to such wonderful developments of plumage and colour as are exhibited by the peacock and the Argus-pheasant; and I may here mention that it was the case of the latter bird, as fully discussed by Mr. Darwin, which first shook my belief in " sexual ", or more properly " female " selection. The long series of gradations by which the beautifully shaded ocelli on the secondary wing-feathers of this bird have been produced, are clearly traced out, the results being a set of markings so exquisitely shaded as to represent " balls lying loose within sockets "—purely

[1] First published in 1879.

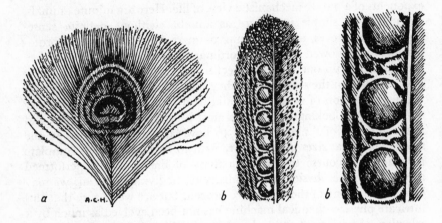

70. *a*, one of the " tail-covert " feathers of the peacock; *b*, a part of a secondary wing-feather of the Argus pheasant, with a portion enlarged in *b'*. Drawn from specimens in the Oxford University Museum.

artificial objects of which these birds could have no possible experience [see fig. 70]. That this result should have been attained, through thousands and tens of thousands of female birds all preferring those males whose markings varied slightly in this one direction, this uniformity of choice continuing through thousands and tens of thousands of generations, is to me absolutely incredible. And when, further, we remember that those which did not so vary would also, according to all the evidence, find mates and leave offspring, the actual result seems quite impossible of attainment by such means.

His solution to the problem, however, was not satisfactory; he attempted to ascribe all such brilliant colouring and ornament to the action of a hypothetical " male vigour ", the bright pigments being supposedly due to a higher male metabolic rate. This idea did not really answer the question he posed and certainly will not explain the courtship behaviour that so frequently accompanies the display of such characteristics which are certainly directed towards the female. Such colour patterns and behaviour, we now realise, are mainly concerned with stimulating the female to co-operate in the sexual act and to maintaining the bond of partnership between the pair till the family are reared.[1] Nevertheless the puzzle which Wallace pointed out of the extraordinarity *constant* nature of the patterns still persists, I believe. I have little doubt that the " design " is coded in the DNA, as is the structure of the feathers and the instinctive reaction of the females to the design; yet with the great variability of the gene complex which we have previously discussed I remain surprised that the design, the *plan* of its layout, is indeed so constant.

I have devoted this lecture to a variety of problems in order to show how much there still seems to be in nature that is not yet entirely accounted for by contemporary evolution theory. I do not doubt that they will be explained in evolutionary terms in time, and I realise that in some of these cases I may well be unreasonably puzzled. In the next lecture I shall discuss some evidence which I believe points to some properties of living things which are not yet recognised by orthodox biology; it is just possible, I think, that they may have a connection with some of the things I have mentioned here.

[1] There are a few cases of polygamous birds, such as the ruff and the black-cock, where the female does appear to select the more brightly coloured males to mate with.

BIOLOGY AND TELEPATHY

Most of my colleagues were surprised when I introduced the subject of telepathy into my Presidential Address to the Zoology Section of the British Association at its meeting in Newcastle in 1949. Many were, and still are, sceptical as to its reality. Some, I think, felt that, even if it existed, it could have nothing to do with Zoology, while others thought that perhaps it might possibly come in to explain certain aspects of animal behaviour such as the sudden change of direction of a flock of birds in flight, as had been suggested by several naturalists such as Edmond Selous.[1] Very few indeed saw what I was really driving at: the possibility that it may reveal something which is fundamental in connection with the process of evolution.

It may be that I am making a tactical, or even strategic, mistake in introducing the subject into this course of lectures. By so doing I may be diverting attention away from the main argument I have presented in support of habit and behaviour as important elements in orthodox evolution theory. I run the risk of perhaps making people believe that I regard something like telepathy as essential to this process; I must make it quite clear that I do *not* regard it as at all *essential* to the principle I have hitherto presented. While for the moment keeping it entirely separate, I wish in this lecture to say why I believe the study of telepathy may be important for biology as a whole, and why I think it *may possibly* have implications for evolution theory. Such a possibility must at present be entirely speculative. It may be unwise so to speculate at this stage, yet I feel we are like proverbial ostriches with our heads in the sand if we refuse to consider phenomena which some very good scientists and philosophers regard as having already been demonstrated beyond reasonable doubt. I believe it is our duty to look at them and see where they might fit

[1] *Thought-transference, or What, in Birds?* 1931.

in. I want in fact to amplify and explain what I meant in my address of 1949; let me recall what I then said. I had been discussing the two forms of selection that I have distinguished in these lectures, that more generally considered as typical natural selection, acting from *outside* the organism and organic selection acting from *within*. I went on as follows:

> There is another matter which I feel it only right to mention if one is not to be intellectually dishonest. There has appeared over the horizon something which many of us do not like to look at. If it is pointed out to us we say: " No, it can't be there, our doctrines say it is impossible." I refer to telepathy—the communication of one mind with another by means other than by the ordinary senses. I believe that no one, who examines the evidence with an unbiased mind, can reject it. ...
>
> It is perhaps unorthodox for a zoologist to introduce such a topic; but I do so for a reason. If telepathy has been established, as I believe it has, then such a revolutionary discovery should make us keep our minds open to the possibility that there may be so much more in living things and their evolution than our science has hitherto led us to expect. Such an idea as I am about to suggest is no doubt highly improbable and would perhaps be better kept locked in a bottom drawer; I mention it however merely as a reminder that perhaps our ideas on evolution may be altered if something akin to telepathy—unconscious no doubt—was found to be a factor in moulding the patterns of behaviour among members of a species. ...

I then very briefly outlined a way in which I thought something akin to telepathy might possibly influence the process of evolution. I will continue the argument later in the lecture after I have presented some of the evidence which I believe to be of such a nature that it cannot be dismissed. With a few notable exceptions, scientists in general have tended to ignore—or perhaps one should say definitely *shun*—the evidence that is available. It is remarkable that the Society for Psychical Research, under the presidency of some great personalities, should now have been in existence for 80 years, yet so few outside its members have thought it worth while to examine the contents of its *Proceedings* and *Journal* which together now make over 90 volumes.

There are at least *four* major reasons why most scientists have an aversion for these matters. It is important that we should consider these points carefully. Some of my friends and colleagues are genuinely shocked that I should be interested in these things; they feel it is impossible to do so and still retain the spirit of science. While I do not share their views, I have a deep respect for the feelings which lie behind them and so I want to discuss them as sympathetically as possible.

The first and most obvious objection is of course that the experiments of psychical research cannot yet be repeated at will and this seems to place them outside science as we know it. Have not the laws of science been built up from observations and experiments which can be repeated anywhere by anyone provided he is working under similar conditions? Add so much hydrochloric acid to so much zinc and you will always get so much hydrogen liberated; a ray of light entering pure water at a particular angle will always be bent through the same angle wherever the experiment is performed—science has grown by the addition of such facts that can be verified by whoever may doubt them. Scientists are apt to say that they are not prepared to consider the findings of psychical research until they can be so repeated. There are, however, many facts of *natural history* which cannot always be demonstrated at will. Animals may usually behave in this or that fashion under these or those particular circumstances, but we cannot be certain that they always will. When this happens we assume that we have not got all the conditions exactly right or that there is something in the animal's psychology we do not yet understand; we don't, however, because of this deny the former observations on the animal's behaviour. Most of the repeatable experiments of science at present deal with the action of matter in the inorganic world or with the chemistry and physics within the animal body; we are only just beginning to understand the laws relating to the behaviour of whole animals under natural conditions. Because the results of psychical research cannot yet be repeated at will I do not myself feel that that is any reason for refusing to acknowledge that on a large number of occasions they have been demonstrated to occur.

Apart from physiology, there is so much of life as a whole which cannot yet be demonstrated by exactly repeatable results. Many of the conclusions from the excellent experiments made in the field of animal behaviour depend not upon getting invariable responses but upon there being more positive than negative results in statistically significant proportions. It seems to me wrong to refuse to examine these other, at present, paranormal events simply because they lie more in the field of observation than in that of laboratory demonstration. In time we may know more about the factors which govern them and so eventually perhaps be able to reproduce them at will; if so we shall have brought them from the domain of natural history into that of exact science. These paranormal phenomena are at present a part of the natural history of Man.

Secondly comes the question of fraud. There has of course been a good deal of deception detected by psychical research among people who have claimed to have unusual gifts. This is certainly a very unpleasant side to the subject. The atmosphere of mystery which surrounds these reported phenomena excites the credulous and makes them easy victims of the charlatans who delight in pretending to have "supernatural" gifts because it gives them a feeling of superiority and power over their fellow men. We must indeed respect the attitude of those scientists who say "Now that fraud has been detected, not once, but again and again, I'm going to have nothing to do with it— to dabble in it is to damage the fair name of science." Yet we all know that the great science of chemistry sprang from the cradle of alchemy, some of those exponents were genuinely striving after the transmutation of metals and the elixir of life, while others were as rank impostors as any false medium or fortune teller of today. This new branch of knowledge which is now struggling to be born will one day, I believe, look back to this period as the chemists of today look back to their own history.

The third objection is one which requires a great deal of consideration; it is, I think, the most important and the most difficult to deal with. The people who work at psychical research often seem to want a particular result. Surely, say the critics, this cannot be the scientific attitude; such an outlook must make us suspicious of the validity of their findings. Are these experimenters not biased? Not that they willingly distort the evidence to support their case—but unconsciously may they not tend to disregard this, and give undue prominence to that, and so unwittingly arrive at false conclusions? I have already referred to this in relation to Lamarckian experiments in lecture VI.

We may have the unbiased scientific spirit (provided we have no pet hypothesis to defend) when we are dealing entirely with material things or with the physical and chemical reactions within the living body; when, however, we come to investigate problems which may have a bearing upon our own relations with the universe—then I think we must honestly admit that such a strictly unbiased attitude is impossible. This does not mean that we must not investigate these problems; it means we must proceed with much greater caution. There is indeed an exact parallel to the Lamarckian experiments already referred to, where the experimenters had an intuition that habit must be important in evolution. They went wrong, however, as did Lamarck himself, in supposing that the direct effects of habit on an individual's body could be inherited; and holding these views so strongly, they sometimes were not sufficiently alive to the possibility of other interpretations of the results they got.

We must not, however, lose the opportunities of making discoveries because we don't like to risk making mistakes. We must face the dangers of bias. If we say science must only be concerned with experiments about whose results we have no emotional feeling—then we can never hope to come to real understanding of living things. Psychical research does indeed appear to hold out a promise of results which may release us from a philosophy of materialism which an intuition seems to tell us is false. We may be interested in investigating the paranormal for this very reason; if so we would do well to admit it frankly and if possible seek the collaboration in our work of someone who holds quite the opposite view. It is fortunate that recently several centres of telepathy research have been set up in Russia based on the belief that it will be shown to be a physical radiation effect.

The fourth reason why some scientists will not examine the claims of experimenters in psychical research is because they believe them to be quite impossible and so a waste of time. It is generally considered, contrary to the Russian view, that telepathy does not appear to fit within the framework of present-day science; but should we, because of that, refuse to investigate it? If we do refuse, are we not just as those who condemned Galileo for his experiments and conclusions? It is interesting that it is the philosophers, rather than the scientists, who tend to take an interest in these matters. Professor H. H. Price, who was then Wykeham Professor of Logic at Oxford, and whom I have the honour to follow here as Gifford Lecturer, writing in the *Hibbert Journal* (vol. 47, pp. 105–13) in 1949, says:

Telepathy is something which ought not to happen at all, if the Materialistic theory were true. But it does happen. So there must be something seriously wrong with the Materialistic theory, however numerous and imposing the *normal* facts which support it may be.

He ends by saying:

In conclusion, I would again like to address myself to the people whom I mentioned at the beginning (I believe they are fairly numerous); to those who agree that Psychical Research has succeeded in establishing various queer facts about the human mind, but think that these facts are mere curiosities and oddities, of no particular importance. Certainly card-guessing does appear at first sight to be a rather trivial occupation. And if a few dreams turn out to be telepathic visions, why should anyone make such a fuss about it? On the contrary, these queer facts are not at all trivial, and it is right to make the greatest possible fuss about them. Their very queerness is just what makes them so significant. We call them " queer " just because they will not fit in with orthodox scientific ideas about the universe and man's place in it. If they show, as I think they do, that the Materialistic conception of human personality is untenable, and if they throw quite new light on the age-old conflict between the scientific and the religious outlooks, we shall have to conclude that Psychical Research is one of the most important branches of investigation which the human mind has ever undertaken.

In the same year Professor C. D. Broad, who was Knightsbridge Professor of Moral Philosophy at Cambridge and who like Price has been President of the Society for Psychical Research, writes in *Philosophy* (vol. 24, pp. 291–309) as follows:

In my opinion psychical research is highly relevant to philosophy for the following reasons. There are certain limiting principles which we unhesitatingly take for granted as the framework within which all our practical activities and our scientific theories are confined. Some of them seem to be self-evident. Others are so overwhelmingly supported by all the empirical facts which fall within the range of ordinary experience and the scientific elaborations of it (including under this heading orthodox psychology) that it hardly enters our heads to question them. Let us call these *Basic Limiting Principles*. Now psychical research is concerned with alleged events which seem *prima facie* to conflict with one or more of these principles. Let us call any event which seems *prima facie* to do this an *Ostensibly Paranormal Event*. . . .

Now it might well have happened that every alleged ostensibly paranormal event which had been carefully investigated by a competent psychical researcher was found either not to have occurred at all, or to have been misdescribed in important respects or to be a chance-coincidence ... (etc.) ... But that is not how things have in fact turned out. It will be enough at present to refer to a single instance, viz. Dr. Soal's experiments on card-guessing with Mr. Shackleton as subject, of which I gave a full account in *Philosophy* in 1944. There can be no doubt that the events described happened and were correctly reported; that the odds against chance-coincidence piled up to billions to one; and that the nature of the events, which involved both telepathy and pre-cognition, conflicts with one or more of the basic limiting principles.

For a full discussion of the subject I would particularly call attention to Professor Broad's *Lectures on Psychical Research*, being the Perrott Lectures delivered in Cambridge University in 1959 and 1960 and published under that title in 1962.

On the theological side Dr. Matthews, the Dean of St. Paul's, in his Maurice Lectures, published by the Oxford University Press in 1950, said:

I believe it is foolish not to recognise that Psychical Research may have much to teach us about our mysterious selves. We should not rule out the possibility that the next great advance in our knowledge will come in this part of the field. Eminent philosophers are now aware of the need to take account of the phenomena and their interpretation; it seems that theologians cannot long remain indifferent. . . .

The case for telepathy is so strong that one is tempted to say that the only way to retain disbelief in it is by steadily ignoring the evidence.

Now let me proceed to some examples of the evidence for telepathy which I regard as so important. There are, of course, many instances of what might be telepathy scattered through history from Grecian times onwards; but the modern experimental study begins with observations of Sir William Barrett, Professor of Physics, Trinity College, Dublin, on what was then called "Thought Transference". He read what I believe to be the first communication to any Scientific Society on the subject, to the British Association, at their Glasgow

Meeting of 1876. He was not allowed to read it to Section "D" (Zoology) but read it before the Anthropology Section on the casting vote of Alfred Russell Wallace. Wallace was greatly interested in this subject, much to the displeasure of Darwin; he did not become interested in psychical research only in his old age, as a senile weakness, as some people seem to think.

The reading of this paper partly gave rise to the foundation of the Society for Psychical Research in 1881. It is with some of this early work that I particularly want to deal, but for a reason I shall explain I will briefly refer to the more modern work first.

For the last thirty years most of the experimental work on telepathy has been using the card-guessing technique developed by Professor Rhine and his colleagues at Duke University in America; similar experiments have now been made in most countries of the world. I welcomed the results of these experiments because they *appeared* to give unassailable statistical proof of the reality of telepathy which actually I felt certain of upon other evidence which, while convincing to me, was not subject in the same way to statistical analysis.[1] My difficulty, however, is that whilst I am sure that the statistical tests applied to the card experiments of Rhine and others are demonstrating the reality of *card guessing*, I cannot be sure that they are in fact demonstrating what *I mean* by telepathy, *i.e.* the transference of a thought, an idea, from one mind to another without the use of the normal sensory channels. It very soon came as a shock to me, when examining the accounts of the experiments, to find that Rhine and others were getting exactly the same kind of results, above chance, with certain subjects guessing cards entirely by so-called "clairvoyance"—*i.e.* guessing the order of the cards in a pack before they have been seen by anyone.

I found it much easier to imagine one mind being in touch with another mind, than to conceive of a mind being able to know what kind of design is on the underside of a card which has never yet been seen by any living being. Then came precognition which seemed equally difficult to imagine, but apparently equally proved by the same kind of statistics. More recently still has come psycho-kinesis,

[1] Professor Camp, President of the American Institute of Mathematical Statistics, stated in 1937: "If the Rhine investigation is to be fairly attacked it must be on other than mathematical grounds"; similar views were expressed by the late Sir Ronald Fisher.

the alleged influence of the mind upon falling dice which is again seemingly established by the scoring of the same sort of degree of probability above a chance result as may be found in the other fields. Then there are some subjects who have repeatedly scored significantly *below* chance results. Whilst I think many of us have felt uneasy at the similarity of the evidence of these four very different alleged phenomena, it remained for Mr. G. Spencer-Brown of Trinity College, Cambridge, to suggest the alternative and simpler hypothesis that all this experimental work in so-called telepathy, clairvoyance, precognition and psycho-kinesis, which depends upon obtaining results above chance, may be really a demonstration of some single and very different principle. He believes that it may be something no less fundamental or interesting—but not telepathy or these other curious things—something implicit in the very nature and meaning of randomness itself. Spencer-Brown has published his hypothesis in a book, *Probability and Scientific Inference* (1957). I am not competent to pass judgement upon his views, but it would seem that his theory could not possibly account for such remarkable results as were obtained in the experiments of Dr. Soal and Mr. Basil Shackleton to which Professor Broad referred in the quotation I have given (p. 240). Whether or not the majority of the card-guessing experiments may be shown to be due to something quite different from telepathy, there is to my mind quite sufficient evidence to prove the existence of a true form of telepathy which seems likely to be of considerable biological significance. In passing, let me say that if most of this apparent card-guessing and dice-influencing work should in fact turn out to be something very different, it will not I believe have been a wasted effort; it will have provided a wonderful mine of material for the study of a very remarkable new principle concerning randomness.

I want now to go back to the experiments that were done in telepathy before the advent of the card-guessing tests; some of this work, done in the early days of the Society for Psychical Research, is as important I believe as anything that has been done since. I particularly want to refer to the series of experiments carried out at Liverpool by Mr. Malcolm Guthrie, J.P., and Mr. James Birchall, a headmaster and Honorary Secretary of the Liverpool Literary and Philosophical Society, between April 1883 and July 1885, during which period 246 experiments were made. The first short report of the early experiments will be found in vol. 1 of the *Proceedings of the Society for*

Psychical Research, pp. 263–83, with fuller accounts in vol. II, pp. 24–42, and vol. III, pp. 424–52. Also in vol. II, pp. 189–200, Sir Oliver Lodge gives a separate account of some of the experiments carried out under his supervision. Sir William Herdman also took part in some of the later ones. These investigations are particularly important because in all the experiments either Mr. Guthrie, Mr. Birchall, Sir Oliver Lodge or another responsible person acted as the agent, *i.e.* transmitter of the impression, so that unless we suspect all of these gentlemen of fraud (for they all at times got positive results) there can be no question of the successes being due to trickery by the use of some code to transmit the impression to the percipient. So important is it to make clear the quality of the Liverpool experiments that I will quote at some length from Sir Oliver Lodge's account:

> Perhaps it may not be considered impertinent, since it bears on the question of responsibility and genuineness, if I state that Mr. Guthrie holds an important position in Liverpool, being a Justice of the Peace, and an active member of the governing bodies of several public institutions, among others of the new University College; that he is a severe student of philosophy, and the author of several works bearing on the particular doctrines of Mr. Herbert Spencer. I may also say that he is a relative of Professor Frederick Guthrie, and that he has exhibited in this experimental research such care and systematic vigilance as might perhaps have been expected on Mr. Francis Galton's principles, and such as would, if properly directed, have placed him in a high rank of experimental philosophers. I may also remind you of what he himself has here said, viz., that he is a partner in the chief drapery establishment in Liverpool, and that it is among the employees of that large business that the two percipients hereafter referred to were accidentally discovered.

> Let it be understood that the experiments are Mr. Guthrie's, and that my connection with them is simply this: that after Mr. Guthrie had laboriously carried out a long series of experiments and had published many of his results, he set about endeavouring to convince such students of science as he could lay his hands upon in Liverpool; and with this object he appealed to me, among others, to come and witness, and within limits modify, the experiments in such a way as would satisfy me of their genuineness and perfect good faith.

Yielding to his entreaty I consented, and have been, I suppose, at some dozen sittings; at first simply looking on so as to grasp the phenomena, but afterwards taking charge of the experiments —Mr. Guthrie himself often not being present, though he was always within call in another room, ready to give advice and assistance when desired.

In this way I had every opportunity of examining and varying the minute conditions of the phenomena so as to satisfy myself of their genuine and objective character, in the same way as one is accustomed to satisfy oneself as to the truth and genuineness of any ordinary physical fact.

I did not feel at liberty to modify the experiments very largely, in other words to try essentially new ones, because that would have been interfering with Mr. Guthrie's prerogative. I only regarded it as my business to satisfy myself as to the genuineness and authenticity of the phenomena already described by Mr. Guthrie. If I had merely witnessed facts as a passive spectator I should most certainly not publicly report upon them. So long as one is bound to accept imposed conditions and merely witness what goes on, I have no confidence in my own penetration, and am perfectly sure that a conjuror could impose on me, possibly even to the extent of making me think that he was not imposing on me; but when one has control of the circumstances, can change them at will and arrange one's own experiments, one gradually acquires a belief in the phenomena observed quite comparable to that induced by the repetition of ordinary physical experiments.

I am particularly interested in the transmission of designs and am reproducing in miniature in figs. 71 and 72 all those diagrams published in vol. II of the *Proceedings*; they have been accurately traced from these facsimiles and then reduced. The six diagrams, originals and reproductions, given in fig. 71 were a complete and consecutive series at one sitting with Mr. Guthrie acting as transmitter (called the " agent " in the following description of the method) and Miss E. as the percipient (called the " subject ") with no contact between them such as touching hands. Fig. 72 gives some selected successes from a number of other experiments. I will quote a brief note from the report showing how they were done, but the complete account should be studied.

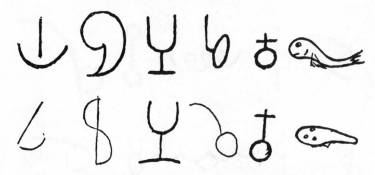

71. Some results from the telepathy experiments conducted by Guthrie and Birchall at Liverpool under strict control conditions in 1883. A complete consecutive series of six drawings (shown in line above) transmitted by Mr. Guthrie to Miss E. who made the corresponding drawings shown in the line below. When the last was being transmitted Miss E. said almost at once " are you thinking of the bottom of the sea, with shells and fishes? " and then " is it a snail or a fish? " and drew as above. Traced from the originals reproduced in the *Proceedings of the Society for Psychical Research*, vol. II, 1884.

The originals of the following diagrams were for the most part drawn in another room from that in which the " subject " was placed. The few executed in the same room were drawn while the " subject " was blindfolded, at a distance from her, and in such a way that the process would have been wholly invisible to her or anyone else, even had an attempt been made to observe it. During the process of transference, the " agent " looked steadily and in perfect silence at the original drawing, which was placed upon an intervening wooden stand; the " subject " sitting opposite to him, and behind the stand, blindfolded and quite still. The " agent " ceased looking at the drawing, and the blindfolding was removed, only when the " subject " professed herself ready to make the reproduction, which happened usually in times varying from half-a-minute to two or three minutes. Her position rendered it absolutely impossible that she should glimpse at the original. She could not have done so, in fact, without rising from her seat and advancing her head several feet; and as she was almost in the same line of sight as her drawing, and so almost in the centre of the " agent's " field of observation, the slightest approach to such a movement must have been instantly detected. The reproductions were made in perfect silence, and without the

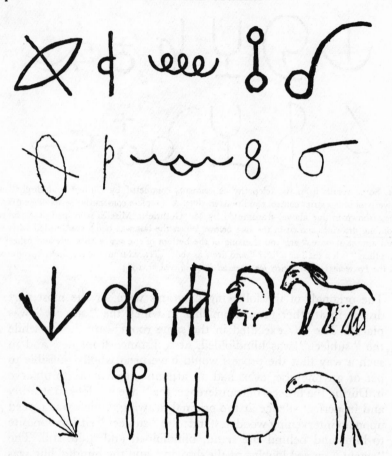

72. Ten further example of drawings transmitted during the Liverpool telepathy experiments; originals with reproductions immediately below in *each* row. These are selected as some of the best examples. No. 1, Mr. Gurney to Miss R., with half a minute contact before drawing was made; no. 2, Mr. Gurney to Miss R., without contact; nos. 3 and 4, Mr. Birchall to Miss R., without contact; no. 5, Mr. Birchall to Miss E., without contact; no. 6, Mr. Steel to Miss R., without contact; no. 7, Mr. Steel and Miss E., contact before reproduction was made; no. 8, Mr. Hughes and Miss E., contact before reproduction was made; nos. 9 and 10, Mr. Hughes and Miss E., no contact. Just before drawing no. 9, Miss E. said " It is like a mask at a pantomime." From the *Proceedings of the Society for Psychical Research*, vol. II, 1884.

" agent " even following the actual process with his eyes, though he was of course able to keep the " subject " under the closest observation.

In a number of experiments *two* agents were used to look at the same drawing to be transmitted to the one percipient. On one occasion Sir Oliver Lodge made an interesting innovation which he recorded in a letter to *Nature* (vol. xxx, p. 145, 1884). I quote from it as follows:

One evening last week—after two thinkers, or agents, had been several times successful in instilling the idea of some object or drawing, at which they were looking, into the mind of the blind-fold person, or percipient—I brought into the room a double opaque sheet of thick paper with a square drawn on one side and a St. Andrew's cross or X on the other, and silently arranged it between the two agents so that each looked on one side without any notion of what was on the other. The percipient was not informed in any way that a novel modification was being made; and, as usual, there was no contact of any sort or kind—a clear space of several feet existing between each of the three people. I thought that by this variation I should decide whether one of the two agents was more active than the other; or, supposing them about equal whether two ideas in two separate minds could be fused into one by the percipient.

In a very short time the percipient made the following remarks, every one else being silent: " The thing won't keep still." " I seem to see things moving about." " First I see a thing up there, and then one down there." " I can't see either distinctly." The object was then hidden, and the percipient was told to take off the bandage and to draw the impression in her mind on a sheet of paper. She drew a square, and then said, " There was the other thing as well," and drew a cross inside the square from corner to corner, saying afterwards, " I don't know what made me put it inside."

A number of experiments similar to the Liverpool ones are also reported in the early *Proceedings* of the S.P.R.; I will refer only to those made in Paris by A. Schmoll and J. E. Mabire (*Proceedings*, vol. iv pp. 324–37 and vol. v, pp. 169–215); the number of successes in this series were more limited but quite beyond mere coincidence—the 10 best results out of 104 drawings made are reproduced in fig. 73.

These results are either fraud or something very wonderful. Some

73. The ten most successful transmissions of drawings (out of 104) during the experiments made by A. Schmoll and J. E. Mabire in Paris. Originals above and reproductions below in each row. From the *Proceedings of the Society for Psychical Research*, vol. v, 1888.

people indeed find them so remarkable that they cannot regard them as genuine, yet they were carried out under scrupulous supervision by most responsible people. They are really, however, no more remarkable than the long series of results of a different kind which the late Professor Gilbert Murray, O.M., obtained. He gave some account of them in a Presidential Address to the S.P.R. in 1915 and more detailed analyses of them were published in the Society's *Proceedings* by Mrs. A. W. Verrall in 1916 and Mrs. Henry Sidgwick in 1924. Let me quote the opening two sentences of Mrs. Sidgwick's report:

Professor Gilbert Murray's experiments in Thought-transference are perhaps the most important ever brought to the notice of the Society, both on account of their frequently brilliant success and on account of the eminence of the experimenter. It is surprising, I think, that they have not attracted more general attention than, so far as I know, they have.

They are indeed worth very close attention. No one can suppose that there is any conscious fraud here. Let me briefly remind readers of the method which, quoting from Professor Gilbert Murray's Presidential Address, " was always the same ";

I was sent out of the drawing-room or to the end of the hall, the door or doors, of course, being shut. The others remained in the drawing-room: someone chose a subject, which was hastily written down, word for word. Then I was called in, and my words written down. I may add that, out of the first 505 cases, Mrs. Verrall estimated the percentage as: Success, 33 per cent.; Partial Success, 27·9 per cent.; Failure, 39 per cent. But it may be remarked that as evidence for the presence of some degree of telepathy most of the partial successes are quite as convincing as the complete successes: this would produce something like 60 per cent. evidential and 40 per cent. non-evidential.

Earlier in the address he says:

At one time, indeed, I was inclined to attribute the whole thing to subconscious auditory hyperæsthesia. I got almost no successes if the subject was not spoken, but only written down. Two or three successes and at least one error could be explained by my having heard or misheard a proper name, e.g. by confusing Judge Davies and the prophet David. But, apart from other difficulties in this hypothesis, there were some clear cases where I got a point or even a whole subject which had only been thought and not spoken.

Careful examination will, I think, lead one to agree with Mrs. Sidgwick when she writes as follows regarding hyperæsthesia after considering many possible examples: " In some cases the evidence against it seems, as we have seen, conclusive and I feel sure that if hearing, however hyperæsthetic, has operated at all, it has done so rarely."

The impressions transmitted to Dr. Gilbert Murray are just as complicated and as often as not agree just as well with the original subject as do the drawings which we have just been discussing. I will quote five consecutive examples taken from the middle of the detailed records given in the Appendix to Mrs. Sidgwick's report. She begins with the following explanation:

In what follows remarks by the agent and contemporary notes are in round brackets; additions by myself, to make things clear, in square brackets.

95. *Subject.* MRS. ARNOLD TOYNBEE (agent): " I'm thinking of the scene in *Marie Claire* where she finds the nun Sœur Marie Aimée crying."

PROFESSOR MURRAY. " This is a book—it's not English, not Russian—It's rather a—I think there are nuns in it—there are a lot of people—either a school or a laundry—and one of the nuns weeping—I think it's French. Oh, it's a scene in *Marie Claire*, near the beginning—I can't remember it, but it is something like that—it's in the place where she goes—one of the nuns crying— a double name—no I can't get the [name] Marie Thérèse."

96. *Subject.* LADY MARY MURRAY (agent): " A monastery that we slept in the first night in Peloponnese with six beds round."

PROFESSOR MURRAY. " I think this is in Greece. I think it is the place where we were so afraid that the arch-priest meant to sleep with us."

(Right.)

97. *Subject.* COUNTESS OF CARLISLE (agent): " The Crimean soldiers after their return receiving their medals from Queen Victoria at [the] Horse Guards."

PROFESSOR MURRAY. " Is it the King giving V.C.'s and things to people? Yes [I] think it's an investiture of some sort."

98. *Subject.* COUNTESS OF CARLISLE (agent): " Sinking of the *Lusitania.*"

PROFESSOR MURRAY. " I've got this violently. I've got an awful impression of naval disaster. I should think it was the torpedoing of the *Lusitania.*"

99. *Subject.* MISS WINIFRED ROBERTS (agent): " I'm thinking of *Caliban on Setebos*, [Caliban] sitting in a cave thinking about things."

PROFESSOR MURRAY. " I think it's a poem. Is it a scene in

a poem or a whole poem?" ("A scene.") "It's like Browning—I think it's Caliban tearing the crabs." (In *Caliban on Setebos.*) [The agent's description applies to the whole poem, of which the crabs incident is a part.]

These are typical of the very many such successful experiments.

In addition to the experimental tests there have been a vast number of spontaneous cases of telepathy most carefully investigated and reported in the Society's *Proceedings*; many of the earlier ones were collected and published in the classic two-volume *Phantasms of the Living*, 1886, edited by Myers, Gurney and Podmore.

I have myself been convinced of the reality of telepathy from two experiences I had many years ago, but they are anecdotal and of no scientific value; yet to me they are as important and as real as any observation I have ever made in Natural History. I will not describe them in the text of the lecture, but for those who may be interested I give an account of them in a footnote.[1]

[1] The following account is taken from the *Proceedings of the Society for Psychical Research*, vol. 50, pp. 105–7, 1953.

"They [my experiences] took place during the First World War. For a time I was in a Cyclist Battalion stationed on the Lincolnshire coast where there lived a Mrs. Wedgwood who was very kind in entertaining some of the officers of the regiment. Sir Oliver Lodge's book *Raymond* had just been published, and after we had been discussing it she confessed that she herself had been an amateur medium. She was, I understood, the widow of a Mr. Arthur Wedgwood who, with his brother Mr. Hensleigh Wedgwood, was much interested in spiritualism towards the end of last century. She then very occasionally, by holding objects, claimed to be able to ' see ' and describe people she had never seen before. Once, by holding a letter she gave a reasonable but not very exact description of my mother who was then alive. I mention this without attaching much value to it only as an introduction to the two cases I consider so important, but in passing I may just say that her description of the path along which my mother and I had so often walked together was much more striking than that of my mother herself.

"Mrs. Wedgwood from earlier talks knew that my brother was an engineering student and that he was a prisoner-of-war in Germany. One Sunday afternoon I went up to her house, to tea. With one or two others I had been trying some table-tilting seances with her—without getting anything but quite meaningless messages spelt out—and that afternoon after tea we sat down at the table. A moment or two after I had put my hands on the table next to hers—I cannot remember now whether they touched hers or not—she suddenly said, ' Oh, I can see your brother in Germany quite clearly.' (I am not reporting her exact words, but as nearly as possible the gist of them.) ' I can see him in a little room in his prison camp with a camp bed, he is sitting at a table drawing what I think must be some engineering plan; on a large sheet of white paper I see him painting what seem to be squares and oblongs of red

In spite of what some of the Russians believe, at present it does not look from the results as if telepathy can be a physical radiation effect. In the experiments conducted at different distances the effects do not

---

and blue.' Actually she had described exactly what I had been doing myself all that afternoon and no one else knew I had been doing it. Our colonel had a great interest in military history and was giving the officers a series of lectures on Monday evenings on various campaigns. He knew I was quick at drawing and he had asked me to make a map for him to illustrate his next talk on the Franco-Prussian War. He didn't know how I was going to do it; it was only that afternoon that I had the idea of cutting out squares and oblongs of card painted red and blue to represent the various units of infantry, cavalry and artillery of the two sides so that he could move them about on pins to their different positions as the lecture proceeded. It was an obvious thing to do, but he had only asked me to prepare a large map of the area. I spent the greater part of the afternoon—in my rather bare room in my billet with a camp-bed in it—looking at the large white map and moving the red and blue cards about following a description of the campaign and making pencil marks where they should be at different stages. After I had finished I put the cards away, rolled up the map, and went straight off on my bicycle to tea with Mrs. Wedgwood: I am absolutely certain that no one could have told her before I went what I had been doing. I would find it difficult to believe that the correspondence of her description of what she thought my brother was doing and what I myself had actually been doing all afternoon was mere coincidence; with another case of almost the same kind I am convinced that coincidence cannot explain it.

"The second case was a year later. I was now attached to the Royal Engineers as a camouflage officer and was attending a special course at the school set up in Kensington Gardens under Solomon J. Solomon, R.A. Mrs. Wedgwood came to stay in London whilst I was there and I went out to dinner with her. The case is remarkably like the other one. That afternoon at the school we were doing experiments in dazzle effects. I had taken a large sheet of white cardboard and then painted it all over with a most vivid pink distemper. I was then going to cut it up into all sorts of shapes to use in our experiments, but I found it took much longer to dry than I had expected so that I had it in front of me and kept looking at it to see if it was ready for some considerable time before I actually cut it up. Again I am quite certain that no one could have told Mrs. Wedgwood what I had been doing, for no one at the camouflage school knew her or knew that I was going out to dinner with her. I had not sat down at the dinner table with her for more than a moment or two when she suddenly said, ' Oh, what have you been doing? I see a large pink square on the table in front of you.'

"There is no need to emphasise further how alike the two cases are; I will only add that I know I have a good visual memory and that colour and shape make a strong impression on me. It was not as if Mrs. Wedgwood frequently made statements as to what she thought I, or people connected with me, had been doing and that these particular cases just described were the only two correct ones. The only other occasion I believe when she made such a statement to me was the one concerning my mother that I have already referred to."

appear to fall off according to the square of the distance law. Again any such message would have to be sent in code and decoded at the other end; we know of no part of the brain that might be so engaged or be a transmitter or receiver. It looks as if there is something here outside the physical system as we at present understand it. I shall say more about this aspect of nature in the next lecture, the last in the present series.

I must now come to the point of saying just why I believe the recognition of the reality of telepathy may be so important for biology. If it is proved to exist in man, and I believe the evidence is overwhelming, and if we believe that man is one with the stream of life then it seems that it is most unlikely that so remarkable a phenomenon should be confined to just a few individuals of just one species of animal. If true, this faculty whereby one individual influences another by means other than through the ordinary senses is surely one of the most revolutionary discoveries of natural history; and again, if true, would it not seem more likely that it is of widespread occurrence but perhaps in the realm of the subconscious, and that only occasionally are a few unusual individuals aware of it? Professor Broad in his 1949 article in *Philosophy*, to which I have already referred, expresses this view in the following way:

If paranormal cognition and paranormal causation are facts, then it is quite likely that they are not confined to those very rare occasions on which they either manifest themselves sporadically in a spectacular way, or to those very special conditions in which their presence can be experimentally established. They may well be continually operating in the background of our normal lives. Our understanding of, and our misunderstandings with, our fellow men; our general emotional mood on certain occasions; the ideas which suddenly arise in our minds without any obvious introspectable cause; our unaccountable immediate emotional reactions towards certain persons; our sudden decisions where the introspectable motives seem equally balanced; and so on; all these may be in part determined by paranormal cognition and paranormal causal influences.

In this connection it seems to me that the following physical analogy is illuminating. Human beings have no special sensations in the presence of magnetic fields. Had it not been for the two very contingent facts that there are loadstones, and that one element (iron) which is strongly susceptible to magnetic influence is fairly common on earth, the existence of magnetism might have remained unsuspected to this day. Even so, it was regarded as a kind of mysterious anomaly until its connection with electricity was discovered and we gained the power to produce strong magnetic fields at will. Yet, all this while, magnetic fields had existed, and had been producing effects, whenever and wherever electric currents were passing. Is it not possible that natural mediums might be comparable to loadstones; that paranormal influences are as pervasive as magnetism; and that we fail to recognise this only because our knowledge and control of them are at about the same level as were men's knowledge and control of magnetism when Gilbert wrote his treatise on the magnet?

Now I should go further than Professor Broad. It would seem to me surprising indeed if such an attribute were confined to just one species of animal. In the next lecture I shall stress how very close man is to the rest of animal creation; his separation from it has only come about in *very recent* geological time with the evolution of speech and the associated greatly enlarged cerebral cortex. For me, at any rate, one interest in telepathy lies in the possibility that it may be the clue to a much more fundamental biological principle.

As I have already explained I am not a vitalist in the old-fashioned sense of believing that there is some vital force or entelechy interfering directly with the physico-chemical reactions of the body in development. I am sure that the laws of physics and chemistry are never broken; yet as I shall explain in the next lecture I am sure we have no right to assume that physics and chemistry as we at present understand them can explain the whole of life—particularly the body-mind relationship. I am not committed as to whether the universe is a dualistic one or not, but I think it more likely that it is. Space and time form a dualism in a sense—perhaps only a dualism of our perception; the physical and psychical may well have a similar relationship. My " vitalism " is a belief that there is a psychic side of the animal which, apart from inherited instinctive behaviour, may be independent of the DNA code that governs the form of the physical frame, but that it may interact with the physical system in the evolutionary process through organic selection.

These unusual people with telepathic gifts may be presenting us with chinks in the material carapace of the living world through which we can probe bit by bit to find out a little more of what at present appears a mystery lying behind it. The existence of such an unconscious telepathic communication between members of the same species of animals might at least help in developing and stabilising common behavioural patterns. The late Mr. Whately Carrington who made some very interesting experiments in the transmission of drawings some 20 years ago, put forward such an idea in his book *Telepathy* published in 1945. After discussing the remarkable web-spinning activities of spiders he writes: " I suggest that the instinctive behaviour of this high order or elaborate type may be due to the individual creature concerned (e.g. spider) being linked up into a larger system (or common subconscious if you prefer it) in which all the web-spinning experience of the species is stored up."

Actually there can be little doubt that truly instinctive behaviour is governed by the DNA gene complex—probably built in by organic selection from gradually formed habits of increasing elaboration. These habits, however, before being genetically fixed, might be spread and stabilised in the population by some such telepathy-like means, for we have seen that they must become widespread before they can be so incorporated. Such a hypothesis might help to explain the development of elaborate instincts in invertebrate animals among which it would be difficult to conceive of new habits spreading by copying and tradition.

There is, however, another possibility I would like to suggest: a similar but more radical application of the same idea. It is, I agree, highly speculative, but I believe there is no harm in such speculation so long as we realise just how speculative it is. Hypothesis is the fuel of scientific progress—it is only by the testing and rejection of ideas that we come nearer to the truth. In the last lecture I drew attention to some problems in biology that, at any rate, to me, presented difficulties in relation to current evolutionary theory. In this lecture I have been discussing some curious, but I believe undoubted, facts regarding at any rate human creatures, facts which have not yet received serious notice by biologists. Their relation to biology may be as puzzling as is consciousness and the body-mind relationship; but that is no reason for refusing to consider them. If we can even vaguely imagine the possibility of some relationship, however fantastic or erroneous it may later turn out to be, it may give an impetus to a more energetic investigation of some of these problems. There must, of course, be *some* relationship between these psychical events, if true, and the biological organism; just as there must be *some* relationship between consciousness and the physical body.

In cosmic science it seems respectable to speculate as to whether the universe is expanding or whether matter and energy are continually being created and so on, but in biology such speculation is frowned upon and the very idea of introducing consciousness, let alone psychism, is taboo! Accepted physical theory has undergone a change that would have seemed impossible to contemplate in Victorian times. I sometimes feel that in biology we are dominated by those who cling to classical materialism for fear of relapsing into a superstition which they regard as the greater of two evils; from this fear they refuse to contemplate either the problem of consciousness or the evidence for psychic phenomena. It is important that we should all realise the nature of the change that has taken place in physics. Sir George Thomson in his Presidential Address to the British Association at the Cardiff meeting of 1960, discusses the quantum theory:[1]

In the course of my life, [he said], the quantum theory has produced a revolution in physics comparable with that produced in biology by Darwin. We have been forced, some of us very unwillingly, to believe that at bottom the laws of physics are not statements of what *must* happen but of the relative chances of a variety of alternatives. . . . Certainty comes with a massive body; or if bodies are small, one must have very many of them so that the laws of statistics can manufacture near certainty out of highly uncertain events, as they do in life insurance.

This makes a difference to the way one regards the world, and I think its consequences are still not realised by the average educated man, though it has been accepted by the majority of physicists for thirty years. It shows for one thing how dangerous it is to extrapolate, to attribute—in this case—to the very small the kind of behaviour that is common sense when one talks of objects of large or ordinary size. That for example, if a particle crosses a flat screen with two holes in it it must have gone through one to the exclusion of the other. This is not true of an electron.

This quotation has no direct connection, as far as I can see, with my speculation; I include it to show that we should keep an open mind in biology towards phenomena that may seem to be contrary to

[1] Published in *Nature*, vol. 187, pp. 837–41, 1960.

common sense, rather than refuse to look at them or to consider how they might possibly be related to the rest of our knowledge.

To return to my speculative idea, it is this. If it is established that impressions of design, form and experience, such as those that we have discussed, can occasionally be transmitted by telepathy from one human individual to another, might it not be possible for there to be in the animal kingdom as a whole not only a telepathic spread of habit changes, but a general *subconscious* sharing of a form and behaviour pattern—a sort of psychic " blueprint "—shared between members of a species?

Let us look back for a moment at figs. 13 and 24 (pp. 38 and 90) to remind ourselves of the physical or genetical structure of the stream of life as it flows along in time. We must now realise that it is most likely that the points of junction in the genetical network, *i.e.* the individuals, are, at any rate in the mammals at least, centres of psychic consciousness, with in addition, like ourselves, a subconscious. If this is so and if something akin to telepathy, but perhaps unconscious, were a general phenomenon, then it is possible to imagine some such pattern of shared unconscious experience: a kind of composite species pattern of life. It is important to remember that in the concept of the individual mind we are faced with a mystery no less remarkable. The mind cannot be anchored to this or that group of cells that make up the brain. The community of cells making up the body has a mind beyond the individual cells—the " impression " coming from one part of the brain receiving sensory impulses from one eye and that from another part of the brain from the other eye are merged together in the mind, not in some particular cells as far as we know. The mystery of the mind and body seems to be as inconceivable as the speculation I am suggesting. I do not expect that my speculation is right, but by being shown to be wrong or impossible it may give rise to better thoughts which may help towards a solution of some of our conundrums.

If there were such a psychic plan it would be something like the subconscious racial memory of Samuel Butler, but it would be a racial experience of habit, form and development, open subconsciously to all members of the species, as in Whately Carrington's group mind, or as in Jung's shared unconscious, if I understand him aright. I always feel that Butler's idea, although it broke down, was a brilliant one: a remarkable evolutionary conception developed by an amateur genius. There were other mnemonic theories of course, such as those of Hering and Semon, but they lacked the vision of Butler's views.[1]

The idea I am suggesting would be in a way akin to Butler's in that it would be somewhat like a racial memory, but not one transmitted from parent to offspring, in the egg. Butler thought that the egg carried on a subconscious memory from the parent of how to develop, of how to manipulate its protoplasm, of how to carry out its instinctive habits. His idea broke down at several points: it could not explain the habits of neuter insects in social colonies, for they could not hand on their instincts by this means; again it could not explain the elaborate instinctive behaviour which some female insects display *after* they have laid their eggs. In the scheme I am suggesting a sort of psychic pool of experience would be shared subconsciously by all members of a species by some method akin to what we are witnessing in telepathy. Individual lives, animal " minds ", would come and go—but the psychic stream of a shared behaviour pattern in the living population would flow on in time parallel to the flow of the physical DNA material.

It would differ from Butler's idea in another important respect: instead of the racial memory acting through Lamarckian use and disuse of parts of the body, as he thought—he was an ardent Lamarckian—it would act by *organic selection*. There would be two parallel streams of information—the DNA code supplying the varying physical form of the organic stream to be acted on by selection—and the psychic stream of shared experience—the subconscious species " blueprint "—which *together with the environment*, would select those members in the population better able to carry on the race. External conditions being equal, those animals with gene complexes which allow a better incarnation of the species plan would tend to survive rather than others whose gene complexes produced less satisfactory versions. There would be the two selective forces at work that we have already discussed. One, the external environmental selection would be tending to eliminate the animals whose gene complexes produce less efficient systems in *direct* relation to the outside world. The other, the internal selection, would be leading indirectly to the elimination of those varieties which failed because their gene complexes strayed too far from the species " design ", *i.e.* they would be those not sufficiently well physically equipped to give a full expression to the shared species " plan of life ".

On the one hand the environment would tend to select individuals

[1] *Life and Habit* (1878), *Unconscious Memory* (1880) and *Luck or Cunning* (1889).

which were better equipped in relation to its various features: with camouflage patterns against predators, strength of limb and claws for capture of prey, etc. On the other hand, the shared, unconscious, species, behavioural " plan of life " would set up an internal selecting standard; those which did not come up to it in one way or another would be less efficient organisms and so tend to be eliminated in the struggle for existence. Such an internal conserving selective element might explain the secret of homology in face of an ever changing gene complex. And then again it might also be supposed that the " racial plan ", linking all the members of the race, might gradually change as the character of the population became modified *both* by the changing environment's external selection and by the development of new behavioural patterns due to the exploring, exploitive, nature of animal life.

If such a highly speculative concept of a " racial plan " were true, then the old ideas of a " morph ", " form " or " archetype " of the pre-evolutionary transcendentalists, which we discussed in lecture II, might not seem quite so quaint as we have sometimes thought them; they might perhaps be the equivalent of what Jung has called the psychological archetype of his shared subconscious in the human species. Again might not this shared subconscious mind, in man, provide some reality for Plato's world of ideas: shared ideas built up with the evolution of conceptional thought?

With this explanation I might now complete the quotation I gave at the beginning of the lecture, that on p. 235 taken from my 1949 British Association address:

> If there was such a non-conscious group behaviour plan, distributed between, and linking, the individuals of the race, we might find ourselves coming back to something like those ideas of subconscious racial memory of Samuel Butler, but on a group rather than an individual basis. . . . If there was such a group habit and behaviour pattern it might operate through organic selection to modify the course of evolution: working through selection acting on the gene complex. If this flight of fancy ever proved to be a fact, it would be a wedding of the ideas of Darwin and Mendel on the one hand and of Lamarck and Samuel Butler on the other!

Such a scheme might also help towards an understanding of the mechanism behind the remarkable transformations pointed out by

D'Arcy Thompson. It seems to me that they have all the appearance of a definite mental conception like that of an artist or designer—a pattern outside the physical world—which in some way has served as a templet or gauge for selective action. My speculative hypothesis, as before, would suggest that it is this plan in the group " mind " which indirectly *selects* those gene complexes presenting (in development) its best expression. It is the species plan mirrored in each individual: a plan which in evolution may be stretched and warped in various ways but always as a *whole plan* is stretched and warped and usually according to a relatively simple formula.

Whilst analogies are dangerous, that of the artist may be helpful if we realise it is *only an analogy* and not part of the hypothesis: useful merely to illustrate the *sort* of way I imagine such a scheme *might* work. I do not doubt that the material body can be completely described in terms of physics and chemistry, any more than I doubt that the pigments and canvas of an old master can be similarly analysed; I do, however, most emphatically doubt that physics and chemistry, as we now understand them, can by themselves tell us why the artist consciously selects the particular paints he uses for a particular effect. Perhaps it might not be carrying the analogy too far to suggest that our hypothetical " group-mind " might be compared to an artist, or better, perhaps, an art critic, who is judging thousands of *mechanically produced* colour reproductions of *one* picture: each one being produced by slightly different sets of coloured inks or dyes—the pigments represent, of course, the DNA genes. Sometimes, by chance, indigo may be replaced by prussian blue, or ultramarine by cobalt. The chaffinch (or whatever it is) species " mind " or " art-critic " is continually confronted with slightly different versions of the chaffinch picture as the available colours vary slightly. Each picture is automatically unfolding according to its DNA code; and at every stage it has to conform within certain limits to the unconscious species plan as well as to survive the environmental selective forces. The finished picture is due to the combined effect of the many pigments; it emerges because in one place one pigment has more effect than in another: as with the genes. By using the word picture I am, of course, introducing an extreme simplification; my " pictures " are really three-dimensional machines of such extreme complexity and detail as the electron microscope is now revealing to us. The general style of the picture (or machine) has as much been determined by selection (organic selection) by the " art-critic " mind (built up from the past) as by selection by the environment. But we need continue no further; these fancies, without more facts from observation and experiment, lead to folly. Nevertheless, such a rash metaphorical speculation is, I believe, no more fanciful than some of the statements that are made with all the confidence of proven fact by some of our mechanistic biologists—such a statement, for example, as that which I quoted more fully on p. 114: " We now find ourselves . . . reducing the *decisive controls* of life to a matter of the precise order in which the units are arranged in a giant molecule." (The italics are mine.)

I venture to think it possible that the biochemists are only analysing the " pigments " of nature's pictures—wonderful as they are—and that it is the naturalists and the students of animal behaviour who will reveal to us the " artists " themselves and the true nature of their works.

LECTURE X

THE PLACE OF NATURAL THEOLOGY

IN THE EVOLUTIONARY SCHEME

We are now coming to the end of the present series of lectures and so far I have said very little *directly* concerning the main subject to which, under the Gifford foundation, they should be devoted: that of Natural Theology. As I stated in the beginning, it is my firm conviction that any Theology calling itself Natural must be linked to the evolutionary system since Man is clearly a part of the great stream of life. It has been my object in the earlier lectures to prepare the way for showing, as I hope now to do, the manner in which I believe Theology and evolution to be related. I have attempted to demonstrate how, geared into the physical framework of the Darwinian-Mendelian-DNA scheme, the ever inquisitive, exploratory nature of animal behaviour, leading to new habits and ways of life, has had an increasingly important rôle in this living stream. It is with this, the psychic side, if you like, of animal nature, that I believe Man's religious feelings are related.

In this last lecture I will try to show how close I believe the link is between such a theology as Lord Gifford envisaged and the natural world. You will remember how he wished the subject to be treated—I quoted from his will in my first lecture. " I wish it to be treated," he said, " as a strictly natural science . . . without reference to, or reliance upon, any supposed exceptional or so-called miraculous revelation. I wish it considered just as astronomy or chemistry is."

Sir Julian Huxley began one of his early essays published in 1923, in *Essays of a Biologist*, with an arresting quotation from Lord Morley: " The next great task of Science is to create a religion for humanity." While I do not for a moment think that science alone can create a religion, I do believe, with the late Lord Gifford, that the scientific treatment of religion is one of the most important, if not *the* most important, of subjects for discussion at the present day.

To my mind nothing could be more urgent than a clearer understanding of the relations between science and religion. Whilst science cannot bring religion into being I do believe that the spirit of scientific enquiry can help in the re-establishment of a declining faith. In this lecture I shall only be able to pursue this line of thought for just a very little way; it is intended as a bridge to the next series of lectures in which I hope to make this subject the main theme.

I am convinced that the world today must have a Natural Theology. Humanism is not enough. Theology, of course, is not religion. Religion is a matter of the spirit. Theology is the study of religion and its philosophy; and it was once called the Queen of the Sciences. Some dictionaries still define it as the *science of religion*; I wonder how many people today really regard that as a true definition—using the term science in its modern sense and not simply in the old sense of knowledge? Very few I think. We are moving—the whole of civilisation is moving—with increasing speed into the scientific age. I believe that only a theology based upon a scientific approach as advocated by Lord Gifford can survive in the intellectual atmosphere of the future.

For those who have a sure faith in the existence of a Divine Power, which they call God, either through their own spiritual experience, or through the spoken or written words of those who claim to have had such experience—for all those who are so convinced—science, of course, can add nothing to their faith. I have no wish to disturb the religious convictions of others. It is clear, however, as I said at the beginning, that more and more people find it increasingly difficult to reconcile the findings of science with a faith in spiritual reality.

Science, in the last 350 years, has completely changed the picture of our relationship with the physical universe from that which our earlier forefathers had. Up to the beginning of the seventeenth century religion and philosophy were firmly united to give western man a comfortable faith in the spiritual nature of his world. It came as a shock to him to find that the earth was not, as he had been led to believe, at the centre of things with all the other heavenly bodies circling round it at only moderate distances. Instead he now knows it is a tiny speck in a universe so vast that his mind boggles at the thought of it. It came, I think, as a much greater shock to Man to find that he himself was not a separate creation, but an organism evolved from lower forms of life and that he had only become Man after some two thousand million years of animal and pre-animal existence. He could

hardly help wondering what God was doing in all those years; and he
may also have pondered the question: if the real purpose *was* the
creation of Man, why were there so many extinct failures on the
way?

The *fact* of evolution could not be denied; those who felt religion
in their hearts still hoped that somehow it might be shown to be the
method of God's creative act. It was not so much the fact of evolution
that was so destructive of faith, but the growing fear, fanned by the
pronouncements of many leading scientists, that it could only be a
materialistic process. That is why I have devoted so much time in these
lectures to showing that the hitherto generally accepted mechanism
of a natural selection by only the *physical* side of the environment is by
no means the whole of the evolution story.

What do I mean by saying that I believe a scientific approach to
religion can help to restore faith? Some people will feel that to suggest
that science can have anything to do with faith and religion is to
introduce a contradiction in terms. Indeed some eminent Gifford
Lecturers have come near to such a view. Sir Charles Sherrington in
his famous lectures *Man on his Nature* delivered at Edinburgh in
1937–8 said (on p. 360 of his published account):

> Now, Lord Gifford in founding these lectures desired their subject
> to be " treated as a strictly natural science ". Though the lecturer
> was not to be under restraint in dealing with his theme, " Natural
> Theology ", he said, " I wish considered just as Astronomy or
> Chemistry ".
>
> His expressed wish was that in regard to Natural Theology the
> facts which seem relevant be followed as in Astronomy or
> Chemistry. Facts as hard facts we have indeed to try to follow
> whithersoever they lead. But the desire that facts or Astronomy
> or Chemistry and the like be taken in examination of, to quote
> his own words, " the relation which man and the universe bear to
> Him " " the First and Only Cause ", is one less simple to fulfil.
> The difficulty arises that such facts are confined to the mechanical
> behaviour of electrons and similar elements and of aggregates of
> them. That must be so since the scope of those sciences is to
> describe those things in those terms. But direct bearing on the
> relation of man and the Universe to the First Cause may find little
> relevance there. More is demanded. There must be considered
> not only " masses " and electric charges but such notions as

ethical values, ideals and motives. In short the theme embraces as well as the perceived the percipient. That seems of its essence.

Today more than when Lord Gifford wrote, Natural Science is suspicious of the intrusion of the narrowly anthropomorphic into its view of Nature and tries as far as may be to exclude it. . . .

Now with all due respect, and my respect for the late Sir Charles Sherrington is unbounded, I venture to think that he is unintentionally misrepresenting Lord Gifford. In the Aberdeen University copy of the will that I have examined[1] Lord Gifford does *not* refer to *the facts* of astronomy or chemistry but says he wishes Natural Theology to be " considered just as astronomy or chemistry is." By this he surely means that he wishes it treated as a science as much as astronomy and chemistry are so treated, and I suspect he wisely chose these two branches for his illustration just because one is largely an *observational* science in contrast to the other which is largely *experimental*.

The idea that science and theology can never be discussed in the same terms is only true if we decide that science can deal with nothing but physical and chemical events. But need science be so limited? Who made such a rule and on what authority? There are certainly those who believe that all life will ultimately be explained in terms of physics and chemistry: that physiology, biochemistry and biophysics are the scientific core of biology, the study of living things. Those branches do indeed at present appear to make up the science of the organism as analysed into its various component parts. We should certainly push these physical methods as far as we can; they will go on revealing more and more that is of benefit to man in understanding the working of his bodily mechanism. As I have said before, the physical laws must hold good within the body as outside it; but it is also a truism to say that when we study living creatures in this analytic physico-chemical way, we can only expect to get physical and chemical answers.

I would deny, however, that we can yet be certain that all that comes under the treatment of science in the wider sense will ultimately be reduced to physics and chemistry—or at any rate to what we at present understand by them. Although I do not altogether follow him in his organistic approach, I have always liked the remark attributed to the late Professor J. S. Haldane: " That a meeting-place between biology and physical science may at some time be found there is no

[1] I have quoted the relevant passage in full in the first lecture (p. 12).

reason for doubting. But we may confidently predict that if that meeting-place be found, and one of the two sciences is swallowed up, that one will not be biology."[1] We can apply the scientific method to the study of certain aspects of living things quite independently of physics and chemistry—and I regard this application as fully worthy of the name of science.

Just as important as the physical analysis of the animal's internal mechanism, is the science of the animal as a living whole, looked at from the outside and in relation to its natural surroundings: the branches of science which we call ecology and ethology (the study of animal behaviour). Many seem to think that the term ecology is just a new-fangled name for natural history; but there is, or should be, a difference. Natural history is the description of nature; ecology is, or should be, strictly a science. (It is unfortunately true that much of what is often called " ecology " is really natural history so labelled because the particular author thinks his pursuit may be thought old-fashioned if it is not given a more modern name.) Ecology is that branch of science dealing with the relationship of animals and plants to their environment both physical and animate. In the first lecture I drew a distinction between science and natural history; let me now illustrate the difference.

When we record that a particular kind of fish is confined to warm oceanic water and feeds upon various kinds of shrimps that is simply natural history. When we can determine the actual ranges of temperature and degrees of saltness of the water which limit its distribution, and when, by the post-mortem examination of the stomach contents of a vast number of freshly caught specimens, we can work out the average percentage proportions of the different species making up its food at different times of the year and for fish of different ages, we are beginning to know a little of its ecology. We are beginning to express the relationships of animals one to another, and to their environment, in numerical terms. From such a quantitative analysis we hope in time, step by step, to discover more of the laws operating in the world of living things. Experiment will come to play as big a part in the study of animals in nature as it has done in the past in the laboratory; as indeed the students of animal behaviour are now so brilliantly showing.

[1] I quote the version given by Dr. Joseph Needham in his *The Sceptical Biologist* (p. 74).

Just as physics and chemistry are based upon statistical laws concerning the behaviour of electrons, atoms and molecules, so this new branch of science, ecology, is a science *in its own right* based upon the statistical treatment of the interactions of animals as *living wholes*. There is no need for it to be wedded to the unproven hypothesis of materialism. Ecology could exist as a true science if the laws of physics and chemistry had never been discovered; although it would indeed be sadly limited. Any one branch of science is handicapped without support from others. Ecology must keep in the closest touch with physiology and the physical sciences; it will, however, be much richer in the future when it gets more help from the rapidly developing study of animal behaviour. Ecology and ethology are both very young sciences feeling their difficult way forward; their performance at present must not be judged in comparison with the achievements of their elder sisters, who not only have been much longer at work, but who deal, I believe, on the whole with simpler phenomena.

There are some people who, brandishing " Occam's razor " and fascinated by it, think it right for science to ignore half the properties of living things because they seem to complicate the issue; Occam's excellent principle must be used with care and not, as so often, waved in front of us to introduce an entirely false simplification of the problem. In the first paragraph of his *Principles of Biology* (1930) Professor Hogben writes: " Because economy of thought (William of Occam's principle: *Entia non multiplicanda præter necessitatem*) is rigorously maintained in any enquiry which is truly scientific, the ultimate goal of biological enquiry is to find generalisations common to the realms of living matter and non-living matter."

In the name of William of Occam, such people would dogmatically limit biology to the physics and chemistry of life-processes; if they wish to do that, let them not call it an entire science of life.

There are certainly some people who, like Dr. Joseph Needham in the earlier period of these fascinating volumes *The Sceptical Biologist* (1929) and *The Great Amphibium* (1931), divide their minds between a physico-chemical interpretation of life, which they regard as the only possible scientific attitude, and a completely separate and more private deeply religious outlook. In the former work (his p. 30) Needham neatly summarises his view at that time:

J. H. Woodger perfectly expressed the essence of Neo-mechanism when he remarked: " Mechanism need not be materialistic. It is possible to maintain it on methodological grounds, while leaving the philosophical question untouched." I am now engaged in trying to show the truth of this statement. In science we have to act as if mechanism were true, though we may really believe it is not.

In his later period, under the dialectical influence of Marx and Engels, as we see in his essay of 1941, *Metamorphosis of Scepticism*[1], Needham revised his views:

The dividing process was succeeded by a uniting one, and an integrated world-view emerged from the differentiated dissected analysed system which I had made. It was bound to follow the lead of the philosophy which most consistently allows for the social background of our thought and being, and explains what is happening, and has for centuries been happening, to human society as the continuation of all biological evolution.

He has lost much of his orthodox Christian ardour, but he retains, and this is most interesting, his belief in the reality of religious experience:

When Society itself has been sanctified by the full incorporation in it of the principles of justice, love and comradeship, religion is destined to pass without loss into social emotion as such. When oppression has been removed, religion as the cry of the oppressed creature will cease to exist, but the sense of the holy, one of man's most fundamental forms of experience, will never disappear.

But let us return to theology and our scientific approach. Sociology is becoming a science; it is in fact human ecology. We now have an interesting statistical study under the title *Religious Behaviour* (1958) by Mr. Michael Argyle, Lecturer in Social Psychology at Oxford. He presents data from Britain and America to show how religious behaviour and belief tend to vary with a number of different factors such as age, sex, environmental experiences, social class and so on; he then attempts to test various psycho-analytical theories against his findings. This is a pioneering beginning of the scientific, ecological approach to religion; it is at present mainly concerned with man's religious activities in relation to different circumstances. I believe, however, that the scientific method will in time have a much more fundamental rôle to play in our understanding of religion by showing more of its true nature. Psychology, of course, will play an important part.

[1] Republished in his book *Time: the Refreshing River*, 1943.

In order to make the matter quite clear let me repeat what I said a little earlier: I do *not* think that science alone can create a religion. No science, not even ecology and ethology, can deal with the emotional side of religion which is its very essence, any more than biology as a whole, which has much to tell us about sex, can touch the poetry of human love. But I do believe, and this is what I am trying to say in these lectures, that just as biology throws much light on the nature of sex, so a scientific theology—a natural theology—will similarly enlighten us about the place of the Divine Power in human affairs; it cannot, however, be expected to touch the rapture of religious experience.

Before we attempt to make a science of theology we must first have an extensive *natural history* of religion. Our newly developed science of ecology has only been possible because of the vast array of natural history observations that has preceded it. Ecology is the conversion of natural history into science. The pioneer naturalists must go in front to map out and describe the ground ahead before the ecologists, as scientists, have sufficient material to deal with. We must first build up a much more extensive natural history of religion which I believe will help to show us more of the nature of the Power we call God.

Lord Gifford was right to cite astronomy as an example of how Natural Theology should be treated. I will now quote a striking passage from Mr. John Langdon Davies's *Man and his Universe* (1930):

> The whole history of science has been a direct search for God, deliberate and conscious, until well into the eighteenth century ... Copernicus, Kepler, Galileo, Newton, Leibnitz and the rest did not merely believe in God in an orthodox sort of way: they believed that their work told humanity more about God than had been known before. Their incentive in working at all was a desire to know God; and they regarded their discoveries as not only proving his existence, but as revealing more and more of his nature ...

We must get back to that spirit and not be too fascinated by the false gods of the DNA, exciting as they are. One of the great pioneer works of the natural history of religion, collecting so many interesting examples, is of course William James's Gifford Lectures *The Varieties of Religious Experience*, first published in 1902. At the very end of the book, in a postscript, he briefly explains his philosophical position. After saying that he cannot accept either popular Christianity or scholastic theism, he goes on to express his belief that communion with the "Ideal" (or God) brings into the world "a new force" which alters events in it. It is particularly illuminating to see how he thinks this comes about; he writes as follows:

If asked just where the differences in fact which are due to God's existence come in, I should have to say that in general I have no hypothesis to offer beyond what the phenomenon of "prayerful communion", especially when certain kinds of incursion from the subconscious region take part in it, immediately suggests. The appearance is that in this phenomenon something ideal, which in one sense is part of ourselves and in another sense is not ourselves, actually exerts an influence, raises our centre of personal energy, and produces regenerative effects unattainable in other ways. If, then, there be a wider world of being than that of our everyday consciousness, if in it there be forces whose effects on us are intermittent, if one facilitating condition of the effects be the openness of the "subliminal" door, we have the elements of a theory to which the phenomena of religious life lend plausibility. I am so impressed by the importance of these phenomena that I adopt the hypothesis which they so naturally suggest. At these places at least, I say, it would seem as though transmundane energies, God, if you will, produced immediate effects within the natural world to which the rest of our experience belongs.

Much I am sure could be done to collect, from all sorts of sources, evidence to support the view that there is something here which is really fundamental and of overwhelming importance to mankind. Let me quote another example, one from the 1950 Riddell Memorial Lectures given by Sir Frederick Bartlett, then Professor of Psychology at Cambridge:

I confess [he writes] that I cannot see how anybody who looks fairly at a reasonable sample of actions claiming a religious sanction can honestly refuse to admit that many of them could not occur, or at least that it is highly improbable that they would occur in the forms in which they do, if they were simply the terminal points of a psychological sequence, every item in which belonged to our own human, day-to-day world. I am thinking not of the dramatic and extraordinary actions which people who write books about religion mostly seem to like to bring forward. They are rare anyway. I remember the ways of life of many unknown and humble people whom I have met and respected. It seems to me that these people have done, effectively and consistently, many things which all ordinary sources of evidence seem to set outside the range of unassisted humanity. When they say " It is God working through me," I cannot see that I have either the right or the knowledge to reject their testimony.

Many more similar observations could be given but these belong to my second series of lectures. By the collection of a vast number of such instances—by the bringing together of the case books of religious experience—the reality of some power, *apparently* coming from outside the consciousness of the individuals, could be shown, I believe, to be a much more widespread phenomenon than it is at present held to be. But such a work must not be confined to the study of just the more sophisticated people, we must also seek for the manifestations of such an influence among the more primitive people of the world. Here the social anthropologists are making great strides to help us. The majority of them have now moved far, I believe, from the view that dominated Frazer's *Golden Bough*—the view that primitive religion was founded on sheer superstition and magic—a will-o'-the-wisp. The late Dr. R. M. Marett, Rector of Exeter College, Oxford, who was formerly Reader in Social Anthropology, was one of the leaders who brought in the new influence.

I will quote from his book, *Head, Heart and Hands in Human Evolution* (1935):

When it is a question of a more or less definitely religious rite of the primitive pattern, we should be wrong in assuming any consistent doctrine to underlie the performance ... It is a common fallacy to suppose that the savage has forgotten what it would be truer to say that he never tried to understand. A play of images sufficiently forcible to arouse by diffused suggestion a conviction that the tribal luck is taking a turn in the required direction is the sum of his theology; and yet the fact remains that a symbolism so gross and mixed can help the primitive man to feel more confident of himself—to enjoy the inward assurance that he is in touch with sources and powers of grace that can make him rise superior to the circumstances and changes of this mortal life.

Or again, Marett writing in his book *Psychology and Folk-lore*, 1920, says (p. 166):

But enough has been said to show that, corresponding to the

anthropologist's wide use of the term " religion ", there is a real sameness, felt all along, if expressed with no great clearness at first, in the characteristic manifestations of the religious conscious- ness at all times and in all places. It is the common experience of man that he can draw on a power that makes for, and in its most typical form wills, righteousness, the sole condition being that a certain fear, a certain shyness and humility, accompany the effort so to do. That such a universal belief exists amongst all mankind, and that it is no less universally helpful in the highest degree, is the abiding impression left on my mind by the study of religion in its historico-scientific aspect.

Perhaps the most illuminating study in primitive religion yet written is that by E. Evans-Pritchard, the present Professor of Social Anthropology at Oxford, on the religion of the Nuer tribe—a cattle- herding people living in the southern Sudan. I quote from his *Nuer Religion* (p. 311), 1956:

The theories of writers about primitive religion have not been sustained by research. During the last century what was presented as theory was generally the supposition that some particular form of religion was the most primitive and that from it developed other forms, the development being sometimes presented as a succession of inevitable and well-defined stages. The form of religion presented by a writer as the most primitive was that which he considered to be the most simple, crude, and irrational; to exhibit most con- spicuously " crass materialism ", " primeval stupidity ", " naïve eudæmonism ", " crude anthropomorphism ", or " dæmonic dread ". Many such origins have been propounded: magic, fetish- ism, manism, animism, pre-animism, mana, totemism, mono- theism, etc. All this was for the most part pure conjecture. The determination of the *primordium*, in the absence of historical evidences, was, as Schleiter, among others, has shown, quite arbitrary.

In summing up after his long study of the characteristics of Nuer religion he writes as follows:

We can say that these characteristics, both negative and positive, of Nuer religion indicate a distinctive kind of piety which is dominated by a strong sense of dependence on God and confidence in him rather than in any human powers or endeavours. God is great and man foolish and feeble, a tiny ant. And this sense of dependence is remarkably individualistic. It is an intimate, personal, relationship between man and God. This is apparent in Nuer ideas of sin, in their expressions of guilt, in their confessions, and in the dominant piacular theme of their sacrifices. It is evident also in their habit of making short supplications at any time. This is a very noticeable trait of Nuer piety, and my conclusions are here borne out by Dr. Lienhardt's observations. He tells me that when he was in western Dinkaland he had in his household a Nuer youth whose habit of praying to God for aid on every occasion of difficulty greatly astonished the Dinka. In prayer and sacrifice alike, in what is said and in what is done, the emphasis is on complete surrender to God's will. Man plays a passive rôle. He cannot get to God but God can get to him. Given this sort of piety, we are not surprised to find that the prophet is more influential than the priest.

Professor Evans-Pritchard took part in a series of broadcast talks which were published under the title *The Institutions of Primitive Society* (1956). In the study of primitive religions he emphasised the need to build up general conclusions from particular ones. We must not ask " What is religion? " but what are the main features of the religion of one particular group of people, and then compare these with the religions of other peoples who are most nearly related to them in their cultures and social institutions. Only after a laborious comparative study, for example, of all the Melanesian peoples can we say something general about the Melanesian religions as a whole. " One can only take this long road; " he says, " there is no short cut." Here indeed is the new science developing on the lines of a kind of human ecology-cum-ethology. He tells us that Wilhelm Schmidt's work *The Origin of the Idea of God* which deals solely, and in summary form, with the religions of primitive peoples, already runs into some 10,000 pages and is not yet completed. " It will give you some idea of the volume of facts now at our disposal and stored for the use of posterity . . ." he says. " We may take legitimate pride in this accumulation of knowledge from all parts of the world." He ends his talk thus:

Without discussing any further examples I can say in conclusion that anthropological studies in the last thirty years or so have constructed at any rate the framework of a science of what is sometimes called Comparative Religion, and that this framework rests on solid foundations of field research, and not, as in the last century, on what was for the most part rationalist speculation. Social anthropology is therefore now in a better position to make a contribution to other subjects concerned with problems of religion —such as Theology, the Philosophy of Religion, Ethics, the History of Religions, and Critical and Exegetical Studies of Sacred Texts, and I believe that its significance for these related disciplines will become increasingly evident and important.

Religion, this feeling of contact with a Greater Power beyond the self, seems to be some fundamental feature in the natural history of man. As one travels through the English countryside,[1] taking the lesser by-ways rather than the great, one cannot, if one goes slowly and is prepared to stop, but be struck by the beauty of the old parish churches and be made to marvel that such glories could be built by such small groups of people, just as one marvels at the great mediæval cathedrals in towns which, at the time of their building, must have had only moderate populations. If one goes inside such an old country church one cannot help feeling that here is something fashioned with real love and reverence; elements of superstition there may well be, but in spite of this, surely here is something created not just by an ignorant craving for magic, but by something of profound depth. A naturalist coming from another planet, if his space-ship had the ability to drift across the countryside like a balloon, could not but be struck by the prominence of these buildings in each small community. Amidst the little groups of houses their spires and towers stand up like the sporangia of some organism and he might well be excused for first thinking them to have the importance of some such reproductive process. Indeed they had an equal importance in the past when devotion to God was as real to the population as was that of sexuality. They hardly have the same significance today and some, alas, stand forsaken like fossil skeletons of the past; this, however, may only be a temporary phase due to the accelerated growth of a physical science, whose findings are difficult to reconcile with many of the old doctrinal dogmas. I say temporary because I believe the dogmas on both sides may be revised as theology becomes more natural and science's mechanistic interpretation of life is shown not to be the whole truth.

[1] As I was lecturing in Aberdeen I had to explain that I really did mean English and not British. I always remember hearing Professor Sir D'Arcy Thompson holding forth on the way in which Calvinism had destroyed the ecclesiastical beauties that Scotland must have had.

74. A balloonist's view of rural England, before the advent of the motorways or the pylons of the electric grid.

Religion indeed seems to be some fundamental feature in Man's make-up: something which can be as powerful as any other urge. Few can doubt that the wars of religion or of rival ideologies are more bitter than those fought for just economic ends; and we must not forget that those on the two sides of a conflict may well, through the lack of a generally accepted scientific theology, be propelled by different ideas of God that they both, in their prejudice, passionately feel to be right. It would not surprise me if the roots of religion went much deeper down into biological history than is generally conceded, and that it *is* part of the very nature of the living stream. If so, you may ask, what about all those failures, those extinctions of the past? As a partial answer to this question I will quote from the late Sir Ronald Fisher's Eddington Memorial Lecture *Creative Aspects of Natural Law* (1950):

> The timid antelope has played its part in the creation of the lion, and species long extinct must have left indelible memorials in their effects on species still surviving. Who knows if the mammals would ever have evolved, but for the creative activity of the dinosaurs!

It is only just being realised, perhaps, how very much closer Man is to the animal world than was thought even by those who were already confirmed evolutionists. An important contribution to this change, I think, is the thesis presented by Professor Polanyi as part of his Gifford Lectures delivered here in Aberdeen in 1951–2 and published, much elaborated, under the title of *Personal Knowledge* in 1958; a little later he condensed the essence of his views into a much shorter book, embodying his Lindsay Lectures, *The Study of Man* (1959). He points out that there are two kinds of human knowledge:

(1) *Explicit knowledge:* that formulated in words, maps, mathematical formulæ, etc.; and

(2) *Tacit knowledge:* unformulated knowledge, *i.e.* the knowledge of what we are actually in the act of doing before it is expressed in words or symbols.

The more primitive forms of human knowing—those forms of intelligence which man shares with the animals—are situated behind the barrier of language. Animals have no speech (beyond some crude systems of communication by signs and sounds); the towering superiority of man over the animals is almost entirely due to his development of language. Speech enables man to formulate ideas, to reflect upon them, and communicate them to others. With its coming came the spread of invention and better tool making.

Babies up to 18 months or so are said to be not much superior to chimpanzees of the same age; only when they learn to speak do they leave the apes far behind. Even adult humans, however, show no distinctly greater intelligence than animals so long as their minds work unaided by language. In the absence of linguistic clues man sees things, hears things, feels things, moves about, explores his surroundings and gets to know his way about very much as animals do. Polanyi quotes Tolman as saying that a rat gets to know its way about a maze as if it had acquired a mental map of it; observations on human subjects suggest that man, however intelligent, is no better at maze running than a rat, unless assisted by notes, whether they are remembered verbally or sketched out in a drawing.

The sudden development of man's reasoning mind, sudden that is in relation to the millions of years of animal evolution, has resulted from the coming of speech and the making possible of explicit knowledge. At first such knowledge and experience were handed on orally, but then by written word. This is the great new development in evolution that

Huxley calles the psycho-social phase. This change, so very recent, is, *at least*, as great a change in the history of life as the separation of animals from plants. It has changed the very nature of evolution. As Medawar so vividly emphasised in the last of his Reith Lectures[1] it has changed the main system of heredity from a Darwinian to (what he calls)[2] a Lamarckian one; it is the *acquired* knowledge, handed on from generation to generation, always drawing new material from the environment as it goes, which now is more important than the DNA genetical system.

What lessons [Medawar asks] are to be learned from the similarities and correspondences between the two systems of biological heredity possessed by human beings? The answer is important, and I shall now try to justify it: the answer, I believe, is almost none.

It is true that a number of amusing (but in one respect highly dangerous) parallels can be drawn between our two forms of heredity and evolution. . . .

He now makes some entertaining comparisons. (Some great dynasties die out—airships, for example, in common with the dinosaurs they were so often likened to . . .) And then he continues:

All this sounds harmless enough: why should I have called it dangerous? The danger is that by calling attention to the similarities, which are not profound, we may forget the *differences* between our two styles of heredity and evolution; and the differences between them are indeed profound. In their hunger for synthesis and systematisation, the evolutionary philosophers of the nineteenth century and some of their modern counterparts have missed the point: they thought that great lessons were to be learnt from similarities between Darwinian and social evolution; but it is from the differences that all the great lessons are to be learnt. For one thing, our newer style of evolution is Lamarckian in nature. The environment cannot imprint genetical information upon us, but it can and does imprint non-genetical information which we can and do pass on. Acquired characters are indeed

---

[1] *The Future of Man*, 1960.

[2] For consistency's sake I must cavil slightly at his use of the term " Lamarckian " here, although I know he is using it in the now generally accepted sense; I believe this to be wrong, as Lamarck did not believe in the direct effect of the environment (see p. 160).

inherited. The blacksmith was under an illusion if he supposed
that his habits of life could impress themselves upon the genetic
make-up of his children; but there is no doubting his ability to
teach his children his trade, so that they can grow up to be as
stalwart and skilful as himself. It is because this newer evolution
is so obviously Lamarckian in character that we are under psychological pressure to believe that genetical evolution must be so
too. But although one or two biologists are still feebly trying to
graft a Lamarckian or instructive interpretation upon ordinary
genetical evolution, they are not nearly so foolish or dangerous
as those who have attempted to graft a Darwinian or purely
elective interpretation upon the newer, non-genetical, evolution
of mankind.

After this digression to emphasise the importance of this, geologically
speaking, very recent evolutionary change that has taken place, let us
return to our consideration of a natural theology. It seems to me likely
that the religious feeling found among so many different primitive
peoples must go back much earlier than the development of speech.
Perhaps it was only with the coming of language that men were able
to compare, one with another, the curious feelings they had—feelings
that seemed to come to them quite apart from those prompted by the
senses; so they may have begun to build up ideas of being in touch
with some power beyond themselves.

The feeling of the holy, of something beyond the individual, may
be as old as consciousness; and where consciousness came in in the
course of evolution we have no idea. To suppose that Man alone is
conscious may be a comforting thought, but I believe it to be very
unlikely; records such as Mrs. Joy Adamson's friendship with her
lioness in her book *Born Free* (1960) or of Miss Len Howard's studies
of *Birds as Individuals* (1952) show that we have almost as much ground
for regarding such animals as conscious as we have for judging our fellow
men to have this quality.

Sherrington, in a memorable passage in his Gifford Lectures *Man
on His Nature* (p. 318) says:

We have, it seems to me, to admit that energy and mind are
phenomena of two categories ... Mind as attaching to any
unicellular life would seem to me to be unrecognisable to observation; but I would not feel that permits me to affirm it is not
there. Indeed, I would think, that since mind appears in the

developing soma[1] that amounts to showing that it is potential in the ovum (and sperm) from which the soma sprang.

To talk of consciousness as a biological problem is generally unfashionable, yet a better understanding of it is of supreme importance for mankind. Is there a dualism in the universe of perceived and perceiver, or matter and consciousness? I was delighted that Sir Cyril Hinshelwood gave such prominence to the problem in his Presidential Address to the Royal Society in 1959.[2] I feel it is so important that I am giving, with his kind permission, a long quotation.

The question, then [he said], of the relation of the internal and the external worlds cannot and should not be ignored by men of science.

It is surprising that biological discussions often underestimate human consciousness as a fundamental experimental datum. In science we attach no value to unverifiable deductions, or to empty qualitative statements, but nobody defends the neglect of experimental data. Among these we cannot validly disregard those of our own consciousness except by a deliberate abstraction for which we must assume responsibility, and which we should not forget having made.

It is tempting to ignore observational facts when they seem intractable, since we rightly abstain from the attempt to arrive at the truth by speculation. But in this we are not always consistent, and indeed very important philosophical conclusions are sometimes propounded by men of science. Moral and æsthetic qualities in man, for example, are not infrequently said to be explained by the operation of natural selection. Again, it is sometimes asserted that suitable combinations of machines could, in principle, produce results indistinguishable by any operational test from animal or even human behaviour.

The mind-matter relation is quite often dismissed as non-existent or meaningless. But moral qualities are not explained by natural selection, human behaviour is not machine-like and the mind-matter relation cannot be ignored in an intelligent consideration of existence.

The approach to the problem of consciousness must admittedly

[1] For those who are not biologists I should explain that the term *soma* means the body as distinct from the reproductive germ cells.

[2] *Proceedings of the Royal Society*, A, vol. 253, pp. 439–49, 1959.

be egocentric. I have to begin logically with the, to me, indisputable fact that I have a wide range of conscious experiences (which are indeed more important to me than anything else). The significance of this fact can be questioned in two ways: first, by the objection that as far as any operational test goes other people may well be behaving simply as machines, and secondly, by the assertion that my consciousness is a more or less irrelevant concomitant of behaviouristic reactions.

I am, it is true, not certain that other people have consciousness. Neither indeed am I certain that the atomic nucleus exists. But I regard its existence as in the highest degree probable. I regard consciousness in other people as equally probable and for similar reasons. The atomic nucleus is not directly observed. It is inferred by elaborate reasoning from many complex experiments, any one of which could probably be given alternative interpretations. What carries conviction is the fact that a coherent body of doctrine emerges from large numbers of varied tests.

We are all the time trying experiments on our relations with other people, informing, asking, ordering, obeying, resisting with varying emotions which are correlated with our actions. Human evolution has developed an elaborate and sensitive communication system, brought into play in innumerable ways. The hypothesis that other people have an interior life not unlike my own enables me to register correspondences at point after point in so intricate a way that I accept the hypothesis, if not as absolute truth, then as something nearly as good. And with most of the basic conclusions of science I am in no position to demand more.

Thus the content of consciousness must rank as something directly experienced by everyone, and therefore as providing observational data. This conclusion is not changed in the least by the consideration that the development of communication between individuals confers a biological advantage and is favoured by natural selection in so far as mutual assistance and the transmission of acquired knowledge can assist survival. The communication mechanisms exist and one of their uses is to enable us elaborately to test the coherence of predictions from the hypothesis that conscious life is on the whole much the same for different people. People like poets and novelists describe this inner life: their writings serve little enough biological purpose, but they are (sometimes at least) intelligible to the rest of us, and evoke memories of our own experiences, which check as significantly as those coincidences of calculations and dial readings on which we base our views about the physical world.

Nor can the observational data of consciousness be relegated on the ground that they are on the whole qualitative rather than quantitative. Science has to come to terms with qualities, and indeed Weisskopf has pointed out that the quantum theory itself introduced fresh qualitative distinctions into a region where classical physics expected only quantitative differences. . . .

After more discussion of the problem he continues:

There is at present no obvious answer to the question of what kind of advance can possibly be hoped for in the problem of psycho-physical concomitance. This, however, is no reason for giving up thought which at least helps to avoid the kind of errors so easily made both about physics and about biology when the problem is ignored.

It would, moreover, be a mistaken policy for men of science to withdraw from the inquiry. Lucretius might well have been asked how any real knowledge of his primordial particles could ever be obtained and would have been unable to answer. Before Galileo and Newton there were no appropriate concepts in terms of which to understand the flight of a projectile. . . .

In the earliest times the description in rational terms of physical nature was not so much an unsolved problem as one which people did not even conceive.

Human knowledge will not be in a satisfactory state until the dichotomy of the internal and the external is somehow removed.

Waddington in his arresting book *The Ethical Animal* has this to say about consciousness:

As soon as one places the problem of free will in juxtaposition with that of consciousness, it becomes apparent that it cannot be solved either by any manipulation of our existing physico-chemical concepts, since these include no hint of self-awareness, or by any analysis of the language used in formulating the situation, since no linguistic analysis can annul our experience of self. We need ideas which depart more radically from those of the physical sciences; something perhaps akin to the thought of philosophers such as Spinoza and Whitehead, who have suggested that even

non-living entities should not be denied qualities related to the
self-awareness and will which we know, in much more highly
evolved forms, in ourselves.

I had hoped to say more in this lecture about the exciting ideas in
this book of Waddington's which certainly bear upon natural
theology, but I now feel that a discussion of them will come better
in the beginning of my next series.

Fisher in his Eddington Memorial Lecture to which I have already
referred (p. 275) also brings in consciousness as follows:

> The surface or limit separating the inner from the outer life of
> each living thing is also, in our experience, the true seat of our
> consciousness, the boundary of the objective and the subjective,
> where we experience, through our imperfect sense-organs, what
> comes to us from outside, and, with at least equal obscurity, that
> which rises into consciousness from within. If consciousness is, as it
> would seem, the symbol, or even the means, of unification in our
> being, this is the region to which creative activity could most fitly
> be traced.

I find this simple concept helpful as something one can get hold of
and, in my visual way of thinking, I like to express it in diagrammatic
form as in fig. 75; Sir Ronald gives no such figure, of course, and I
do not know whether he would have approved of such symbolism. In
my diagram each circle is meant to represent this " surface ", shown
here as spherical, separating the inner and outer life of a conscious
individual; in each, of which two are shown, A and B, the arrows from
above represent the impressions coming from the sense organs and
that from below those " with at least equal obscurity " rising from
within, from the subconscious. It is the possibility of some link between
the subconscious minds of A and B that gives the great interest to the
results of such experiments in telepathy as were discussed in the last
lecture. It is in this field that I believe science will come to make its
second great contribution to natural theology by showing the reality
of part of the universe outside the world of the physical senses. It is in
this *apparently* non-material part of the world that the power we call
God must lie: some source of influence to which Man can have access
in an extra-sensory way by the communicative act we call prayer.

I have suggested that the power we call God may well have some
fundamental link with the process of evolution. In saying this I hope
I shall not be thought to be belittling the idea of God; I would rather

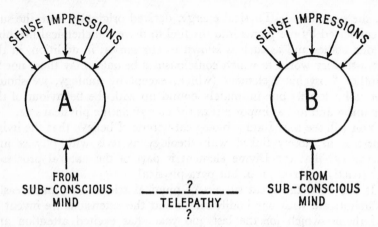

75. Diagrammatic representation of consciousness in two individuals A and B with a hypothetical " telepathic " connection between the subconscious elements of each.

appear to be saying that the living stream of evolution is as much Divine as physical in nature, which is what I believe.

I think there may well be much more significance, than many suppose, in the association of the feeling of love and devotion that accompanies the communication with the Divine in prayer; those who are devout make their approach as if they were confronting a person. It does not worry me a bit if the psychologist tells me that this is just the projection into adult life of a child-parent love relationship: *Our Father which art in Heaven.* I think the psychologists are likely to be right, but that only explains the form of the approach and does not effect the reality of *the Power and the Glory.*[1] No biologist will deny that two of the great forces operating in nature are those of sex and the binding together of parent and offspring by parental and filial love. Such love, even sexual love, when not abused by man and turned to lust, may well be related on *a lower plane* to the same Divine power we know in our communion with what we call God.

We remember the words of the author of the fourth gospel: *God is Love.*

Who knows? Perhaps all true love—animal, human or Divine— may be part of one tremendous " force " animating the organic world

[1] I shall be discussing the Freudian concept of the " super-ego " in the next course of lectures and will say why I do not consider it to be the whole explanation.

on the psychic side. Physical energy, derived originally from the sun, is converted by the plants into the fuel to drive the chemical machine of our bodies and as such is known to our senses; in addition, in the extra-sensory world to which consciousness belongs, may there not be another " psychic " element (which, except by analogy, we should not call a force): one intimately bound up with the behaviour of the organism and just as important as the energy on the physical side.

You will see that I am a biological heretic. I believe that the living world is as closely linked with theology as it is with physics and chemistry: that the Divine element is part of the natural process—not strictly super-natural, but para-physical.

It has been the great success of physical science—so much easier to investigate with our bodily senses and the extensions we invent to aid them—which for the last 300 years has excited attention and tended to push the study of the psychic side of life into the background. I believe that a truer biology, one which will not sell its soul to physics and chemistry for quick results, will emerge and tackle the more important and more difficult aspects of life about whose nature we are almost as ignorant as when physics and chemistry began. I say more important because in this field lie consciousness, the nature of memory, the feeling of purpose, love, joy, sorrow, the sense of the sacred, the sense of right and wrong, the appreciation of beauty—indeed all the things that really matter in life. Some of them, of course, are likely always to lie in the field of natural history rather than of science. Natural theology will extend from science, through natural history to religion.

I shall shock some of my colleagues when I say that I sometimes feel a sympathy for Shaw's elderly gentleman in Back to Methuselah who said, " They tell me there are leucocytes in my blood and sodium and carbon in my flesh. I thank them for the information and tell them there are black beetles in my kitchen, washing soda in my laundry and coal in my cellar. I do not deny their existence but I keep them in their proper place." We must keep physics and chemistry to their proper proportions in the scheme of life.

So many people seem to think that science has banished all the non-material side of life—all that we might call the psychic and the spiritual—to a limbo with superstitious fantasy: that a materialistic view must be the truly scientific, and hence the only valid one. Our present civilisation was founded in the days of a sure faith and a belief in spiritual values; today only to a minority is God a living reality. We are, as Lord Elton said in a broadcast, " for the present living on our spiritual capital."[1] Those who are concerned lest our civilisation will change its nature under the influence of a materialistic philosophy might, I believe, do well to consider how they might encourage further research into the nature of personality in the hope of finding out more about man's spiritual side and the nature of God.

The great institutes for scientific research having a bearing on man's bodily comfort—upon medical problems, direct and indirect, agriculture and fisheries, food, transport and so on—are dotted about the country, and are as symbolic of the present age as our glorious cathedrals and parish churches are symbolic of our spiritual past. Since I began to give these lectures the Trend Report has appeared.[2] In it we see that Government expenditure on civil research (*i.e.* not including military research) has risen from just over $9\frac{1}{2}$ million pounds in 1946 to $151\frac{1}{2}$ million this year. If only 1 per cent of the money spent upon the physical and biological sciences could be spent upon investigations of religious experience and upon psychical research, it might not be long before a new age of faith dawned upon the world. It would, I believe, be a faith in a spiritual reality to match that of the Middle Ages; one based not upon a belief in a miraculous interference with the course of nature, but upon a greatly widened scientific outlook. If East and West could come to have a common ideology through such a new perspective, would not that be worth so much more than the results of rival physical research?

What might Man not do if he used the tools of modern science with the faith and inspiration of the cathedral builders?

As our natural theology must be based upon a scientific approach so I believe our religion itself should be a dynamic faith—an experimental faith—a faith in the receiving of Grace in answer to prayer. Let us experiment and see. I don't mean selfish prayer for one's own safety or betterment or prayers to alter physical events, like praying for rain, but prayers to have help in our actions. Somehow, in some extraordinary way, I do believe that there is a vast store of wisdom and spiritual strength that we can tap in this way—something which is of the utmost importance to mankind.

[1] *The Listener,* January 4th, 1951.
[2] *The Report of the Committee of Enquiry into the Organization of Civil Science* (under the chairmanship of Sir Burke Trend), H.M. Stationery Office, 1963.

Lord Elton, in the broadcast talk to which I have just referred, said: Perhaps the most obvious argument for Christianity is the argument from experience: " it works " . . . Countless very ordinary Christian citizens have been conscious of the overruling of their lives by God, or of an overwhelming sense of His presence, which, they would tell you, the argument of a man who has never known God can no more discredit than the argument of a man who has never seen a car could persuade a life-long motorist that cars do not exist . . .

I am far from being an orthodox Christian. Perhaps I should here make my position a little clearer. For me it is the spirit of Christianity, not any hypothetical dogma of theology, that matters. Evidence of the working of a Divine Power that we may call God, the reality of religious experience and the sense of the sacred, and a belief in the way of life as taught in the Gospel of Jesus—a belief men have died for—these, to my mind, are vital; for me they form a far more substantial foundation for a theology than the blind acceptance of supposed events in the past—events which cannot satisfy the accepted rules of evidence used in other fields of historical research. My views on religion are very close to those of the late Dr. L. P. Jacks so well expressed in his Hibbert Lectures of 1922, *Religious Perplexities* (published 1923):

God, said Jesus, is spirit: a man is spirit no less; and when the two meet in fellowship there is religion. Religion will give us power rather than satisfaction; courage to face danger rather than safeguards against it; inspiration rather than explanation. . . .

All religious testimony, so far as I can interpret its meaning, converges towards a single point, namely this. There is that in the world, call it what you will, which responds to the confidence of those who trust it, declaring itself to them as a fellow-worker in the pursuit of the Eternal Values, meeting their loyalty to it with reciprocal loyalty to them. It is a Power which can help, deliver, illuminate and gladden; the companion of the brave, the upholder of the loyal, the friend of the lover, the healer of the broken, the joy of the victorious—the God who is spirit, the God who is love.

Our natural theology must be fearless. We must have the scientific approach and not shrink from what it may point to. At the *very least* I expect this power of which we speak may be some subconscious shared reservoir of spiritual " know-how " which we call Divine (perhaps something like the species " mind " that I have suggested); I think, however, it is *far more likely* that above this there is something much more wonderful to which we give the name God. But even if it *should* be shown, and I don't believe it will,[1] that this whole conception is a purely psychological one and, if, in some way, this mind factor *should* eventually be proved to be entirely of physico-chemical origin —it would not to my mind destroy the joy or help of *the experience we may still call Divine* any more than it would destroy the glorious beauty felt in poetry or art. I remember as a very young man ending an argument with an adversary by saying " If you should prove that God is made of chlorine—or whatever other chemicals you like—it would not to my mind be so much the worse for God, but so much the better for chlorine! " Then I was very young, today of course I should have said not chlorine by DNA! If this came about chemistry would indeed look different from what it does today—it would be Divine alchemy.

Above all, our natural theology must be based on the records of religious experience. To be *religious* such experience must be more than cold intellectual meditation. An attempt at prayer must be a matter of deep feeling—and as I have said before, one of love—as of love towards a person, although we know that this is just a simplified way, a childish way, if you like, of approaching this great Divine experience. Dr. Marett in his Gifford Lectures: *Faith, Hope and Charity in Primitive Religion* (1932) said: " Thanks to the predominance of emotion over reason in it, religious experience is always hot. Gone cold it has gone out. Rationalism can at most serve to temper a flame which it does not light and may easily extinguish."

There is always a danger that we may stifle the spirit in our determination to stamp out superstition. We must try to combine a scientific approach to theology with a burning spiritual faith. Again, as I have said before, but think it worth repeating, just as a knowledge of the biology of sex does not destroy the love of a lover, so a religion linked with science through a natural theology need not destroy the rapture of our communion with God.

We must have more studies of the nature of religious experience and

[1] I do not believe it will because of the evidence from human experience I shall discuss in the next series of lectures which will be published with the title of *The Divine Flame* as a sequel to the present volume.

more research into the psychic side of man. Let us go forward to reclaim the ground that has been lost in the world through a false belief that science points only to materialism. Let us have the faith of Lord Gifford and, making it alive with the spirit of experiment, show the way to a re-establishment of the idea of God as both a philosophical and a scientific Reality.

INDEX